To our dear
friend Priscilla.
This book is of our
home town. Springfield
Ohio the Parker Sweeper Co
is the company I worked at
for 15 years. Hope you
enjoy the book.
Rita & Sandy Eisman
2014

"THIS BANNER" IS AWARDED BY THE FAIR TO CLARK COUNTY, WHOSE PEOPLE CONTRIBUTED $5,580. THE GREAT WESTERN SANITARY FAIR. PAID $234,000 to SANITARY COMMISSION. CINCINNATI, O. Dec. 21ST 1863.

HEARTLAND

AN EXHIBITION FROM THE COLLECTION OF THE HERITAGE CENTER OF CLARK COUNTY

Burton K. Kummerow

Clark County Historical Society   Heritage Center of Clark County

Springfield, Ohio

2 0 0 1

Copyright © 2001
by Burton K. Kummerow and the Clark County Historical Society

ISBN 0-9707625-0-X

FRONTISPIECE PHOTOGRAPH:

Sometime after 1900, a newly-invented panoramic camera took a photograph of a large gathering in the heart of Springfield.
The unidentified group includes a band with two lady horn players, military personnel, some VIPs and many adults all dressed up
for the occasion. The location is Pennsylvania Railroad Park and the photograph is a time capsule of
downtown Springfield during its Golden Age. Starting on the first page with the Arcade in the background, the viewer can follow
the skyline of half of the community, past St. Raphael Church, the Big Four Railroad Station, the sea of puffing factories in
the east end, St. Joseph Church and the Pennsylvania Railroad Station. Regular folks are going about their business. A trolley car
is rolling by and, among the people in buggies looking on, two young men are on motorcycles on the right of the last page.
If the camera were turned around, the Esplanade, Kelly Fountain and the new City Building would be in the picture.

TITLE PAGE FRONTISPIECE:

Well over a century old, the Springfield City Building has a new life as the Heritage Center of Clark County.
The structure is again the focus of attention for visitors to center city.
(Photograph by W. Fred Boomer)

Design and production: Gerard A. Valerio, Bookmark Studio, Annapolis, Maryland
Typesetting and production: Sherri Ferritto, Typeline, Annapolis
Photography: Unless otherwise noted, all photographs are by W. Fred Boomer Photography, Dayton, Ohio
Illustration Editor: Patricia B. Kummerow
Index Editor: Ernest Scott

Contents

Foreword

To visit the Heritage Center of Clark County is an exciting, educational and entertaining journey through America's Heartland. That is so because when we tell the stories of the men, women and children of Springfield and Clark County, amply illustrated by the rich array of artifacts in the collections of the Clark County Historical Society, we also tell the story of the people who settled the Northwest Territory—America's first frontier—one of the nation's heartlands. Clark County, Ohio, is the area *Newsweek* Magazine called "the true story of America."

That true story is presented in this museum catalogue aptly entitled *Heartland*. Your tour of the museum is enriched by this handsome volume by Burton K. Kummerow who captures the excitement of our lives and places them within the broader context of the nation's great saga.

Bringing the Heritage Center into being is a dramatic story in itself, one equal to many others in the long history of building community in this area. It was, first of all, a community effort to preserve a landmark. The 1890 City Building, designed by native son, Charles Cregar, is a fine example of Victorian architectural style called "Richardson Romanesque." The building served as a community center for the better part of a century with a farmers' market, government center including police department and jail, an opera house, and a gymnasium where my father played basketball. Today it is a museum, education center, library, conservation laboratory, historical society office, veterans service center, restaurant and store.

For the past quarter of a century, the Society has been staffed with well-trained professionals in curatorial sciences and museum management. The dedicated work of our staff, professional consultants and trained volunteers brought this outstanding collection to the point where its value became self-evident.

At that point, leading citizens advanced a plan that brought the building and the collection together.

County Commissioners passed a one-year, half-a-percent sales tax. The owner of the building gave it as a gift. The City Commission forgave a mortgage on the building and contributed the parking lot. Private citizens raised a large endowment to provide for operation of the center. Our representatives in state and federal government, energized by the community's more than eleven-million-dollar contribution, enlisted another nearly eight-million-dollars to complete the project. This was a great example of public and private cooperation to achieve a great end, the kind of bipartisan interaction that built the Heartland in the first place.

Burton Kummerow's presentation of our stories in this volume salutes the thousands of citizens who came together to build community and those who do so now in erecting the Heritage Center to preserve those stories for posterity.

WILLIAM A. KINNISON
President, Clark County Historical Society

Acknowledgments

It's not often someone has an opportunity to profile a community that has been an important player on the national level. *Newsweek* Magazine was the pioneer almost twenty years ago when it used its fiftieth anniversary to declare Springfield/Clark County a matchless illustration of the ongoing quest for "the American Dream." This volume is verification of the wisdom of *Newsweek's* choice.

The hard work of this project was accomplished by decades of perseverance, keeping the past alive while American downtowns everywhere went through cataclysmic changes. The small staff at the Clark County Historical Society, and especially Floyd Barmann, kept the community's attic from ending up in a landfill. With the able assistance of Virginia Weygandt in recent years, he has put together a body of information about the local history and outstanding collections that has made our work possible. It is Floyd's faith in our abilities that got us involved in this wonderful project in the first place. Virginia also has our gratitude for always being helpful, even when our numerous requests got in the way of other deadlines.

The vision of local leaders, especially Richard Kuss, William Kinnison, Richard Foster, Thomas Loftis and their Development/ Steering Committee, has put Society efforts on the front pages of local newspapers. Working closely with a committed Board of Directors, they have planned and accomplished a multi-million dollar initiative that is the envy of historical societies and downtowns all over the country. They will soon get well-deserved attention for their efforts beyond Clark County. The proof of their success is the large stable of donors they have attracted to their cause. Richard and Jane Heckler led the way in helping to make this publication possible. We are honored that we have been chosen to put the exciting story of their hometown on the printed page.

Along with unprecedented private support, the Historical Society has attracted enthusiastic and pivotal assistance from the Clark County Commissioners, the Springfield City Mayor and City Commission, the State of Ohio and Federal elected officials. The County Commissioners, aided by County Administrator W. Darrell Howard and Assistant Administrator Jeff Johnson, have been especially helpful in our work to complete this catalogue.

Much of the credit for the quality of this volume goes to Gerard Valerio of Bookmark Studio in Annapolis, Maryland. He guided us through the time-consuming process of putting together almost four hundred illustrations and making visual sense out of two hundred years of people, institutions and events. We were lucky to find someone with his wisdom, experience and good-natured patience. Another essential part of this process was photographer W. Fred Boomer of Dayton, Ohio. He produced most of the stunning photographs in this volume and did it without once complaining about our short deadline and often confusing needs. The staff at Explus, Inc. in Dulles, Virginia, particularly Trish Seddon and Karen Werth, also deserve our thanks for letting us piggyback on the graphics schedule for the Heritage Center exhibits. Many museums, conservators and private collectors helped us meet our tight graphics deadlines. We especially thank Lee Grady, the curator of the McCormick Collection at the State Historical Society of Wisconsin and Brian Dunnigan at the William Clements Library, University of Michigan, for their assistance and Greg Lennes and Julia Haley for opening up the archives of the International Harvester Company in Chicago.

This book began with an exciting exhibit design that gave us our outline. William L. Brown, III and David McLean of More than a Museum, Ltd., Linwood, Maryland, did much of the preliminary research on graphics and objects which would best represent Clark County history. David Williams Design of Frederick, Maryland, assisted with the early selection of artifacts and themes used in the book. In the process of our research we worked with two scholars, Professor Thomas Taylor of Wittenberg University and Martin West, Director of Fort Ligonier, Pennsylvania, and Adjunct Professor of History at the University of Pittsburgh. Tom took time out to research local newspapers for topics that would add human interest to our text. Martin is the premier authority on the 1780 Battle of Piqua and was kind enough to share his most recent research on the subject.

We met many collectors, buffs and hobbyists in the last three years who helped us understand some of the topics in this volume that demonstrate what an amazing manufacturing universe existed in Springfield/Clark County over the last two centuries. Doug Smith and Andy Munkres of Carriage Hill Farm and Preserve near Dayton, Ohio, gave us a crash course in horse drawn and steam farm equipment. Richard Durig called our attention to the Quick Manufacturing Company's pioneering work on rototillers. Jim and Sarah Campbell, Mindy Barmann and Harry and Roseanne Van Pelt showed us that the bicycles of the nineteenth century actually worked. The Van Pelts also gave us insights into the Westcott Motor Car and Mr. Burton Westcott himself. Fred McDaniel was always ready to share his knowledge of the era of steam and John Bartley answered questions about the extensive collection of Springfield advertising art he so graciously donated to the Society. We also thank Howdy Weber for so willingly sharing his remarkable life story and giving us a wonderful epilogue to inspire present and future generations. Having hopefully benefited from all of this tutoring, any mistakes in this volume must be mine alone.

On a personal note, I grew up on the coasts of America and discovered the culture of the Heartland as an adult. My daughters Elke and Cassandra accompanied me on occasional trips to midwestern museums where we explored the rich history of middle America. And now I have found a soul mate in my wife Tricia who not only puts up most of the time with my all-consuming passion for things historical but has also become an essential partner in those pursuits.

BURTON K. KUMMEROW
Historyworks, Inc.
Baltimore, Maryland

xvii

Introduction:
A County in the Heartland

BURTON K. KUMMEROW

Clark County begins at a rest stop and ends in an intersection of interstates. That's the way most of the world sees this county in the Heartland. It's a race across the newest ribbon of pavement, about twenty minutes from east to west on I - 70. The interstate is a major national artery. The eighteen-wheelers roll through the county, an endless parade, hood to tailgate. Everybody's going somewhere else.

The rest stop always has a line up of trucks spilling out on the highway. Exhausted drivers from every part of the continent catch an hour or two of rest at the side of the road before they rush on to their destinations. It was the same long ago, a different time but the same. Canvas-topped "schooners" pulled by jingling teams of heavy horses. It was two days crossing the county if the weather was right, exhausted teamsters putting their teams to bed and finding a spot near the fire. An endless parade, nose to tailgate, rolling on the "People's Highway."

We measure ourselves with our roads. It's a ceaseless quest for more lanes, better pavement and speed with safety. The old "National Road" came straight through in 1836 and created "the Town at the End of the Pike" in the process. The new road still comes straight in, but dips south and then heads west. Springfield, formerly a destination, has become a detour. We have to find a faster way to get where we're going. It's a pity what we lose in the process. No time to look around and explore.

There are over three thousand counties, parishes and boroughs spread over the American landscape. They are the places where our federal system meets the people, where the political rubber hits the road. Among the eighty-seven other Ohio counties, Clark is an average sort of place. Almost a hundred and fifty thousand call it home, close to half in the county seat at Springfield. It has always been conveniently on the road to other, bigger places like Dayton, Columbus and Cincinnati. The Chamber of Commerce proudly proclaims that the county is within ninety minutes by air of fifty-nine percent of the U.S. population. The serene, rolling, rural landscape is typical of western Ohio. There are hints of the prairie to come. As the drivers glide through on automatic pilot, dashing on the interstate across the long reach of the Buckeye State, Clark County becomes a glaze of green signs and green farmland. But what happens should a traveler slow down and abandon the mind numbing motorcade?

The first county exit, heading west, is South Vienna/Catawba. The early settlers had the honor and the challenge of picking catchy names for a sea of crossroads communities. Some went for the grand, like South Vienna and South Charleston (south of where?). Others went for the local, like Catawba and the south county metropolis of Pitchin. Cellular phone towers, dwarfing the old signature water towers, now punctuate the entrance to South Vienna. Only a few blocks of the village's neat and orderly vintage buildings separate the interstate from U.S. Route 40, the original National Road.

A wide, divided and now practically deserted thoroughfare heads west toward Springfield. Once hated as two lane bottlenecks, the classic American highways are again cherished as reminders of a simpler past.

The exit to Route 40 is a ticket to another America. There's time to look around and find out how interesting our landscape still is. Going west on the old road, the countryside

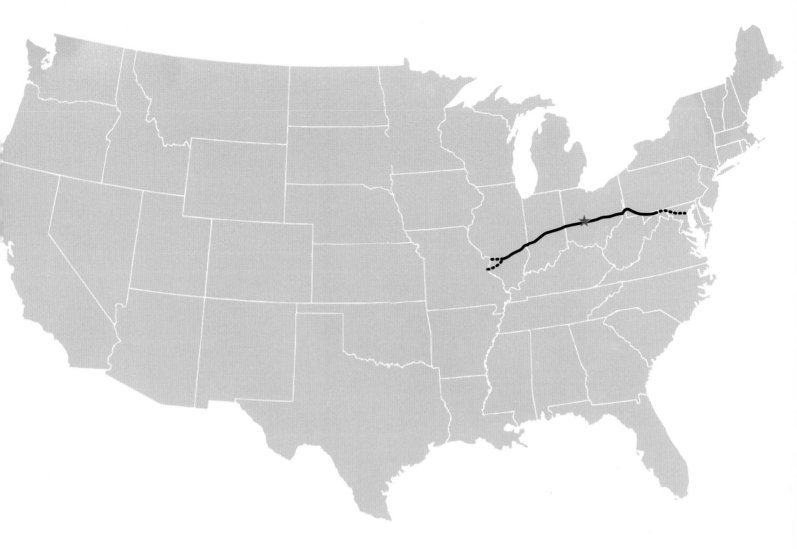

somehow looks better. Only ten percent of us may be tilling our fields, but agriculture remains important in this land of A. B. Graham. Clark County raises respectable crops on handsome farms. The communities out in the county, like South Charleston with its impressive collection of grain elevators, are connected to the soil of their ancestors. Along with the silos and barns, there are substantial old homes, the kind they don't build anymore. There's also lawn art, signature mailboxes and homey roadside businesses.

Passing under the interstate, the old road heads straight for the county seat. It's four miles to the fast food on the east end of Springfield. On the way, a venerable drive-in movie, rambling motor hotels and roadside stands, all from previous generations, line the highway. The top of a hill suddenly reveals the edges of the Champion City.

Welcome to the country's 347th largest city. Eleventh in Ohio, Springfield has been the engine of Clark County. Two centuries old, the community has pursued the American Dream with a relentless spirit. Seven generations have put their hearts and souls into finding success in the Mad River Valley.

A mile through the strip development and the old city looms ahead. It's the same rousing vista that greeted the stagecoaches and conestoga wagons of the 19th century. Down to the banks of Buck Creek with Wittenberg University on the bluffs beyond. Nearby, an Art Deco Post Office and the block wide halls of county government stand on the site of the frontier settlement. A turn to the south on Fountain Avenue and it's two blocks to the heart of Golden Age Springfield. A core block, once filled with lively downtown business but now the new home of city government and a black skyscraper, opens up in city center. Once past the modern, glass-enclosed city building, the old Springfield is just ahead.

A lone survivor of a rich heritage stands piercing the sky with its steepled clock tower. It is the wellspring of the Champion City's history. It holds the keys to the marvelous story of America's Heartland.

Springfield is right in the center of America's first interstate federal project. In spite of detours in Pennsylvania, the National Road was aimed like an arrow at St. Louis in the heart of the continent. The federal funds ran out at Springfield in 1836, but the road eventually extended six hundred miles and carried millions into the states of the Midwest.

In 1891, Gustavus Frankenstein setup his easel on the rolling farmland northeast of Springfield and painted the profile of a Champion City (below) pulsing with Gilded Age industry *(Springfield Museum of Art)*. Photographer W. Fred Boomer captured the city profile more than a century later (above).

A Building for a Champion City

A thirty-year-old City Building hums with activity during a typical day in the 1920s. Several trucks and cars filled with produce are lined up around the first floor market. The structure was at the heart of a busy Springfield center city until the 1950s when most business migrated to the growing suburbs.

Mayor and businessman Oliver S. Kelly carved out a piece of downtown Springfield that he could call his own. When the Champion Reaper Company moved to the east end of town, he gave the company's original downtown brick factory a new life as the Arcade Hotel and Shops. The city center was moving south from the first Public Square, near Buck Creek, to Market Square and now to what was called the "Esplanade," a new plaza that had been swamp only a few decades earlier. Kelly dipped into his own deep pockets to decorate the plaza with a towering fountain. Justly proud of this impressive addition to the booming city, townspeople also grumbled that you could be drowned if you passed by when a gust of wind hit the cascading water.

When Mr. Kelly became mayor in the late 1880s, he set out with the City Council to complete the mid-city development by building a thoroughly modern city building. Clark County had built an ornate courthouse at the beginning of the decade. It was a Victorian wedding cake, a collection of columns, arches and towers spreading in all directions. Soon Springfield was discussing its own replacement for the city's old market house where the

> accumulated fragrance of the…annual crops of pork and cabbage – not always the freshest – ascended to the upper floor – and where the fumes of tobacco and possibly stronger stimulants, penetrated from the time-honored Springfield forum to the vicinity of the market stalls…

In five years, the cost grew to a quarter of a million dollars. Charles Cregar, talented young local architect, was chosen to fit an elaborate new structure into the only space still available facing the Esplanade. It was a long and narrow lot, about fifty feet by close to five hundred feet, and Cregar decided to build up toward the sky. The result was a building like nothing Springfield had ever seen. Described as "Romanesque and Venetian in character," the style was imported from Boston where an architect named Richardson had invented a "back to the Middle Ages" movement that swept America. The tower on Fountain Square pointed up one

hundred and fifty feet, the tallest in the city. The block long brick and stone profile averaged seventy feet high with hundreds of windows spread over three expansive floors.

Springfield picked a midwinter evening in 1890 to christen its new wonder. Mayor Kelly and the City Council planned a celebration that, for the first time, illuminated the downtown with natural gas. They chose red, white and blue flags, bunting and paint to decorate the streets and buildings. The *Springfield Republic-Times* newspaper, overwhelmed by the festive occasion, gushed about everything:

…The streets down town were taken possession of by out of town visitors who had come to see old Springfield unbutton her vest and 'holler…' By 6 o'clock the mass of people was immense in magnitude… The crowd was restless, bent on seeing the whole show and the continuous moving and removing, rushing and crushing, laughter and talking, was not the least interesting phase of a pregnant evening. The adjacent buildings were covered with people, the roofs, balcony and every available space was being taken up.

The huge crowd was not disappointed.

They didn't have to wait long . . . the lighting of the natural gas standpipe on Fountain Square at

The 1890 winter night coming out party for the majestic new City Building was one of the biggest events in Springfield history. The national newspaper *Leslie's Illustrated News* recorded the festivities with a lively illustration that depicted part of the parade as well as a "natural gas illumination" that almost received more attention than the brightly-lit building itself. Note the gas-lit arch to the left as well as the seventy-foot high black tube next to the fountain, "a glorious beacon of light" that "reminded one of [a] rushing, foaming Niagara."

half past five seemed like the famous signal fires of old… The black tube rearing its flaming head from out the center of the human sea, seventy feet below, shot out into the sky a glorious beacon of light illuminating with startling distinctness the grand buildings on each side and converted the waters of the majestic and beautiful Kelly fountain into a gleaming, silvery mantle of spray.

The Fountain Square standpipe, another "four-inch monster at the corner of Spring and Columbia Streets," and their companion thirteen lighted arches "stationed about the city" consumed about fifty-four million cubic feet of natural gas in just one night.

The dull murmuring of the gas…reminded one of [a] rushing, foaming Niagara… The blueish, yellowish flames would surge and sway and adapt themselves to the motion of the wind…One could have studied the scene for hours without weariness.

A parade followed the illumination,

…Winding its low and noisy way along the flame-kissed street… It was a huge, rip-roaring demonstration, a people's proud, joyous and regal spectacle, an united exhibition of a noble city's pardonable pride in a structure of unsurpassed magnificence and architectural beauty…

The crowd next rushed to the new city building for the "Dedication Exercises."

The City Building has been a landmark in downtown Springfield. A turn of the century postcard (above) records the standard Esplanade view of the one hundred and fifty-foot clock tower with the block long building stretching west. The Esplanade or east-side of the City Building was the scene of parades and ceremonies for decades.

The building was lighted both by electricity and gas in every department, from the basement to the third story. Never before in the history of Springfield did nature and the art of man combine in the creation of such brilliant splendor... Minute by minute the crowds increased and jostled and crowded each other as they promenaded the hallways, filed into the council chamber, ascended and descended the stairways to the third floor, and looked in upon the police court and offices in the west end, and the public school superintendent's room and armory court in the east. It was interesting to note the many expressions of surprise at the magnitude of the building... It was a matter of but a comparatively short time before every seat in the [city] hall was occupied, and still they came, until the aisles were filled both below and in the balcony, and an unnumbered host went away without gaining entrance at all.

The overflow and noisy audience was treated to the long-winded speeches, homegrown entertainment and "marvelous and daring physical exhibitions" of the era. Young Mr. Walter Davis sang "I Rise from Dreams of Thee," laboring

"under the disadvantage of the continued noise in the rear of the hall." The double bar exercises performed by the gentlemen's class of Turn Verein "took the house by storm." Judge F. M. Hagan, chairman of the event, summed up the evening's enthusiasm.

...The more the [east tower] and the building... are looked upon and studied from year to year, the more their simple but tasteful adornment and massive proportions be admired and esteemed, as a lasting and fitting monument to the genius

A Beckley and Myers ice truck, decorated for the Fourth of July about the time of the first World War, poses in front of the Esplanade entrance. Photographer W. Fred Boomer captured the impressive early morning profile of the recently renovated City Building, now preserved as the Heritage Center of Clark County.

of the architect and to the taste and public spirit of our people…Our new market house is inferior to none known, even in the great cities of America and Europe. It is doubtful if any city in the world, with 40,000 people, has such a splendid town hall as ours.

Judge Hagan was prophetic. The City Building remained unique and was eventually nominated to the country's honored "National Register of Historic Places." It harbored a city market for over a century and the functions of city govern-ment almost as long. A growing Springfield serving the different needs of a larger population could not keep reinventing an old building, but the new city hall stands only a few hundred yards away.

The Champion City's bold statement of its Golden Age optimism has now stood for half of the community's history. The City Building is still a touchstone for Springfield's spirit and vitality. Now, more than ever, it houses the memory of a powerful past.

xxvii

Thirty-eight Presidents and a Dozen Wars
The Sweep of Springfield and Clark County History
1768–1977

The history of Clark County and Springfield has mirrored events throughout America. Divided into the terms of thirty-eight of the forty-three U.S. Presidents, local affairs are compared and contrasted with our national history. Local events are in bold throughout this eventful timeline.

George Washington (1789–1797)

1768-69	Tecumseh is born.
1775	American Revolution begins.
1776	Declaration of Independence is written.
1780	**Battle of Piqua.**
1783	American Revolution ends and Britain cedes the Ohio Country to the United States in the Treaty of Paris.
1785	Land Ordinance lays out the Northwest Territory.
1787	Northwest Ordinance provides for self-government in the Northwest and prohibits slavery.
	Constitutional Convention in Philadelphia.
1789	George Washington becomes the First U.S. President.
1790	**John Paul settles at Honey Creek near New Carlisle.**
1791	Shawnee and Delaware Indians defeat St. Clair's forces in Ohio.
1794	Anthony Wayne defeats the Indians at Fallen Timbers.
1795	Treaty of Greenville.
	David Lowry and Jonathan Donnel settle in the Mad River Valley.

John Adams (1797–1801)

1797	Congress receives the earliest known petition by fugitive slaves which is rejected after vigorous argument.
	The frigate Constitution "Old Ironsides," is launched.
	First cash crop from the area is floated down the river system and sold in New Orleans.
1798	Congress passes law abolishing imprisonment for debt, ending the practice in the U.S.
1799	Former President George Washington dies.
	Simon Kenton leads twelve families to the confluence of Mad River and Buck Creek.
1800	Congress opens its first session in the new capital city of Washington.
	The Library of Congress is established.

Thomas Jefferson (1801 -1809)

1801	**James Demint lays out the town of Springfield and opens its first business, a distillery.**
1802	**Simon Kenton builds a gristmill, a carding mill and a sawmill.**
1803	Ohio becomes the 17th state in the Union.
1804-06	Lewis and Clark explore to the Pacific.
1804	**Road opens to Dayton.**
1807	**Townspeople hold a council with Tecumseh in Springfield.**
1808	Congress outlaws importation of slaves.
	The National Road begins in Cumberland, Maryland.

James Madison (1809–1817)

1810	**New Carlisle founded.**
1810-11	**Religious revival led by Mrs. Walter Smallwood.**

1811	First steamboat on the Ohio and Mississippi Rivers.
1812	War begins, Tecumseh and Indian allies join the British.
1814	British burn the Capitol and White House.
	Tecumseh dies at the Battle of Thames.
	Clark County Militia includes Springfield Artillery, Clark Guards, Osceola Plaids and Springfield Cadets.

James Monroe (1817–1825)

1815	**South Charleston founded.**
1816	**Medway founded.**
1817	**Clark County created from parts of Greene, Champaign and Madison Counties.**
1818	National Road reaches the Ohio River.
	Springfield is chosen as the county seat over New Boston. James Demint fined for dealing with slaves as free men.
1819	Panic in the banking industry, economic effects felt for years.
1820	Missouri Compromise and the debate over slavery.
	First Federal Census lists Clark County's population at 9,533.
	Weekly newspaper The Farmer begins publication.
1822	**Pennsylvania House opened.**
1824	**African Methodist Episcopal Church founded.**

John Quincy Adams (1825–1829)

1825	Erie Canal officially opens.
1828	Ohio and the nation elect Andrew Jackson, first western President.
	Mail coach arrives daily with newspapers from Baltimore only five days old.
	North Hampton founded.

Andrew Jackson (1829–1837)

1830	**Clark County's population is 13,114.**
	Johnny Appleseed visits relatives who live on Chapman's Creek in Clark County.
	Donnelsville founded.
	Peter Cooper and B&O Company introduce first steam railroad.
1830's	**German and Irish immigrants arrive.**
1831	Cyrus McCormick demonstrates first practical reaper.
1832	**Harmony founded.**
1832-33	Nullification Crisis.
1833	**South Vienna is platted.**
1835	**Enon and Tremont City are founded.**
1836	Siege of the Alamo.
	Federal funds for the road cease.
	Springfield becomes known as "The town at the end of of the Pike." Center of town shifts southward to line up with National Road (current Main Street).
	1,200 Conestoga wagons pass through Springfield in June.
1837	National Financial Panic hits entire country.

Martin Van Buren (1837–1841)

1838   **The village of Catawba is platted on land owned by George Dawson.**

1840   First modern political campaign– "Tippecanoe and Tyler, too" and "Van, Van he's a used-up man."
James Leffel builds foundry on Buck Creek.
First County Agricultural Exposition.

William Henry Harrison (1841)

1841   President Harrison dies thirty days after taking office.
Leffel and the Barnetts construct a 1^1/$_2$ mile mill run along Buck Creek.

John Tyler (1841–1845)

1842   **Anti-Slavery Society forms.**
Selma founded.

1843   The first wagon in a party of about 1,000 persons bound for Oregon pulls away from Independence, Missouri.

1844   Samuel F.B. Morse, inventor of the telegraph, sends the first telegraph message "What has God wrought!" from Washington to Baltimore.
Pitchin founded.
Wittenberg College moves to Springfield from Wooster.

James K. Polk (1845–1849)

1846   **Little Miami Railroad arrives in Springfield.**
First Clark County Fair held in South Charleston.

1846-48   Mexican War begins with significant opposition in Clark County.

1847   **First water pumping windmill in Ohio, located in South Charleston.**

1847-49   **Telegraph lines arrive in Springfield.**

1848   First National Women's Rights Convention held in Seneca Falls, NY.

1849   California Gold Rush
Cholera epidemic. Over fifty Irish railroad workers die.

Zachary Taylor (1849–1850)

1849   The Great St. Louis fire.
Compromise of 1850, debate over slavery in western territories continues.

1850   **Springfield incorporated as a city and has six gas street lights downtown.**
Phineas P. Mast begins production of farm equipment.
The census lists Clark County population at 22,178.

Millard Fillmore (1850–1853)

1850's   **Anne Aston Warder organizes Springfield Underground Railroad Association to aid runaway slaves.**
Many Clark Countians move to Minnesota to make sure it enters the Union as a free state.
Nativist (Anti-immigrant) groups peak: Know Nothing Party.

1852   Uncle Tom's Cabin by Harriet B. Stowe is published.
First city directory lists forty-two "persons of color" as heads of households or in business.
Plattsburg founded.

Franklin Pierce (1853–1857)

1854   Kansas-Nebraska Act opens Kansas to slavery which leads to bloody conflicts.
Know Nothing Party sweeps School Board.

1855   **The play, *Uncle Tom's Cabin*, is performed in Springfield.**

Member of the Basey family becomes the first African American to purchase land in Springfield.

1857   Supreme Court decision in Dred Scott case opens the nation to slavery.
Local residents prevent U.S. marshals from seizing fugitive slave Addison White in Mechanicsburg.
Fassler and Whiteley are joined by O.S. Kelly to produce the Champion reaper.

James Buchanan (1857–1861)

1858   Lincoln-Douglas Debates.

1859   John Brown's raid on the Federal Arsenal at Harpers Ferry, West Virginia.

1860   South Carolina secedes from the Union.
Clark County elects Samuel Shellabarger, a Republican and abolitionist, to Congress.
The census lists Clark County population at 25,300.

Abraham Lincoln (1861–1865)

1861-65   **Springfield factories make cloth for uniforms, wagons and linseed oil for the army, and farm machinery for labor short farms. Women assume new roles in industry and agriculture and support the war effort.**

1861   Fort Sumter bombarded on April 12, Civil War begins.
The Springfield Zouaves, Washington Artillery and Jefferson Guards form. By War's end, three-quarters of the eligible men, including half of the voters see service.

1862   **James Leffel receives patent on his double turbine waterwheel. He was producing 150 turbines a day by 1864.**

1863   Lincoln announces the Emancipation Proclamation.
Battles of Gettysburg and Vicksburg indicate the tide of the War is shifting to the North.
J. Warren Keifer sent to New York to command Provost Marshal's troops putting down draft and race riots.

1864   Sherman's Army of Cumberland marches through Georgia and the Carolinas.
The 5th U.S. Colored Regiment is raised mainly in Clark County.
First labor union, the Iron Molders #72, is organized in Springfield.

1865   General Robert E. Lee surrenders to General U.S. Grant at Appomattox, Virginia, April 9.
President Lincoln is assassinated at Ford's Theater in Washington on April 14.
First Hebrew Congregation forms.

Andrew Johnson (1865–1869)

1866   Samuel Shellabarger plays a major role in passage of first Civil Rights Act.

1867   **Former slave children taken in by families in Clark and Greene counties.**
Six companies form to produce Champion farm equipment to fill the demand for reapers in southern and western states as a result of the Homestead Act.
Daniel Hertzler mysteriously killed.
Local economy booms: 250 new buildings erected in 1868; five-story, 140-room Lagonda House opens in 1869.

1868   President Andrew Johnson impeached but not removed from office.

1869   First Transcontinental Railroad completed.

Ulysses S. Grant (1869–1877)

1870's — Nine major manufacturers of farming equipment.

1870 — First street cars in Springfield, drawn by mules.

The census lists Clark County population at 32,070.

1871-72 — Ohio State Fair held in Springfield.

Rise of the Labor Union movement.

Rise of the Temperance Prohibition movement led by "Mother" Eliza Daniels Stewart.

1876 — U.S. Centennial Exposition in Philadelphia.

Battle of Little Big Horn.

Disputed election of Hayes and Tilden.

Samuel Shellabarger attorney for Hayes in disputed election.

1877 — Last federal troops withdrawn from southern states.

Rutherford B. Hayes (1877–1881)

1878 — Thomas Edison receives patent for his phonograph.

1879 — Thomas Edison demonstrates his new "incandescent lamp" at Menlo Park.

1880's — Bicycling clubs are the rage for young people who become major advocates for paving the National Road.

1880 — First commemoration of the Battle of Piqua.

Mad River Valley Pioneer and Historical Association founded.

P. P. Mast founds *Farm and Fireside* to promote Champion farm machinery sales.

James A. Garfield (1881)

1881 — President Garfield assassinated.

Annie Oakley gives first professional performance at the Crystal Palace in Springfield.

Chester A. Arthur (1881–1885)

1883 — Buffalo Bill opens his "Wild West" shows in Omaha, Nebraska.

Kelly's Springfield Arcade opens.

1884 — Mark Twain's *The Adventures of Huckleberry Finn* is published.

Citizens fund construction of Recitation Hall, second building on Wittenberg's campus.

Grover Cleveland (1885–1889)

1885 — The Washington Monument in Washington, D.C. is dedicated.

1886 — Dr. Russell tests the Russell steam car, first automobile patented in the U.S.

Congress enacts The Interstate Commerce Act.

Whiteley locks out Knights of Labor workers.

1887-90 — Designed by local architect Charles Cregar, The City Building (now the Heritage Center) is constructed.

1889 — O. S. Kelly's gift enables construction of the 41-foot fountain on the Esplanade.

Benjamin Harrison (1889–1893)

1890's — Interurbans connect Ohio cities with a hub in Springfield. Several statewide homes open and Springfield becomes known as "Home City."

Indians massacred at Wounded Knee, South Dakota.

1890 — Springfield Trades and Labor Assembly founded, promotes the celebration of Labor Day.

1892 — Landsdown (Avalon and later Spring Grove) Amusement Park opens adjacent to Leffel's Lane.

Populist Party founded.

1893 — Young Men's Reading and Social Club founded. Later it becomes the Center Street YMCA.

Grover Cleveland (1893–1897)

1893-97 — Economic Depression.

1894 — Pullman strike cripples the nation.

1897 — The Mitchell Post, GAR and local businessmen form the Clark County Historical Society.

William McKinley (1897–1901)

1898 — Snyder Park opens on land donated by the Snyder brothers.

Lillian Gish moves to Springfield.

1900 — Rise of the city: One-third of the U.S. population lives in cities, 150,000 phonographs and three million records sold and 4,000 automobiles manufactured.

Clark County population is 58,939, including 12,686 men and 2,809 women in the workforce.

1901 — Marconi invents the radio.

Springfield celebrates the centennial of its founding.

Buffalo Bill's Wild West Show in Springfield.

New Carlisle's "Fighting Fred Funston" captures Emilio Aguinaldo in the Philippine Insurrection.

President McKinley assassinated in Buffalo, New York.

Theodore Roosevelt (1901–1909)

1902-03 — A series of major fires in Springfield.

1903 — Wright Brothers pilot the first plane at Kitty Hawk.

1904 — Formation of International Harvester with corporate headquarters in Chicago.

Construction begins on Panama Canal.

A.B. Graham founds Boys and Girls Club, forerunner of the 4-H Club movement.

1904-06 — Whites riot in black neighborhoods.

1905 — Gus Sun opens vaudeville theatre and booking agency in Springfield.

Frank Lloyd Wright designs and builds a home for Burton J. Westcott.

William Howard Taft (1909–1913)

1911 — Daytons Charles Kettering demonstrates first electric self-starter for automobiles.

1912 — On maiden voyage, the British Liner *Titanic*, sinks after striking an iceberg in the North Atlantic.

1913 — Morgan and Rockefeller interests control more than 10% of the nation's wealth.

Springfield voters adopt a home rule charter government with a professional city manager.

Woodrow Wilson (1913-1921)

1915 — *Lusitania* sunk by German submarine.

1916 — Westcott Motor Car Company begins production in Springfield.

1917 — U.S. enters World War I.

Five million cars in the U.S.

Revolution in Russia.

1918 — World War I ends and President Wilson unsuccessfully campaigns for the League of Nations.

Springfielder Leon Roth carries Armistice to the front.

1919   **International Harvester Company converts Springfield plant to trucks only.**

Crowell Publishing acquires *Collier's* Magazine and moves headquarters to New York.

1920   Women are guaranteed the right to vote with ratification of the 19th Amendment.

The census lists Clark County population at 80,728.

1921   **Edwin Parker begins making lawn sweepers in Springfield.**

Ohio National Guard in Springfield to preserve order as new racial fighting erupts.

Warren G. Harding (1921-1923)

1921-23   Teapot Dome scandal

1922   **Civic Orchestra founded.**

Calvin Coolidge (1923–1929)

1923   **Ohio Ku Klux Klan meets in Springfield.**

1924   **Springfield becomes known as "Rose City."**

1925   **Credit Life is founded.**

Scopes Trial in Dayton, Tennessee.

1927   Lindbergh's transatlantic flight.

Herbert Hoover (1929–1933)

1929   Beginning of the Great Depression, stock market crash.

1930   **150th anniversary of Battle of Piqua.**

George Rogers Clark Park founded.

1931   The "Star Spangled Banner," song written by Francis Scott Key is officially adopted as national anthem.

1932   Twenty-month-old, Charles Lindbergh, Jr. is kidnapped from his home in New Jersey.

Franklin Delano Roosevelt (1933-1945)

1930's   **Chakeres' theaters spread across Ohio.**

New Deal programs help build City Hospital, U.S. Post Office, Clark Park and many streets.

1932   **Bonded Oil Company opens first service station in Urbana.**

1933-41   New Deal programs enacted by Congress.

1935-39   Dust Bowl in the mid-west.

1939   Germany invades Poland, World War II begins.

1941   Japan bombs Pearl Harbor and America enters World War II.

1941-45   **Springfield industry turns to supplying war materiel; diesel engines for liberty ships, M-5 half-track trucks, torpedoes, military trucks, artillery shells, parts for the Norden bomb sight and numerous other items.**

1942   Allies invade North Africa and begin counter attack in the Pacific.

1943   Allies invade Italy.

Air Force cadets train at Wittenberg College.

1944   Allied D-Day invasion, Marshall, Mariana and Philippine Island chains retaken.

1945   Iwo Jima and Okinawa retaken.

President F. D. Roosevelt, only four-term President, dies.

Victory in Europe on May 8.

Atomic bombs dropped on Hiroshima and Nagasaki, Japan surrenders on August 14.

Harry S. Truman (1945–1953)

1946   GI's return home, Baby Boom begins, growth of suburbia.

Marshall Plan to rebuild Europe.

Cold War begins.

"GI Bill" sends former soldiers to college.

Wittenberg College enrollment reaches 1,364 students.

1947   **Clark County Fair takes over the old Springfield Airport.**

1950   North Korea invades South Korea; UN forces land at Inchon; China enters the war.

Mercy Hospital opens.

Clark County population is 111,661 according to the federal census.

1953   Korean War Armistice signed.

Dwight D. Eisenhower (1953–1961)

1954   In Brown v Board of Education of Topeka, Kansas the Supreme Court orders end to segregated public schools in U.S.

1955   **Park Shopping Center, the first one in Springfield, opens.**

Montgomery Bus boycott.

1956   **Crowell-Collier closes its printing plant on Christmas Eve, 2000 workers lose their jobs.**

1957   Soviet Union launches Sputnik, first successful satellite.

1960's   Nationwide Civil Rights Movement.

1960   **Local chapter of NAACP starts with Dorothy Bacon as secretary.**

John F. Kennedy (1961–1963)

1961   Bay of Pigs invasion of Cuba is defeated.

Robert C. Henry, first black person elected to Springfield City Commission.

1962   Cuban missile crisis.

1963   March on Washington, Martin L. King Jr.'s "I Have a Dream" speech.

President Kennedy assassinated in Dallas.

Medgar Evers assassinated.

Lyndon B. Johnson (1963–1969)

1964   Gulf of Tonkin incident, escalation of U.S. involvement in Vietnam.

Maurice K. Bach becomes first Jewish mayor of Springfield.

1965   Malcolm X assassinated.

1965-73   Anti-war protests across the nation.

1965-68   Urban riots throughout the U.S.

1966   **Robert C. Henry becomes first black mayor of Springfield.**

1968   Tet Offensive in Vietnam.

Martin L. King, Jr. assassinated.

Robert Kennedy assassinated.

Betty Brunk becomes first woman mayor of Springfield.

1969   Neil Armstrong and Buzz Aldrin, first men to walk on the moon.

Richard M. Nixon (1969–1974)

1970's   **Businesses begin to relocate around newly opened I-70.**

1970   Invasion of Cambodia, Kent State and Jackson State shootings.

The federal census shows Clark County population at 157,115.

1971   **Upper Valley Mall opens and draws business from downtown.**

Robert Burton announces plan to revitalize downtown. Core Renewal Corporation formed.

1973   U.S. forces leave Vietnam.

1973-74   Watergate scandal culminates in Nixon's resignation.

Gerald Ford (1974–1977)

1974   American Indian Self-Determination Act.

1975   Fall of South Vietnam.

1976   The Nation celebrates its Bicentennial.

One millionth truck leaves new International assembly line in Springfield.

1977   **Construction of new City Hall on the "Core" block, downtown Springfield.**

HEARTLAND

1801–1980

THE NATIONAL ROAD

A "Peoples' Road" into the Heartland

America's First Interstate Helps Build a New Nation

Like so much of early American history, the first "national road" is linked to the amazing career of George Washington. Gaining access to the vast interior of North America was a lifelong, almost religious, mission for the first president.

> Settling the west will fulfill the first and greatest-commandment, increase and multiply.

Washington had good reason to be zealous about westward expansion. He first visited the "Ohio Country" in 1753 as a twenty-one-year-old Virginia diplomat. For the next five years, he regularly risked life and limb with British and colonial troops who successfully chased the French out of North America. His reward was an abundance of land in a wilderness he was certain held the key to America's future. Throughout his long service to the new nation, he steadfastly saw huge potential beyond the Appalachian Mountains.

Many joined Washington, enthusiastically supporting settlement in the still dimly understood western frontier. Citizens of the restless new nation were looking to the vast wilderness for their piece of the American dream. It was a pattern that would continue for a century across the entire continent.

First, a trickle of hardy frontiersmen would push out the perimeter, trading and living with Native Americans. Next came the flood of settlers, cutting down the forest for agriculture and livestock. The native population, befuddled by the surveys and fences of land ownership, fought valiantly to preserve their way of life but could not stem the tide. Many of the early settlers of the Ohio Country were Revolutionary War veterans, paid for their service with warrants for western land. As they moved out to the frontier, they demanded federal protection and outlets to the markets in the east.

After the American Revolution, the British and Spanish continued to seek footholds in the Ohio and Mississippi Valleys. George Washington, concerned that these interests might lure away frontier settlers, advocated a road to link west and east like none before it.

> [The nation must] open a wide door, and make a smooth way for the produce of that Country to pass to our Markets before the trade may get into another channel.

Westerners were used to steep mountains, dark forests and briers that tore skin and ripped clothes during the trickle of annual migrations to eastern markets. Water transport was the salvation for travelers, but all the great interior rivers faced west and south. Only about forty miles separated the headwaters facing east and west. The problem in Pennsylvania, Maryland and Virginia was that those forty miles covered some of the roughest terrain east of the Mississippi. The Appalachian Mountains, a great backbone across the path to the west, stymied road building for generations.

The breakthrough came in the early 1800s. Along with the tough terrain, politics made solutions difficult to find, but, somehow, the U.S. Congress and the small list of new western states found a way to build a revolutionary new road. Many felt that the federal government had no right to build roads that benefited individual states. The states, for their part, competed

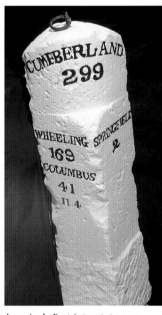

America's first interstate was built to last. Sturdy stone columns marked every mile. They reminded travelers how far west they were from Cumberland, Maryland, where the road started. Many of the battered old stones still mark the way after more than 150 years.

This lively recreation of the "Peoples' Road" in Maryland demonstrates that traffic jams are nothing new. For a half century, the thirty-foot roadbed carried an endless stream of wagons, stage-coaches, livestock and ordinary families headed west. Stone taverns, the truck stops of another era, stood every ten miles along the road to America's Heartland. *(Maryland Historical Society, Baltimore, Maryland)*

vigorously for a share of a road that would link their economies with the unbounded riches of the American interior.

The country was beginning to preach the gospel of "Manifest Destiny." An editor at the New York Evening Post predicted,

> The destiny of North America belongs to the United States. The country is ours, ours is the right...to all the future opulence, power and happiness which lay scattered at our feet.

South Carolina Senator John C. Calhoun lobbied for what came to be called "Internal Improvements."

> Let us...bind the republic together with a perfect system of roads and canals. Let us conquer space.

Beneath that currency of national expansion, every state fought for its slice of the economic pie.

The brand new state of Ohio provided an imaginative solution to the bickering. A talented Swiss immigrant named Albert Gallatin settled in western Pennsylvania and became Secretary of the Treasury in the Jefferson Administration. The little remembered but influential Gallatin proposed that five percent of the revenues from

public land sales go to building good roads to the west. He boldly titled his idea "Origin of the National Road." When Ohio came into the Union in 1803, Congress accepted Gallatin's proposition. An 1805 senate committee report envisioned a "Cement of Union" that would

> make the crooked ways straight...the rough ways smooth... [and] remove the intervening mountains.

It took twenty years to chart a path and develop a formula for building the road.

Following George Washington's vision, the Potomac River and the new national capital seemed a logical route, but the other major eastern cities also wanted the honor and profits associated with the "United States Road." It took a presidential commission to sort out the claims. Humble Cumberland, Maryland, an early gateway to the frontier soon to be linked to Baltimore by a private turnpike, finally received the nod. Surveyors headed west to mark a course across the rugged mountain terrain. Local settlements along the 131 miles to the Ohio River battled to get the road to detour through their community. With close connections to national leader Henry Clay, Wheeling, then part of Virginia, won the much coveted honor of Ohio River terminus. From that cross-

roads, travelers could head down the river on a flatboat or west into Ohio.

Construction finally began in 1811 and, seven years later, a thirty-foot-wide, stone-covered highway was cut through the mountains and carrying a flood of travelers. Profiteers had inflated the cost of the new road to $13,000 a mile, but America finally had the sought after artery that joined the watersheds of east and west. Beautiful and sturdy stone bridges over the many streams and rivers remain engineering marvels today. Carved and painted stones marked each mile on the north side of the right of way. A Maryland traveler was euphoric.

> …This great Turnpike Road…is the Salvation of those Mountains or Western Countrys and more benefit to the human family than Congress have any knowledge…

The fine new thoroughfare raised expectations that points further west would get the same treatment. An inexpensive Ohio road, called Zane's Trace, featured foot high stumps that broke wheels and rattled coach passengers. Another constitutional argument about federal funding for state projects ensued until President James Monroe broke the logjam. By 1825, work crews were headed west on the rolling Ohio landscape. A decade of non-stop travel on the

road east of Wheeling had taught designers that they needed a harder surface to prevent deep ruts. The answer came from a Scotsman named John McAdam. He recommended replacing gravel with broken stone layered and rolled across the graded thirty-foot-wide roadbed. It was a labor intensive method but the new surface revolutionized travel. Horses and coaches could now glide across the landscape at up to twelve miles per hour!

The first interstate faced traffic jams from the start. The road was a magnet for every freight wagon, every stagecoach, every single traveler headed west. One observer noted,

> This is the people's highway, and the people crowd it from rim to edge until their carts, wagons, stages and carriages challenge one another for the right of way.

Another was amazed by the traffic.

> As many as 20 four-horse carriages, have been counted in line at one time on the road and large, broad-wheeled wagons…laden with merchandise… are visible all the day long…besides innumerable caravans of horses, mules, hogs and sheep.

It was a world where nothing moved faster than a horse. The rugged, distinctive blue and

OVERLEAF:
Benjamin Hiner stands proudly beside his fully-rigged Pennsylvania style freight wagon in this rare pre-Civil War photograph taken near Virginia's Shenandoah Valley. The graceful, bow-shaped "schooners," pulled by teams of six horses or mules, were the "eighteen wheelers" of their day. (Courtesy of Richard M. Hamrick, Jr.)

continued on page 12.

The David Crabill Family Moves to Clark County

The most common travelers on the National Road were the "movers," humble farm families walking slowly alongside their earthly possessions piled high on the family wagon. Some immigrants pushed wheelbarrows and carts ahead of them as they plodded hundreds of miles.

David Crabill left Virginia in 1807 to find a new home on the Ohio frontier. Crabill's long trip on horseback is recalled in the journal of Joseph Keifer, another settler who rode twice to Clark County from Maryland in 1811 and 1812. On the first trip, Keifer details the miles traveled together with brief remarks about the towns, the agricultural potential of the land and the quality of his lodgings. Finding a place to put your head at night could be a hard bargain. One woman found "slim treatment, space on the floor, meager food and surrounded by loud, drunken, dirty men." Almost matter of fact about his adventures, Keifer notes that he was able to travel 660 miles for $40 in forty-eight days (about fourteen miles per day).

Mr. Crabill returned to Clark County in 1810 with his family and a newly purchased heavy Pennsylvania style wagon, known to the world as a Conestoga. It was

Jacks and grease buckets were critical tools in the days of wooden axles and rough roads. The jack, dated 1773, is an elegant handmade example of blacksmith ingenuity. The humble wooden grease bucket is a graceful marriage of style and function.

a fine addition for the migration. Piled high with all the family possessions and pulled by a yoke of oxen that did double duty dragging plows and harrows, the wagon rolled across the National Road with the Crabills marching alongside. Once at their farmstead, northeast of the growing hamlet of Springfield, the family used the old Conestoga for generations. As the Crabills prospered in Clark County, they kept their wagon while others discarded the obsolete machines of their grandfathers. It became a source of nostalgia during local parades. Now, carefully restored by the Clark County Historical Society, it has a place of honor in the Heritage Center.

The wagon making traditions of England and Germany came together during the 18th century in Lancaster County, Pennsylvania. The result was one of the most famous early American icons. There is no better known symbol of the National Road. Tens of thousands rolled continuously down the Road for two generations. When they lost out to the Industrial Revolution, their memory survived as an important piece of the American success story. The Conestoga illustrates how craft, applied to perform a function, can become art. The blue body has a graceful bow, designed to keep loads from shifting in the mountains. The ironwork, applied to reinforce the harness and the wood structure, is a combination of Pennsylvania folk art and the best of the blacksmith's craft. A teamster, handling a large six horse team with only his voice and a whip, was pure magic. The total effect of giant wagon and horses, lumbering down the road must have been electric.

The Crabill Family Conestoga Wagon is a rare survivor connected to a family's history. Most of the surviving wagons have long since lost their identity. They were humble working machines, discarded when their usefulness ended. The Crabills might have used their wagon to haul freight, but it survived because its value on the farm only ended when the gasoline engine ushered in a new age.

In spite of repairs over two centuries, the rare ca. 1810 Crabill Family Wagon still has the look of a Pennsylvania style freight wagon. The trademark blue of the box, the red of the running gear and the decorative iron work on the tool box (detail above) were all common features on the wagons of early America.

What Clark County Immigrants Brought with Them

Two hundred thousand people poured through Ohio on the National Road during the early years. Ninety thousand of them decided to settle in the Buckeye State. They came from New England, New York, Pennsylvania, Maryland and Virginia. They came from Ireland and Germany. Some of them

Many of the Clark County settlers preserved the treasures associated with the fragile lives of their children. Along with a favorite doll, the Van Tassel christening dress and the Kinney Bible, filled with family history, made the trip to the Ohio frontier. The Swayne family brought along a high style tall clock to add dignity to their new home.

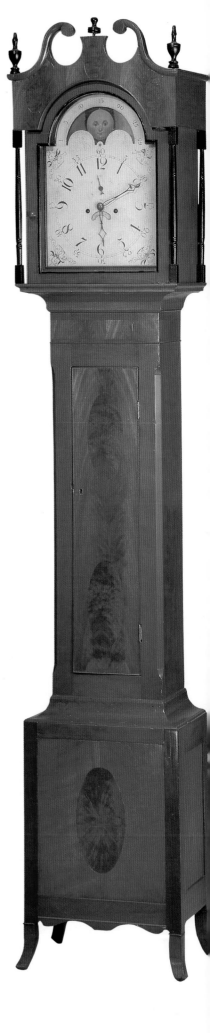

trunk. The christening dress worn by five of the eight Van Tassel children might be in another. You might find the wool plaid day dress that Swedish immigrant Annalisa Arronson made for her trousseau, or a fine white bedspread that Mary Schooley Spining inherited from her mother, or the Kinney Bible filled with records of family births, marriages and deaths.

The Swayne family couldn't imagine life without their Pennsylvania-made tall clock. It found its way into a wagon, made it to Clark County and still, after

brought slaves. Others brought the desire to abolish slavery. All brought the hope that they would prosper in the Heartland.

Faced with the dilemma of packing all their possessions into a wagon or cart, they were forced to bring along only the bare necessities. Whatever came over the mountains had to survive a lurching and lumbering ride for hundreds of miles. The everyday farm tools and cookware were first on the list. A farm family could not survive without the basics. But, along with the butter churns, broadaxes, iron roasters and cook pots, there were treasures tucked away in trunks and carpet bags.

A special doll with a real bisque head might be in one corner of a

more than two centuries, is able to chime the hour. There was always room for precious personal things.

For frontier families, the work was hard and the pleasures few. Musical instruments brightened an often dreary existence. Local businessman Pierson Spining, a contractor who built part of the National Road, decided in 1832 to give something special to his twelve-year-old daughter Mary Catherine. Mary was then attending the Cincinnati Select Boarding School run by future author Harriet Beecher Stowe. She had developed an interest in the

Luxuries we take for granted were rare in early Ohio. When Pierson Spining brought the first piano to Springfield in 1832, most of the community turned out to hear his daughter Mary play it.

pianoforte. Mr. Spining ordered a new piano from Philadelphia. It was the first of its kind to make the long trip over the mountains. After being freighted by wagon to Pittsburgh, it was loaded on a flatboat to Cincinnati and again put on a wagon to Springfield. Its arrival caused quite a stir in a frontier community still starved for regular contact with the rest of the world. Mary Spining kept playing her father's pioneering gift until her death in 1905.

Family heirlooms, like the 18th century Schooley/ Spining Family quilted bedspread called a "counterpane," were lovingly preserved in trunks. The sturdy trunk to the left originated in Hamburg, Germany.

red freight wagons, with sturdy six horse teams each sporting sets of jingling bells, carried three to five tons of freight about fifteen miles a day. Springfield Mayor Oliver S. Kelly recalled how important those wagons were to Clark County.

> The big 'schooners,' hauled by four [or six] horses, brought all the drygoods from Baltimore; it used to take six to eight weeks to make the trip one way. I remember a man named Lucas once hauled 11,100 pounds at one load and the county talked about it for some years.

The colorful stagecoaches, regularly scheduled both east and west, could go faster provided a drover with a large flock of geese or sheep didn't block their way. Old time Springfielder Thomas McGrew remembered his father's experiences as a teamster near Cincinnati.

> ...The stagecoaches had the right of way because they carried the mail. When you met a stagecoach you had to give all the road especially in muddy roads...[My father] drove three yoke of cattle with a pair of leaders he called Buck and Bright, big fellows with long horns. They resented giving more than half the road and never would unless he was there to guide them. When they would meet a stagecoach the driver would blow

his horn for them to give way. The teamster would be on the wagon pretending to be asleep but the oxen would go along, pay no attention to the horn until the horses came close, then they would throw down their heads, give a snort, and the horses would lunge to one side and give them a wide berth. He always managed to be awake and out of the way of the stage driver's whip when he came up, as they were experts with the whip.

At night, the noisy, crowded taverns provided fodder for animals and a kettle of "bubble and squeak" stew along with ever present whiskey for the teamsters. National politicians, even presidents, traveled the road to and from the national capital and engaged in some old-fashioned "stump politics" at every stop.

America's first "Main Street" was eventually six hundred miles long. Millions used the highway to get to their piece of the American dream. Many found that piece in newly-settled Clark County, Ohio. George Washington's vision was realized as a sea of immigrants flooded into the Heartland on his imagined "smooth way." The National Road was the main route west for almost half a century.

Politics Stop the Road and Launch a Community (1836-1846)

Throughout the 1830s, work crews pushed the National Road west. It was taxing and tedious work, but immigrants jumped at the opportunity. The road bosses were pleased to have the large labor pool.

> German and Irish immigrant gangs worked on the road for the princely wage of ninety cents a day and a jigger of whiskey. The jigger boss was a familiar sight, passing down the lines of men with his jug.

Four separate parties of men worked on the thoroughfare. The first surveyed and cleared the brush. Another followed, building the bridges and culverts. A third graded the thirty-foot-wide roadway with picks, shovels and dumpcarts. The last then poured the three inch stones into the right of way and packed them down with a roller. Laborers sat on piles of rocks and hammered away, making pieces that would fit through a three inch ring. Many wore primitive goggles because slivers of rock flew in all directions.

The process was revolutionary for its day. The rest of the American roads hardly deserved the name. Travelers used terms like "wretched,"

"infernal" and "the Devil turned loose." An early settler described a typical road in Clark County.

> The road through the bottoms was hardly any road at all, and in soft weather, nearly every wagon and stage would be swamped in the mud. Sometimes there would be as many as fifty of them, and it would look like the wagon train of an army. They tore down the farmer's rail fence to get levers to pry the coaches out; they drove over the farmer's fields...At night, we could see them coming with their lights, a mile or two away, winding about in an effort to find the best places in the road.

But the "smooth way" also had its faults. Storms washed out the pavement stones. Culverts put in to divert the water bounced the stagecoaches unmercifully and were christened "thank-you-marms." The roads we all take for granted were a century away. On the other hand, the graceful stone bridges along the route of the National Road were well received and many survive today. When the road builders approached the prairie and good stone became scarce, they built covered wooden bridges to cross the many streams and rivers. Clark County had its own wonder spanning the Mad

River west of Springfield. The Mad River Covered Bridge was literally a "dual carriageway" (the locals called it "double-barrelled"). Almost one hundred and fifty feet long, it became a landmark on the road for ninety-five years. It finally succumbed to age and rot and was torn down in 1932. A 1,700 piece scale model was lovingly constructed from its original wood.

By 1838, the federal government had spent almost $7 million on what some enthusiastic boosters called "the Appian Way of America." The road inched west while Congress, the states and local communities continued the familiar bickering. First Newark, near Zanesville, then north and south Columbus and finally Dayton lobbied to have the road curve through their neighborhoods. The federal surveyors had their orders, straight west through the state capitals. The national arguments, for and against federal

funding for internal improvements, reached a crescendo.

> The U.S. Congress does not have the right of jurisdiction and construction. If a community wants a road or canal, let them build it!

> How are we, on the frontiers of American Civilization, going to play our part to cement the Union without federal assistance?

Congress, tired of the endless arguments, handed the road to the states in 1838. It was not a good bargain. The highway was unfinished west of Ohio and damaged by overuse everywhere else. Pennsylvania and Ohio decided to charge toll to pay for overdue repairs. Within a few years, there were tollhouses every ten to fifteen miles collecting cash for the maintenance of the road. A horse and rider paid a couple of cents and a stagecoach with four horses had to

As late as 1890, hardworking laborers on the National Road still used the same tools and looked the same as their fathers and grandfathers. The arrival of the horseless carriage would soon put a scene like this in the history books.

This handsome scale model is all that remains of the majestic two-lane covered bridge built across the Mad River with federal funds in 1837. The bridge finally succumbed to age and rot after ninety-five years, but the community kept its memory alive with a 1,700 piece model made from the salvaged wood.

Tolls were common after the federal government handed the National Road over to the states in 1838. Private citizens often banded together to build local toll roads as profit-making ventures. The ten-mile-long Springfield and Clifton Turnpike probably made money because other local roads were practically non-existent.

Clark County surveyor Thomas Kizer used his hundred-year-old Ludlow-Symmes Compass, already famous for the original surveys of the cities of Cincinnati and Springfield, to plot out the National Road in 1875. This highly-detailed section, from mid-Springfield east toward Columbus, illustrates how straight the road was.

cough up twelve cents. Users dipped into their pockets and complained about highway robbery. There were fistfights and one toll keeper took to shooting at cows if a drover passed his herd through the gate without paying the toll. Finally, sullen complacency set in and, while Ohio raised over $1 million during the next fifty years, the road continued to deteriorate.

One community benefited from the end of federal funding for the National Road. The magnificent thirty-foot right-of-way swept through the middle of downtown Springfield and then abruptly stopped just west of town. Not until the 1850s was the road "graded up." Nearby Dayton, trying to lure travelers in that direction, had built a road of its own. The Dayton road ran right by old-timer J. J. Snyder's house.

> Well, a good many people, when they reached Springfield…were thoroughly tired out, and rather than go on decided to settle here, especially as Springfield seemed to be an attractive sort of place. The town gained many inhabitants in this way.

Adventurers who traveled further met the usual tree stumps and mud for a decade until Indiana found its own funds to continue the road. Suddenly Springfield became the bustling "Town at the End of the Pike."

Nobody had paid much attention to Springfield during its first three decades. It was growing apace but, until the 1830s, it was just another sleepy frontier community. Locals were

fond of calling it a "hard lookin' place" and "[no] city by any means and manners." James Johnson, Sr. came to town when he was six,

> One could not see fifty yards in front of him, on account of the thick growth of hazel bush and scrub oak. My good Irish mother used to sit and cry for fear we'd be attacked by bears – and even Indians were seen not unfrequently. And game!
> Why it was nothing to see flocks of…a hundred and fifty wild turkeys, and you could go out any morning before breakfast and knock a dozen quail over with a stick. Springfield was a little bit of a place at that time; I suppose that there were no more than…thirty at the most, brick houses in town.

Like all settlements on the edge of civilization, Springfield had its rough edges. John Ludlow, an early chronicler, commented on what the settlers called recreation.

> The morals of the people…were in a low state. Drinking, horse-racing and gambling were of frequent occurrence; and on Saturday, when a large number of people from the country were accus-

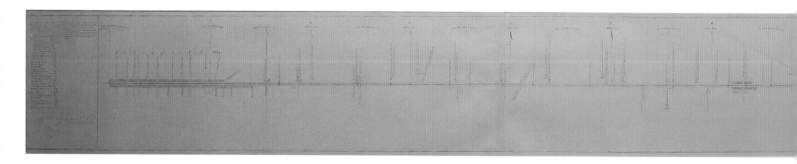

TOLL SHEET

OF THE NATIONAL ROAD AS ESTABLISHED BY THE BOARD OF COUNTY COMMISSIONERS OF FRANKLIN COUNTY, OHIO.

Ordered the tolls on that part of the National Road in Franklin County, Ohio, shall be and the same are hereby established as follows, for every ten miles of travel:

For every Cart or Wagon if drawn by One Horse or other animal,	12 cents
For every Cart or Wagon if drawn by Two Horses or other animals,	25 cents
For every Cart or Wagon if drawn by Three Horses or other animals,	35 cents
For every Cart or Wagon if drawn by Four Horses or other animals,	45 cents
For every Cart or Wagon if drawn by Five Horses or other animals,	60 cents
For every Cart or Wagon if drawn by Six Horses or other animals,	70 cents
For each Horse in addition,	12 cents
For every Gig, Sulky, Buggy or Dearborn with One Seat, drawn by One Horse or other animals,	12 cents
For each Horse in addition,	6 cents
For every Buggy, Carriage or Dearborn having Two Seats, drawn by One Horse or other animals,	20 cents
For each Horse in addition,	6 cents
For every Coach or Hack with Two or Three Seats, drawn by Two Horses or other animals,	30 cents
For each Horse in addition,	12 cents
For every Omnibus drawn by Two Horses or other animals,	40 cents
For every Coach with Four Seats or Omnibus drawn by Four Horses or other animals,	75 cents
For each Horse in addition,	12 cents
For every Sled or Sleigh drawn by One Horse or other animals,	12 cents
For each Horse in addition,	6 cents
For every Horse, Mule or Ass with Rider,	6 cents
For every Horse, Mule or Ass led or driven,	5 cents
For every Score of Cattle,	25 cents
For every Score of Hogs,	12 cents
For every Score of Sheep,	12 cents

And in the proper ratio with the above for any number of miles less than ten, provided that any person residing on the road within ten miles of any gate, may compound by paying quarterly in advance such sums as the Gate Keeper may deem just and reasonable, which sum together with 25 per centum on the same shall be credited to such person, and the distance traveled by them, their families or servants, shall be charged to them at the above rates.

OFFICE OF THE BOARD OF COUNTY COMMISSIONERS, COLUMBUS, FRANKLIN CO., OHIO.

I HEREBY CERTIFY, That the foregoing Rates of Toll on the National Road in this County, as established by the Board of County Commissioners, and the proviso annexed thereto, are correctly taken from the Journal of the Board.

W. H. HALLIDAY, AUDITOR, FRANKLIN COUNTY, OHIO.

---

tomed to visit the town, quarreling and fighting was frequently the order of the day. It was the custom at the stores to keep a bottle of whisky by the side of the water pitcher…the whisky bottle was thought to be as necessary an article in the harvest field as the sickle or cradle. Such evil practices as these were making bad work upon the morals and social condition of the people of both town and country…

…all who desired, and had the money to pay, could get a dram and drink it…no concealment was thought of – the liquor straight and the drinking was straight, in full sight of all present or passing by…

James Johnson, Sr. had a different view of all the drinking.

There was not nearly so much drunkenness then, although whiskey was almost as free as water… In the taverns two of you could get a drink for a flip-and-a-bit, you know we hadn't any cent pieces, or nickles, or dimes then. Our change was 6 1/4 cents (a flip-and-a-bit) and 12 1/2 cents. And

---

everybody drank whiskey then…But nobody ever thought of taking a glass full of whiskey like they do now, about one finger was the usual drink.

The population of Springfield was pushing 1,000 by 1830. When the National Road showed up in the 1830s, the town was ready. Back in 1828, the local newspaper *Western Pioneer* detailed at least 115 local businesses which included six blacksmiths, four coach and wagon makers, three saddle and harness shops and three "good houses of entertainment." A flood of stagecoaches and conestogas came to town with the road and the number of taverns and hotels skyrocketed. Twelve hundred wagons a day were lumbering through town by 1836. A weekly newspaper was only one of the amenities adding some luster to daily life. A four-horse coach arrived daily to pick up the mail and a letter could get to the east coast in just five days. There was a not very bellicose but "best drilled and neatest equipped" militia company called out for special occasions. There was also a brand new bookstore, a courthouse bell with a "long and clamorous tongue" and a $50 sixteen-foot-square brick jail with a mean looking black

---

The Franklin County Toll Sheet lists the fees typical for ten miles of travel on the National Road. Any animal-pulled vehicle cost at least twelve cents and a six-horse freight wagon paid a pocket-book emptying seventy cents. Stagecoaches paid even more, but there is no mention of fees for pedestrians or "movers" who often pulled or pushed carts themselves.

One surviving Clark County National Road tollhouse was photographed after its toll-taking days had ended. These structures, which contained spartan living quarters, were much simpler than the handsome brick tollhouses on the original Maryland/ Pennsylvania sections of the road. Nearby gates on the roadway could be raised and lowered to control traffic.

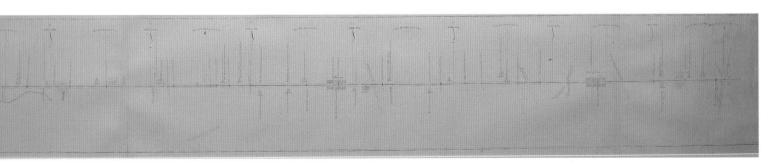

Tippecanoe and Tyler, too

The rare 1840 political ribbon below depicts the Springfield "Whig" Club building a mock frontier log cabin to honor general and presidential candidate William Henry "Tippecanoe" Harrison. "Tippecanoe" won the presidency only to die a month after his inauguration.

A whimsical 1845 Springfield Whig Party ribbon (above right) promotes success in recruiting Clark County "mechanics and farmers" and looks forward to the 1846 election. Militiaman Peter Ebersole used the highly decorated scarf at right to carry his silk hat as he rode in a parade honoring his hero General Harrison.

The 1840 presidential election campaign sparked the Heartland's imagination. Americans embraced their own unique brand of politics and produced ribbons, banners, songs and slogans. Clark Countians gathered to celebrate their own western candidate. It was a rip roaring time remembered fondly by many early settlers.

Kentucky Senator Henry Clay had been the continuing Whig candidate against the Jacksonian Democrats. Clay had always been a strong advocate of westward expansion, but, in 1840, a new candidate eclipsed him. William Henry Harrison was a War of 1812 hero, credited with defeating the famous Shawnee Chief Tecumseh. While his view of the presidency was limited, all the westerners knew he supported federal funding for the National Road. Harrison's handlers created a strong frontier image for the campaign. It was log cabins, hard cider, coon skins and an 1814 Battle called Tippecanoe, all for a candidate with aristocratic ties to Virginia. Clark County joined the country in extolling the "Log Cabin" Harrison with unbridled enthusiasm, or as one local put it, "There was never in this country so much nonsense in a campaign."

Fifteen thousand citizens raised a log cabin in honor of Tippecanoe Harrison and Tyler (John Tyler of Virginia) too.

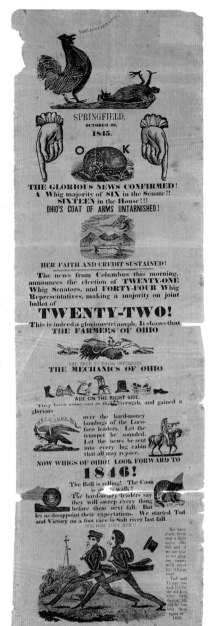

Everywhere, and especially on Main Street [in Springfield], five hundred flags…flapped in the morning breeze. A multitude repaired to the Market House where a table 1,000 feet in length was loaded with provisions.

In South Charleston [Clark County's second largest community], a pole was raised in the town center and topped with a keg marked 'Hard Cider for Harrison.' Excitement exists all over the Union for General Harrison.

Springfield was always a great political town. I remember in 1840, during the Harrison campaign, Tom Corwin made a speech here, in the woods on west Main St…There were several acres of people to hear him. A big stump, six feet across, had been brought from the woods for him to stand on…

This village… held an even row with all others in the 1840 excitement. The Carlisle boys brought the great ball and kept it rolling. Two men, one on either side, rolled it down the street, while the third man stood on it, walking backwards as the men rolled it along, and sang a song. A thunderstorm overtook them in the West End and spoiled the imposing appearance they intended to make…The Democrats said it was a judgment sent upon the Whigs for their folly. By being put upon a store box…I got a clear view of General Harrison. The afternoon was fair and the multitude was harangued by speakers on horseback.

I recollect that big Harrison convention of 1840. The National Road was just built, and there were toll gates at intervals along it. I remember that when the immense procession came along from Columbus with high poles and log cabins with coons clambering over them. The poles of the toll houses had to be removed to allow the procession to pass.

I remember, also, that when Gen. Harrison was called home by a letter announcing the death of his son, the opposition campaign papers and orators said it was because he was an ignorant man that could not make a speech to such a large crowd, but their minds were disabused of that, for the general returned in about two months and addressed an immense concourse of people at Urbana. I heard that speech and it was a very good one.

No more federal funds were destined for the National Road. William Henry Harrison, the "Log Cabin" President, died of pneumonia only a month after his inauguration.

bear chained to its front door. Double reflector street lights began to dot the streets. Households had to pay 12 ½ cents for oil and wicks and were required to keep the lamp in front of their home lit.

Like Mississippi steamboats, the stagecoaches caused quite a stir when their horns blared and they "came tearing into town." Old John Monahan remembered what a pleasure it was for a twelve-year-old to watch twenty stages stop every day.

> Springfield was a great stagecoach town; after the National road was built the greatest part of the travel of the state passed through here. The stages...[were] drawn by four horses, or six when the road was rough, and carrying from eighteen to twenty-four passengers, baggage, and mail from Vienna Cross Roads, eleven miles in fifty minutes. Yes sir, they did make good time. Why, after the National road got settled it was as smooth as this floor, and on a still night you could hear the coach when it left Harmony. And it was a mighty fine way to ride, too, just as easy as a rocking chair.

The old stage-yards and barns were usually packed...full of coaches. The stables often held four or five hundred horses. The stage drivers were a lot of fine fellows, and to see them about the hotel you would think they were congressmen or something. They always dressed in the latest and always kept themselves spic and span. They got $13.00 a month and were boarded at the best hotels. Their runs were from ten to twelve miles.

> The drivers had to be men of some grit; it was no easy job, I tell you, especially in the winter time before the pikes were built. Often on the old Sandusky Line the passengers would have to get out and help pry the coach out of the mud and then wade through it themselves...
>
> They used some mighty fine horses, horses that any gentleman would be proud to drive to his carriage, and they were always kept in the pink of condition.

The stagecoaches and the freight wagons only lasted for two generations, but they captured the drama and romance of America's first western migration.

Thomas Wharton sketched this earliest view of Springfield from the east in 1832. A cluster of buildings, dwarfed by rolling countryside, appears the way approaching travelers saw it. The first Clark County Courthouse, built in 1827, dominates the town skyline while a large house stands atop a hill on the left of the drawing. *(Cincinnati Museum Center)*

Amazing Innovations Bring More Development (1846-1861)

By the 1840s, the horse had a rival that moved ahead with "irresistible momentum." While America experimented with rails to help horse drawn vehicles down bumpy roads, the English first noticed the value of using steam engines for land transportation. But it was an American businessman, Peter Cooper, who, in 1830, first successfully married a practical steam engine to the stage coach. His experimental "Tom Thumb," able to pull four tons at fifteen miles per hour, lost a race with a horse but proved the technology could work. The race was on to find

A blurred early photograph opens a rare window to the evolving steam railroads that converged on Clark County in the 1840s. In spite of their shortcomings, the railroads were a huge technological leap over the wagons, stage-coaches and canal boats that brought the first generation of settlers to Ohio.

The cutting edge 1837 Pioneer "Fast Line" promised a four hundred mile combination railroad and canal boat trip from Philadelphia to Pittsburgh in just three and a half days. From Pittsburgh, you could take your chances, booking passage on a steam packet down the Ohio River. *(Courtesy of the Penn Central Post)*

an efficient steam engine and good rails for it to ride on. The rails turned out to be the greater challenge, not totally met until steel appeared in American factories.

The canal builders fought the railroads at every turn. They had the support of legislators and were able to block rail development for a time, but railroad mania trumped all the other interests. There was something uniquely American about the belching, dirty, noisy "Iron Horse." It could feed everyone's incessant desire to travel. It could subjugate, while canals and roads could only adapt, nature. Its wide-spread development was a new source of jobs for an increasing flood of Irish immigrants. It created new factories as the industrial revolution kicked into gear. Davy Crockett may have called it "hell in harness," but what other technology could propel you through the landscape at thirty miles per hour?

New England poet Ralph Waldo Emerson was ambivalent about this revolutionary new technology. At first, he was euphoric that the railroad could help the United States conquer the continent. Then he considered how these ugly machines could pollute the garden that nature had given America.

> The character of [railroad] work...violates the primal...forms of nature, the villages of shanties at the edge of beautiful lakes, the blowing of rocks, explosions all day.

Others only saw the dawn of a breathtaking new era that would change everything for the better. One thing was certain. In places like Clark County, the pioneer age soon came to an end.

The railroad age ushered in the next western frontier. The new industry brought civilization to the Mississippi River and the new city of Chicago. By 1850, almost six thousand miles of roadbed linked up the countryside as never before. The quality of the rail was often second rate, accidents were common and many of the trains could still only go twenty miles per hour. Judge E. G. Dial, who left Cincinnati on his first train trip in 1844, liked it that way.

> In the afternoon, we came as far as Xenia, where we had supper and went to bed like civilized human beings. The next morning we started out again and...in the afternoon reached Columbus – making a trip from Cincinnati to Columbus in two days. We thought it no particular hardship to travel so slowly – indeed, we thought we got along at a rapid rate.

There was, however, an inevitable and reckless emphasis on speed both in steamboats and trains. Engines were soon able to go a mile in sixty seconds. The result was a rash of boiler explosions and wrecks that took many lives. New Yorker Philip Hone was worried about the future.

> ...This world is going too fast. Improvements, Politics, Reform, Religion – all fly. Railroads, steamers, packets, race against time and beat it hollow. Flying is dangerous...Oh, for the good old days of heavy post-coaches and speed at the rate of six miles an hour!

Clark County welcomed its first railroad in 1846. Local investors had worked long and hard to help the community participate in the new technology. The "Major," William Hunt, moved his family to Clark County and negotiated a railroad charter way back in 1832. He always claimed that the Mad River and Lake Erie Railroad was the "father of western railroads," but the Little Miami got to Springfield first. Both lines faced huge obstacles as they laid their tracks.

Cholera was often a killer among the work crews and sometimes visited the community itself. One epidemic near Springfield in 1849 killed between fifty and seventy-five Irish rail workers. And, beyond the incessant "right of way tangles, delayed supplies and political wrangles," Clark County was noted for bottomless swamps. Mrs. George Frankenburg remembered a childhood incident.

> It was a very swampy country around here and it was necessary to lay rails and sometimes even logs across the roads to keep the wagons from miring. When I was quite a small schoolgirl, I remember we all came down from the school one day to see some men dig several cows out of a big swamp, right where the Arcade building now is [today it is the site of the Springfield Inn].

The Little Miami line came up from Cincinnati. Scrap iron was spiked onto wooden rails that were first laid in mud sills cut in the ground. Oliver S. Kelly recalled that it proved to be a less than perfect rail system.

All that remains of the first Clark County railroads is a handful of artifacts. A spike, a hammer, a Dayton-made lantern, a fragment of original track and a 1907 model of the first jerry-rigged Little Miami Railroad track recall a hundred and fifty year old revolution that gave Clark County never imagined access to the rest of the world.

Along with the railroad, the 1840s brought the "electric spark" telegraph to Clark County. In 1848, the magic dots and dashes of Samuel Morse's code announced General Zachary Taylor's election to the presidency directly from Washington, D.C. Telegraph keys like the New York model to the right were clicking out messages that linked every city and town in America.

Every once in a while the end of one of the iron rails would come loose, and turning up would make what we called a gooseneck, and would run into a car, smashing things in general.

But long-term durability was the last thing on the railroad builders' minds as they raced to be the first to reach Springfield. On August 6, 1846, excited townspeople heard the lonesome whistle of the locomotive, "Ohio," for the first time. Regular passenger travel to Cincinnati began five days later to toasts all around and at least five longwinded speakers. Two years later, the locomotive, "Seneca," representing the Mad River and Lake Erie Line, made the trip south from the Great Lakes. Clark County now had railroad links to all the points of the compass.

With its piece of railroad mania, the County suddenly had never imagined access to the outside world. An 1852 map charted the two railroad lines bisecting in downtown Springfield. Nothing could ever be the same again. In that year, a promotional booklet, "Sketches of Springfield," noted the all-important change.

This was an important event in Springfield's history, for with the completion of this road, the town began to increase still more rapidly in improvements and business importance.

The community with the "goahead" attitude was launched into the modern era.

The changes were breathtaking. Just twenty years earlier, Springfield was a brawling, frontier town and now a mysterious new invention had arrived the same year as the Mad River and Lake Erie Railroad. An artist turned inventor, with a passion for the mysteries of electricity, was convinced he could use "the electric spark by way of telegraph." After years of tinkering, Samuel F. B. Morse sent his first public message from the U. S. Supreme Court Chamber in 1844. The words "what hath God wrought" literally electrified the nation.

…This is incredible. My faith is staggered. I see that the result is produced, but I have no faith of the understanding of it.

The perfect success of Professor Morse's electric magnetic telegraph has excited the astonishment and admiration of the community…The experiments have satisfied the public that the magnetic telegraph is not merely a beautiful illustration of a philosophical principle, but an agent that may be made of practical and every day utility in the business transactions of the country.

Within four years, 5,000 miles of telegraph line were laid across the land. When they were setting the poles and stringing the wire in Clark County, a lady in Harmony Township observed that the "new fangled clothes line is being hung too high. The wind will blow the clothes to tatters." In 1848, Clark County received the announcement of Zachary Taylor's election to the presidency instantaneously from the National Capital!

Taverns and Churches

With thousands of tired and hungry souls passing through, first on the National Road and then on railroads, taverns and hotels were big business in the "Town at the End of the Pike." There were massive stone and brick "public houses" for all classes of traveler every ten miles or so on the National Road. The Pennsylvania House, literally at the end of the pike in west Springfield, was one of those structures, catering to the many teamsters transporting tons of freight. But, in a community overrun with strangers, any shelter was fair game. Privacy was often simply non-existent.

> I had twenty teamsters pay fifty cents to sleep on my floor and they were glad to escape the rain and cold.

While taverns were licensed, no keeper needed a good housekeeping seal of approval. There were several nice lodgings in town, including Pierson Spining's hotel which featured an open courtyard with galleries around, and the "Buckeye House" where well heeled guests could expect to be "brandied." In an age rarely noted for its hygiene, however, some establishments were downright disgusting.

> I spent the night in a bed with four other godforsaken souls, never knowing whether I would get my pocket picked or be carried off by vermin.

The incessant whiskey drinking also often made pub stays noisy and risky.

> A pair of teamsters found reason to square off over a matter of no consequence. The result was a grand contest of vigorous ear biting, much to the delight of the drunken revelers.

In the midst of this confusion, there was a hospitality giant in Springfield for decades. Col. "Billy" Werden, called "one of the best known men of the West," ran the "world renowned" National Hotel and later the larger Werden House. A Delaware transplant with no known military connections, the "Colonel" was a big, boisterous, generous man. His instincts included a thoroughgoing understanding of quality service for customers. His career spawned dozens of cherished community stories.

> Uncle Billy Werden...sat at the head and front of everything. He was a great big, jolly fellow, whom everybody liked, and he kept a mighty fine hotel, and set a mighty fine table. I remember he had in his yard a coop 30 feet long, that he kept filled with quail that he purchased for thirty-seven cents a dozen from boys who trapped them.
>
> His sign was that of a stagecoach, and horses under full speed, suspended on a tall post at the

The Pennsylvania House (below), now operated as a museum by the Daughters of the American Revolution, was literally at the end of the National Road just west of town. John Thomas hung out his Black Horse Tavern sign in 1834 (left) and ran his log "public house" in North Hampton for two decades.

> outer edge of the sidewalk...When a weary traveler stopped at his door, Mr. Werden was the first to meet him and conduct him into the house, where his muddy...boots were removed by a servant, and a pair of clean slippers supplied. The frequent attentions of the polite host, and warm fire, soon caused the stranger to feel at home, and a bountiful meal well prepared under the direction of Mrs. Werden, with a clean bed and a good night's rest, were well calculated to gain the good will of the traveler.
>
> Two Kentuckians who were stopping at the house saw [Mr. Werden's] boots in the hall as they were about to leave in the morning. Astonished at their size, they asked...Colonel Werden...who wore those immense boots. The Colonel replied, "Oh, a man who stays here"... They ordered their horses back to the stable and sat down to await the appearance of their curiosity. Colonel Werden allowed them to wait until ten or eleven o'clock, before he appeared before them with the boots on.

William Werden was one of several bigger-than-

Early taverns featured gallons of whiskey and few frills. Note the pitcher, probably filled with "spiritous liquor," the announcements of public sales and the snakeskins tacked on the wall, the stuffed raccoon and the "bar," able to be closed denying over zealous patrons access to the bottles and the jugs on the shelves. One nod to fashion is the decorated wall clock. In a world where tobacco chewing was universal, the spittoon on the floor was a necessary part of the décor. *(Painting by August Kollner, Chicago Historical Society)*

Many taverns catered to rough teamsters and drovers so vividly drawn by George Caleb Bingham (above). *(The Nelson-Adkins Museum of Art, Kansas City, Missouri. Lent by the People of Missouri through the generosity of Mr. and Mrs. Herman Robert Sutherland)*

An 1831 handwritten receipt has somehow survived one hundred and seventy years to give us a glimpse of early Springfield bureacracy. "Colonel Billy" Werden, "one of the "best known men of the West," had to plunk down his ten dollars like everyone else to "keep a tavern in the town of Springfield for the term of one year."

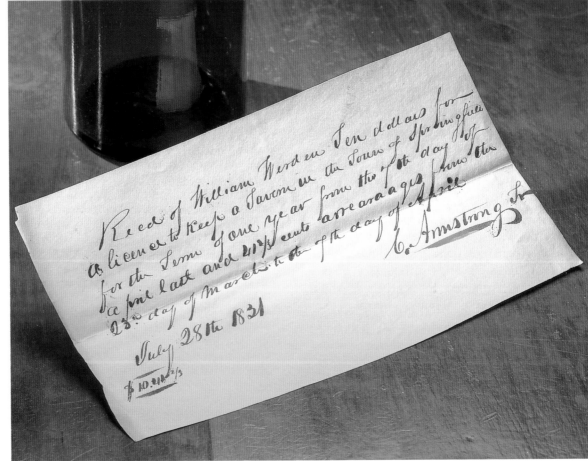

life settlers who put their special stamp on early Springfield and Clark County.

After the Civil War, rough taverns turned into more respectable bars and saloons. An assortment of ale and whiskey houses lined Main Street, ready to relieve the community's many factory workers of their paychecks every Friday night. The rowdy, unbridled drinking in nineteenth century America was funny to some and pathetic to others. Newspapers have always printed stories about local drunks. South Charleston had its own example in January of 1880.

> A man named Coffee got saturated...and while trying to get out of town slid gently from his horse, concluding to take a nap before he went further. Policeman Schietz, with great gentleness, plumped him into a wheelbarrow and carried him to the Bastille. After his nap was about out, Mayor Barret called for $4.70 in payment for lodgings, which was paid, and Mr. Coffee went home to tea.

For many, this amusing anecdote hid a terrible truth. Free flowing spirits often ruined lives and destroyed families. The tension between drinkers and teetotalers was present from the very beginning.

Religion played a big role in efforts to tame a roughhewn settlement. It seems fitting that the first religious services, organized by Mrs. Walter Smallwood's Methodist Society in 1803, were observed in the first tavern, built of logs by Griffith Foos. Tough frontiersmen often would drink to excess and then humble themselves at religious revivals. Mrs. George Frankenburg remembered her father's battle with the bottle.

> I am sorry to say that nearly every man went home from [military] muster drunk, for when I was a very small child every man drank intoxicants...It was the summer of 1832, at the time of the first great temperance move here - the Washingtonians, the pledge signers were called... After the speeches my father went up and signed the pledge. I will never forget how my mother talked to him on the way home. She was frightened, for such a thing had never been heard of. She reminded him that he had a large number of harvest hands...and that probably every one would quit work. In the morning my father called the men about him and told them what he had done and explained that, of course, he could not give them liquor, either. Well, sir, not one of them quit work...They took out [several barrels of whiskey and cherry-bounce] and knocked the heads in. I remember the whiskey ran down a little gulley where the hogs were, and every one of them got sot-drunk. I never see a drunk man that I do not think of those hogs.

"Uncle Billy" Werden's self-styled "world renowned" National Hotel survived in Springfield into the era of photography. The boisterous Mr. Werden put up a tall sign depicting a stagecoach and horses running at full speed and then set a high standard for service and hospitality. Werden and his hotel were at the center of the budding community's social life as the "Colonel" pampered, "brandied" and "gained the good will of travelers" for decades.

This 1844 painting by James Goodwyn Clonney shows a politician "stumping" in his "claw hammer" coat and pushing a chair aside to make his point as he argues with a working man. The others are looking on in bemusement. *(Photograph by Richard Walker, New York State Historical Association, Cooperstown, New York)*

After the Civil War, Springfield saloons became homes away from home. Whole paychecks disappeared in this friendly environment. Compare the women bartenders with the young lady in the painting above. Enormous social changes had occurred in just one generation.

The presence of so much whiskey undermined civil behavior and "there were men and women in Springfield who were anxious for a remedy." On the frontier, the remedies erupted as revivals filled with religious fervor.

During the winter of 1811, there was quite a religious revival in Springfield. A number of 'New Light' preachers converged on the town to conduct a 'season of religious excitement.' Their revival meetings were lively, accompanied by a lot of jerking and falling down of converts 'seeing the new light' unknown to them before. Numbers of non-churchgoing frontiersmen were converted to Christianity as a result. Their enthusiasm was so great that they erected the first real church in Springfield. Two years later, the Methodists built the second church...

Three Methodist circuit riders tended to the Springfield faithful until the Reverend Saul Henkle arrived with his wife and two-month-old child in 1809. For the next twenty-eight years, "...scarcely a man and woman joined in matrimony, or citizen committed to the grave, but that Mr. Henkle performed the religious rite." He was a devout and tireless missionary, determined to bring godliness to the frontier. During the many funerals he attended, he was fond of singing an old-fashioned hymn as he followed the coffin to the grave.

Hark! From the tomb a doleful sound!
　　Mine ear, attend the cry!
Ye living men, come view the ground
　　Where you must shortly lie.

More than just a preacher, the Reverend Mr. Henkle was a politician, temperance leader and newspaper editor. In an unforgiving land where life was hard and short, he was a solid moral example, "setting a high bar so all sinners could know and face their Creator."

The "New Lights" built the first church of logs with a rough, unpainted pulpit that stood high off the floor. Fitting the mood of piety the evangelists brought to Springfield in 1810, Griffith Foos subscribed "a fine horse at ten dollars" requesting that the structure be available to other denominations that had no place of
continued on page 35.

Peter Keller first showed up in the 1876 Springfield City Directory as a brewer of ale and lager beer. By 1882, he had opened his own saloon and hung out this sign. His business, vying with a sea of drinking establishments in Golden Age Springfield, lasted only four years.

After a sect called the "New Lights" brought a religious revival to Springfield and built a log church in 1811, a community of churches grew quickly. On the eve of the Civil War, there were fourteen denominations with a total of two thousand communicants. The Springfield skyline became noted for its tall spires. The 1848 Old Covenant Presbyterian Church was a feature of Main Street. The county communities had their own attractive chapels like the Greek Revival Christian Church built in 1846 at Plattsburg near South Vienna.

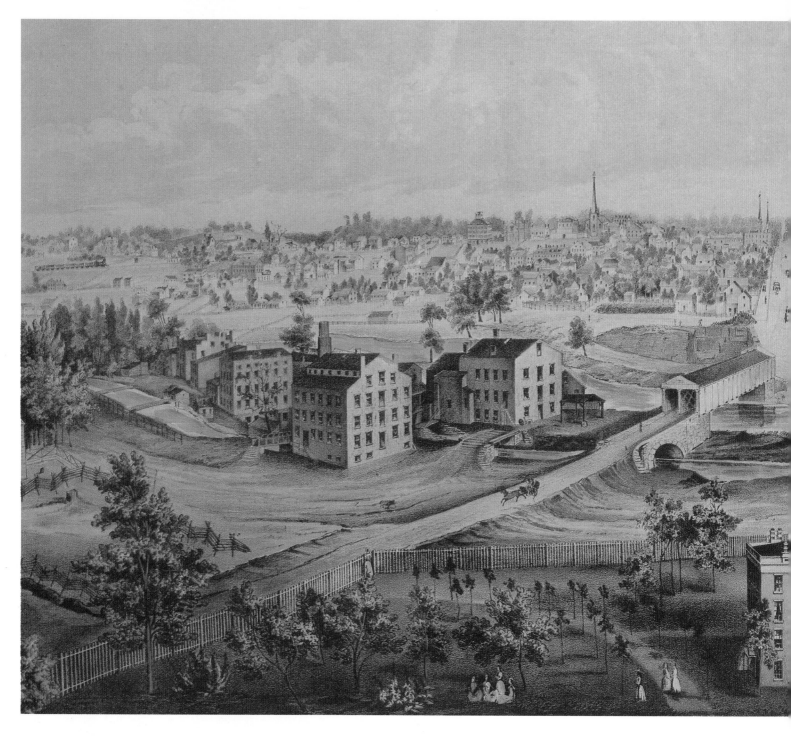

Springfield at Mid Century

This romantic 1854 "View of Springfield" depicts a growing community on the verge of an era of major prosperity. Smoking factories are nowhere in evidence and the railroad is still off in the distance. The emphasis, in the foreground, is on an idyllic school for females and a set of brick mills powered by the abundant waters of Buck Creek. Limestone Street is a wide way moving toward downtown and a busy Main Street on the National Road. The National Road became a busy Main Street (opposite page) as it passed through Springfield. (*Cincinnati Museum Center*)

By 1850, the newly incorporated "City" of Springfield and its elected mayor were proclaiming a graduation, in just two generations, from wilderness to developing industrial powerhouse. There was a bold sense of achievement trumpeted in the "Sketches of Springfield," an 1852 promotional booklet.

The advantages of Springfield in point of location and general health – its means of moral and intellectual improvement – its abundant water privileges for manufacturing – its Railroad and Telegraphic facilities – and its unbounded resources for building – are scarcely excelled, and are such as will cause the city to move onward in improvements and prosperity for years to come.

There was also, for the first time, a real snapshot of the budding community. Springfield sponsored its first color lithograph in 1854, an overview of the city. The aim of the illustration is to show a prosperous, but still idyllic place. The new railroad and the downtown are still in the far distance. Homes, churches and schools are featured.

Limestone Street, pointing to the center of town with a few discreet carriages and riders in the roadway, is a wide swath aimed at the horizon. A large brick school and a cluster of mills are front and center.

The handsome Springfield Female Seminary, in a "prosperous and flourishing condition, with four acres of beautiful premises…[and] bright prospects for the future," fills the foreground. The mill complex to the left was part of the water-run industry that was making Springfield famous. Flour mills, around since the beginning of settlement, were annually generating the "snug sum of a million dollars." Five large woolen mills were replacing the home weaving so popular in eastern Clark County.

Jerome Fassler sits on his "Champion" mower in the bleak and dusty Springfield Market Square. A separator (threshing) machine and several horses stand idly in the background. This pre-Civil War photograph documents the city's downtown on the eve of Fassler's phenomenal manufacturing partnership with William Whiteley and Oliver S. Kelly.

Steam power was still rare because the neighborhood was blessed with water that gushed down Lagonda (later Buck) Creek on its way to the Mad River. An inventor named James Leffel learned how to effectively harness that power and revolutionized the design of water wheels in the process.

The 1856 directory, complete with a list of twenty-four city officers, chronicled how the changes were accelerating. Springfield could now boast two new railroads and tracks heading out in five directions. There were five newspapers including the popular daily and weekly *Nonpareil*, claiming to be "Independent in Everything – Neutral in Nothing." There were

two telegraph offices and a resident dentist promising "safety and ease to his patients." The new "Photographic Art" was now represented by three studios, giving Clark County another magical invention, black and white images of loved ones for their posterity. The Springfield Gas and Coke Company was installing street lights and piping gas for lighting into several downtown buildings.

Sometime late in the decade, a photographer captured one of the earliest surviving photographic images of downtown Springfield. The town square is a bleak, dusty place.

In the foreground, a machinist named Jerome Fassler sits on a mowing machine. He and a young

inventor named William Whiteley had been building new-fangled devices to help farmers mow and reap their wheat. The 1856 Directory mentioned Whiteley's efforts in an addendum.

"Mr. Whiteley, whose Reaper met with uniform and remarkable success last season, is preparing to manufacture for the coming season fifty Reapers and Mowers. Already is his enterprise in active operation. Success to Young America and his model machine."

That photograph and that footnote heralded the birth of a business that would bring the world's attention to Clark County.

Springfield was beginning to

tured educator Horace Mann among its five speakers in the 1855-56 season. The Young Men's Christian Association, advocating the "moral and religious improvement of young men and relieving the want and suffering of the destitute poor," was eighty members strong. Out in Donnelsville, two expert violinists put together a string band for school exhibitions and "those who tripped the light, fantastic toe."

One long-term cultural achievement had happened almost by accident. Springfield wasn't much interested in adopting a Lutheran college. Many in the religious community looked at the Lutherans as beer drinkers who were "liberal" in their observance of the Sabbath. For its part, the budding institution was just looking for a good, central location in Ohio. Springfield beat out Xenia when it offered a slightly better deal. In 1845, eight students, with little fanfare, met in the basement of the local Lutheran church.

Four years later, Wittenberg College was ready to move to its permanent home on a beautiful northside site originally planned for a cemetery. The College was "entirely new [for a community like Springfield]. It had its own future to make." But, by 1856, the town was boasting there were 164 students at an institution that "enjoys a reputation which seems to be deserved and will doubtless prove enduring."

For all of its pretense to urbanity, Springfield was still a town of tough neighborhoods divided east and west by the swampy, meandering Mill Run and later north and south by Buck Creek. Mill Run ran several of the town's earliest mills as it cascaded north into Buck Creek. The National Road crossed Mill Run on a wooden bridge,

> an ugly structure [that] divided the business of Springfield into two parties quite jealous of each other. The boys would meet and fight on this structure,

reminding Thomas McGrew of

> How well [the Roman hero] Horat[ius] held the bridge in the brave days of old...Property was rated in reference to which side of the bridge...The west side was named Old Virginia...the east side, Springfield.
>
> Men and boys became partisans...When I arrived in Springfield in 1856 this partisanship was still

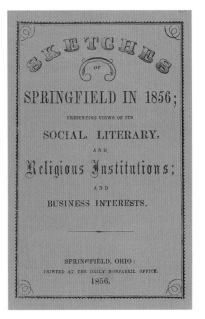

cultivated and at times was quite violent.

The source of this neighborhood rivalry was born of the original migrations to Clark County. "Old Virginia" was populated by Kentuckians and Virginians, traveling from the south on old military roads. One of the unsavory parts of this section was christened "Rat Row." Many easterners, more sophisticated immigrants from New England and Pennsylvania, came to the east end on routes through the Western Reserve in northeast Ohio. Money and status continued to reside in the east and north into the twentieth century.

There were tribal conflicts from other sources in pre-Civil War Springfield. The community's young "blades" found exciting "action " in the volunteer fire companies.

> Great times the fire companies of this city used to have; the rivalry was of the very interested kind. When I [James R. Cushman] was in the old 'Rover' Company, the 'Neptunes' used to be their greatest rivals. The 'Neptune' Company was composed mostly of young fellows; ten or fifteen of them boarded together...Whenever one of them saw or heard of a fire, instead of raising an alarm, he would hustle up to the boarding house, route out the company out of bed and get their engine and reel out before the other company heard of the fire. A few sparks were enough to get the companies out. The companies were always anxious to make a run, anxious to get a stream of water on a fire. It was considered a big disgrace to go to a fire and not throw a stream of water; so no matter how small the fire there soon would be two or three streams of water play-

grow up in the 1850s. The population had more than doubled in a decade to almost seven thousand souls. Back in the rough frontier days of 1829, the Reverend Henkle had declared all benevolent and literary causes in a possibly fatal "distemper." The sophisticated Warder family had come to the rescue from Philadelphia. Blessed with business sense and good breeding, Jeremiah Warder built a local empire and then shared that success with his adopted community. The results were evident in Springfield's growing sophistication. The Warders' own creation, a Springfield Lyceum, now had three hundred volumes in its library. The brand new Irving Lecture Club fea-

Only four years after the first "Sketches" of Springfield, a second edition trumpeted the town's energy, industry and livability. With a slate of city officers, four railroads and two telegraph offices, Springfield was in tune with America's progress. The "Sketches" were printed by the Catholic and immigrant hating "Know Nothing" newspaper *Nonpareil*, indicating all was not perfect in the soon-to-be "Champion City."

ing on it. I remember especially one house… where there was only a small blaze, I don't suppose the department now would even turn the hose on it, but every company got a hose laid and together they ruined the house and the furniture. It was to prevent such work as that, that City Council appointed Jerry Klinefelter of the 'Neptunes,' Chief of the Fire Department. Of course, the appointment met with strong opposition of the 'Rovers' and they refused to take orders from him. The quarrel grew so bitter that finally the 'Rovers' disbanded.

The "Rover" Company attracted young Republicans, considered radicals for their abolitionist views. Everyone who worked at the Driscol Carriage Works was a member and one worker, Green Michael, was the captain. Driscol made a fancy hose reel for the "Rovers" for $1,000. Many of these men joined the Union army and served with the Company's most famous member, General J. Warren Keifer. The "Rovers" left behind one of Clark County's most touching pre-Civil War artifacts, a set of over one hundred ambrotype case photographs of members grouped in a frame around a photograph of their favorite fire engine. Here are the men who fought the Civil War, staring proudly into the camera in 1859, only two years before the upheaval that would change all of their lives.

Old-timer William Diehl once said that Springfield "has been noted for more curiosities of different kinds than any other city in the Union." One of those curiosities was one of the first of the local promotional events that are now so common around the United States.

I believe Springfield was the first town to have a baby show… Along…about '47…a lot of old bachelors…got up a baby show. Three large prizes were offered and the contest was open to the world. Well, sir, it brought babies from all over the Union, and it was spoken of and published all over America… Travelers who met each other would say: "Well, where are you

Two features on the map of 1852 Springfield point to future success. The new railroads crisscross in the center of the community. Just north of downtown, Buck Creek, with its Mill Race tributary, snakes its way toward the Mad River. The marshy Mill Run divides the town center as it flows north.

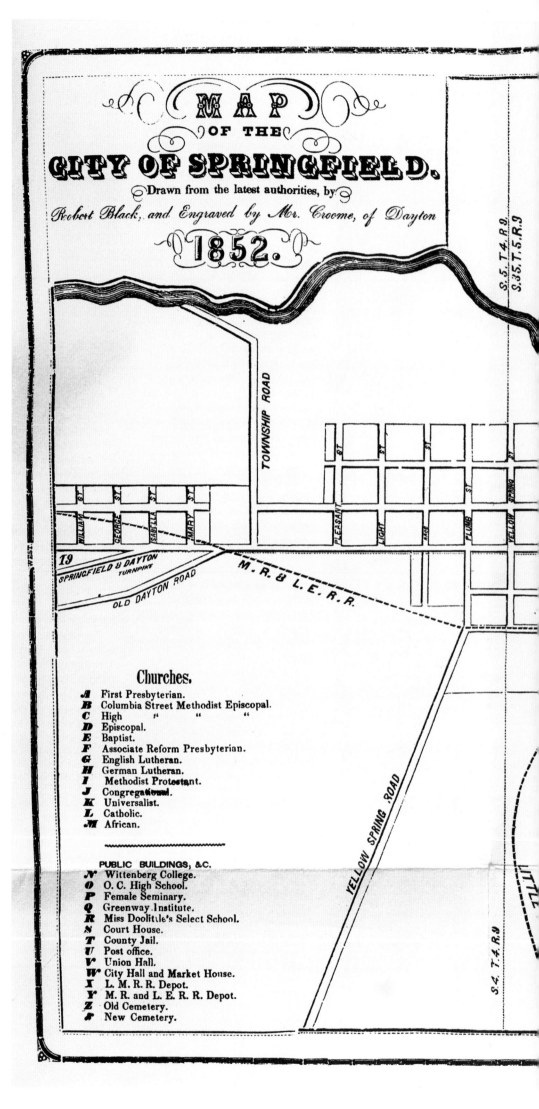

Churches.

A First Presbyterian.
B Columbia Street Methodist Episcopal.
C High   "   "   "
D Episcopal.
E Baptist.
F Associate Reform Presbyterian.
G English Lutheran.
H German Lutheran.
I Methodist Protestant.
J Congregational.
K Universalist.
L Catholic.
M African.

PUBLIC BUILDINGS, &C.
N Wittenberg College.
O O. C. High School.
P Female Seminary.
Q Greenway Institute.
R Miss Doolittle's Select School.
S Court House.
T County Jail.
U Post office.
V Union Hall.
W City Hall and Market House.
X L. M. R. R. Depot.
Y M. R. and L. E. R. R. Depot.
Z Old Cemetery.
& New Cemetery.

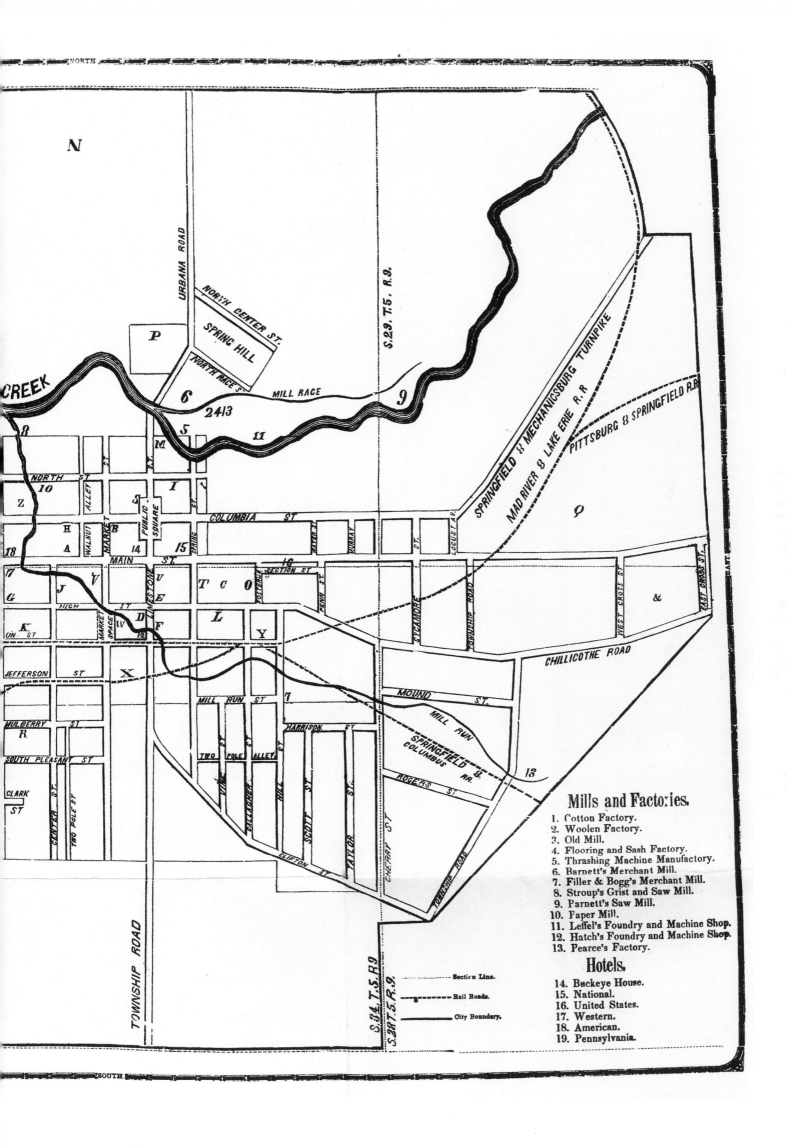

Mills and Factories.

1. Cotton Factory.
2. Woolen Factory.
3. Old Mill.
4. Flooring and Sash Factory.
5. Thrashing Machine Manufactory.
6. Barnett's Merchant Mill.
7. Filler & Bogg's Merchant Mill.
8. Stroup's Grist and Saw Mill.
9. Parnett's Saw Mill.
10. Paper Mill.
11. Leffel's Foundry and Machine Shop.
12. Hatch's Foundry and Machine Shop.
13. Pearce's Factory.

Hotels

14. Buckeye House.
15. National.
16. United States.
17. Western.
18. American.
19. Pennsylvania.

- - - - - - - Section Line.
─┼─┼─ Rail Roads.
───── City Boundary.

going - to Springfield to see the baby show? A committee of ladies and gentlemen was appointed to view the babies and pass on their merits, and, so far as I know, the prizes all went to babies in this city and county. But a most curious coincident occurred: soon afterwards every one of the babies died. It set people to thinking that maybe the show wasn't right: it seemed to make a mockery of God's creatures.

One hundred and fifty infants, all under two, competed in the first "Grand National Convention of Babies," attended by 15,000 spectators. A ten-month-old girl from South Vienna (in Clark County) won first prize, but there were winners from Columbus and Cincinnati. Back in New York, newspaperman Horace Greeley wrote that Springfielders were so busy admiring baby flesh that they were losing sight of the buying and selling of human beings in other parts of the country.

In spite of bouts with cholera and periodic financial panics, Springfield was poised to capture the country's attention. Abundant water power, a location that looked out in all directions, home-grown geniuses who were reinventing the way people lived, all of these factors were conspiring to produce a Golden Age.

In examining the map of the United States, what more central, more prosperous region can be found in which to ply largely and remuneratively the cunning handicrafts of man? Let the facilities be created, and the capital and skill, beyond a peradventure, will flow in apace, until Springfield shall become the third city in Ohio.

This unique 1859 set of photographs chronicles a generation on the eve of America's greatest tragedy. Most of these "Rovers" volunteer firemen have been identified. Several hold the tools of their trade. Soon-to-be General J. Warren Keifer stares out three photographs to the right of the hand drawn fire engine. Green Michael, "Rovers" Captain and head blacksmith at the Driscol Carriage Works, is just right of the engine. The Civil War musician Henry Hawken is the fifth from the right in the third row from the bottom. National Road surveyor Thomas Kizer is pictured with his survey equipment right above the fire engine.

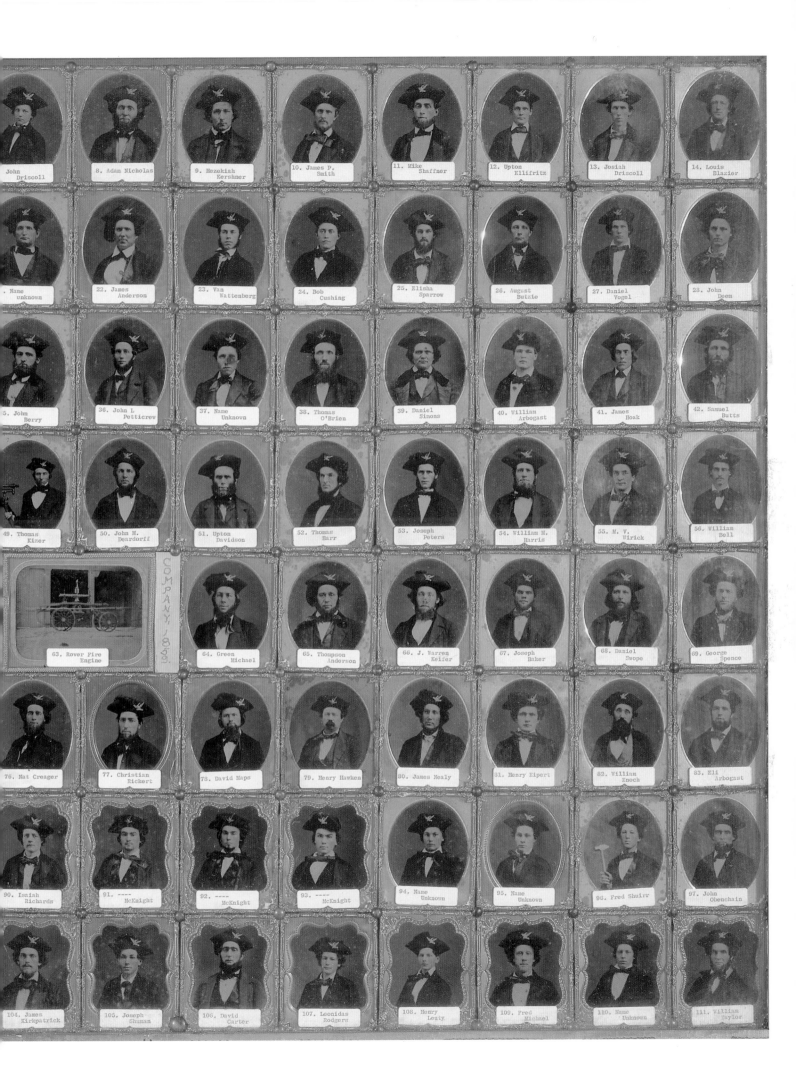

worship. By 1825, the church was a shelter for cattle and hogs, and the Methodists and Presbyterians had built more permanent sanctuaries. The African Methodist Church soon followed, serving a community of African Americans that already numbered fifty. Three decades later, fourteen denominations, including the Episcopalians, Baptists, Lutherans, Congregationalists, Universalists and Catholics had planted congregations with a total of two-thousand communicants. Springfield was now increasingly noted for its handsome downtown churches, but the war against "the devil whiskey," about to find a bold new champion, continued undiminished.

A Golden Age of Prosperity (1861-1929)

The Civil War Fuels a Boom

Twice in Clark County history, a war touched off a period of economic prosperity. While the community sent off its sons to an uncertain fate, a huge national appetite for goods to feed the war effort gave local businessmen unprecedented opportunities. World War Two brought good fortune to the workers and factory owners all over the country and lifted the nation out of the worst depression in its history. Eighty years earlier, the county had been visited by a similar bittersweet boom.

The Civil War brought enormous social as well as political change. As the fighting sacrificed young men by the tens of thousands, eventually snuffing out over six hundred thousand lives, women went into the farm fields to pick up the slack at home.

> A hundred thousand agricultural laborers are gone; how are we to meet the deficiency?..At the present time so perfect is machinery that men seem to be less of a necessity. Of all the labors of the field, mowing was formerly deemed to be the most arduous, and the strongest men were required for it. We have seen, within the last few weeks, a stout matron whose sons are in the army, with a team cutting hay,.. and she cut seven acres with ease in a day, riding leisurely upon a cutter. This circumstance is indicative of the great revolution which machinery is making in production.
>
> ...We have reapers, mowers, separators, sowers, drills, &c., making a great aggregate of agricultural machinery, which does the work of three fold the number of men, who...would have been required to do it. Indeed, without this machinery, the wheat, oats, and hay of Ohio, in 1862, could not have been got safely...At Dayton, Springfield, Lancaster, Canton and Cleveland, large factories are engaged in turning out agricultural machines... The mode in which the harvest of 1862 has been principally got is this. One farmer in the neighborhood buys a machine, whether reaper or separator, and goes round doing the work for his neighbors at so many cents per bushel. It is thus that machinery has done the work of thousands of men, who have thus been spared for the war...

> ...Substituting animal and mechanical power for hand labor...is one of the compensations of the war, and no slight one either. Its influence will be felt long after peace shall have called the absent laborers to their homes. It is, in fact, an emancipation of thousands of men from the necessity of severe toil...

A farming revolution like no other before it had been accelerated by a war like no other before it. As Clark County farmers were astounded by fundamental changes, the Springfield mills were running night and day to keep up with an unprecedented demand for goods.

At the beginning of the war, northern doomsayers had predicted,

> When war wages its wide desolation, the country will be ruined and not one stone left upon another of all that commercial and manufacturing greatness which is our pride and boast.

As nurse Clara Barton said, "the armies left mischief and misery in their wake," but the fortunes of the conflict had exactly the opposite effect on northern industry.

Clark County capitalized on a market for new farm machines created by the Civil War. With few men to do the farm work, the home front demanded the newly-invented mowers and reapers that efficiently did the work of many. Young inventors and entrepreneurs like William Whiteley were happy to oblige and Springfield soon became the "Champion City."

In the fall of 1861, the spit and polish, Washington-based 67th New York Infantry Regiment joined hundreds of thousands of other Union and Confederate soldiers in serious preparations for war. The result was a four-year nightmare that took six hundred thousand lives, but fueled a boom in northern industry that continued for decades. *(Library of Congress)*

There are no less than 218 patents, reissues, designs, &c...of recent origin...It shows convincingly that war, instead of being an evil to general manufacturing interests, lends increased impetus to all branches of it...Iron is in such demand that the producers of it command their own price, paper is the same, woolen goods are the same...

Charles Rabbitts came to Springfield in 1847 looking for a good site for a woolen mill. He liked the town's potential; good water power for a reasonable sum, the promise of good railroad facilities and nice people. After carding and fulling wool for local farmers, he began to produce cloth in exchange for the farmers' wool.

We carded wool for farmers – having a special machine for the purpose – we made yarns, flannels, blankets, cloths, and later satinettes and jeans. During the war, for about a year, I made cloth for the government contractors. The government would contract, mostly with eastern men, for thousands and thousands of suits of 'army-blue;' and the contractors, of course have to sub-contract for the goods with which to make them. The wholesale clothiers of Cincinnati made a great many army garments. My first contract in that line was for 10,000 yards, for which I received seventy-five cents per yard. It took us about sixty days to make it.

The Rabbitts Mill was one of at least a half dozen in the Springfield area, each turning out several thousand yards of cloth a week. All but a handful ran on water power, because, as Rabbitts explained, "water power does service for twenty-four hours a day at no greater expense than for twelve hours, while the expense of steam power is, of course, double."

duced his new turbine to the Springfield millers. They appreciated any opportunity to make their overburdened operations more efficient.

> He built that old oil-mill upon the cliffs near Factory St., to show what the turbine wheel would do. He had great difficulties in getting the race made, but little trouble in running the mill.

Millers far and wide knew a revolutionary innovation when they saw it. By the time he died a few years later, Leffel was selling his turbine to Europeans as well as Americans.

At times, Unionist Clark County was disturbingly close to the battlefields. A scare in 1862 brought out almost five hundred Clark County volunteers to defend Cincinnati. Known to history as the "squirrel hunters" because of their civilian hunting rifles and shotguns, these "thirty day wonders" chased a non-existent Confederate raid. The only casualty was a Springfield mill that burned to the ground when there weren't enough men around to fight the spectacular fire. The next year, John Hunt Morgan's rebel raiders passed within fifty miles of Springfield so quickly that no one had time to respond.

Like thousands of northern communities, Springfield spent the war nervously following the news of the armies and attempting to keep life normal. An Englishman's wartime description of Racine, Wisconsin, could have described any other small Yankee town caught up in the conflict.

> The amusements... are about as limited as if it stood in our [English] midland counties...a passing circus, an itinerant exhibition of Ethiopian minstrels, and an occasional concert...A Mrs. Francis Lord Bond was to lecture on Sunday evenings on spiritualism; a fancy fair was to be

Springfield inventor James Leffel introduced his innovative water turbine in the middle of the Civil War and revolutionized the efficient use of waterpower. This diagram illustrates how the horizontal wheel uses the rushing water more effectively than the old-fashioned vertical models.

The local millers could boast of the blessings of water power because of a homegrown genius who was obsessed with harnessing the abundant waters of Buck Creek. James Leffel, described as a "very energetic man, a great talker, and a person who would undertake almost anything he set his mind to," began his career making stoves. He and a talented colleague named Mr. Jayne invented the Buckeye Stove which "threw the flame and smoke down around the oven - something on the principle of...base burners." Having earned a princely sum from the manufacture and sale of the stove, Leffel turned his mind to water power. The result was a new mile long mill race along Buck Creek and, later, a water turbine that revolutionized water power throughout the world.

While the Civil War raged, James Leffel intro-

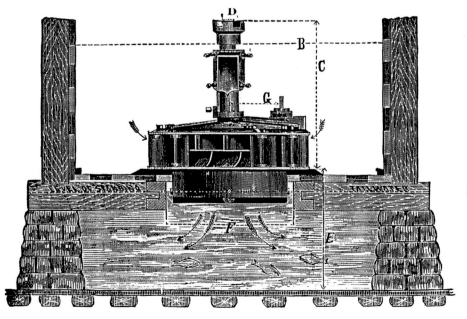

This damaged photograph sums up the tragedy of the Civil War. Private Leonidas Jordan, going to war with the 31st Ohio Infantry, tentatively holds his musket and stares uncomfortably at the camera. His father Hiram, presumably holding a bible, offers his painfully young son to the Union cause. *(U. S. Army Military History Institute, Carlisle Barracks, Pennsylvania)*

held for the Catholic convent…and a German 'choralverein' was to meet weekly for the performance of sacred music. Then…there were the war advertisements. The Mayor announced that a great battle was expected daily before Corinth, and requested his townspeople to provide stores beforehand for the relief of the wounded. The Ladies' Aid Committee informed the female public…that there would be a sewing meeting every Friday in the Town Hall, where all the ladies were requested to come, and sew bandages for the Union soldiers; every lady to bring her own sewing machine. Then, too…there was the Governor, calling for recruits to fill up the gaps in the ranks of the…regiments, who were cut to pieces on the field of Shiloh.

The town press…is of the regular unwieldy English four page size…The advertisements, which occupy two of the four pages, are chiefly of

patent medicines, business-cards, and foreclosure sales. The local news…is extremely meager…The politics of the paper are staunch Republican and anti-slavery, and the leading articles are well written, and all on questions of public not local politics…There were letters from the war, copied out of New York newspapers, and the list of killed and wounded in the…regiments; but fully one page of the paper was occupied by short stories and poems.

Society…is still in a primitive stage. Dinner-parties are unknown, and balls are events of great rarity; but tea parties, to which you are invited on the morning of the day, are of constant occurrence. Probably there is as much scandal and gossip here as in an Old World country-town; but there are not, as yet, the social divisions which exist with us. If you inquire the names of the owners of the handsomest houses,.. you will find that one, perhaps began life as a stable boy, another was a waiter a few years ago...and a third a bricklayer in early life. On the other hand, some of the poorest people are persons who were of good family and good education in the Old World... This very mixture of people which you find throughout the West gives a freedom, and also an originality, to the society of small towns, which you would not find under similar circumstances in England...

Everyone in Clark County lived their lives as best they could during this time of tragedy. The county sent more than three thousand of its men, white and black, to the Union armies. Scores were killed or died and were buried in far off places. Springfield set aside a special place for the war dead in the new Ferncliff Cemetery, but few were ever buried in their home soil. Other soldiers returned home sick and maimed, trying to pick up their lives after being shattered at Chickamauga or Gettysburg.

When the war ended, five thousand gathered in Springfield to celebrate and "upon every house, upon every shop, upon every available spot, was displayed the flag of our country." Then, suddenly, in a twist of fate that characterized the national nightmare, word arrived by telegraph and newspaper that President Lincoln had been shot. When the townspeople gathered for a meeting at city hall, the audience sat in stunned silence for fifteen minutes before anyone could speak.

The four years of indescribable carnage had brought some good along with the bad. The veterans returned to a community that was ready to exploit its wartime economic successes. William Whiteley led a nucleus of smart and ambitious young entrepreneurs who had turned successfully to government contracts to help the Union win the war. Now they were eager to use their profits in a postwar expansion that would again change the face of Springfield and Clark County.

Whiteley, Fassler and Kelly Manufacture a Champion City

"William had always been of an inventive turn of mind; when he was a boy he was always making machines of different kinds and hiding them from me." Andrew Whiteley, the father of the future "Reaper King," knew his son was something special.

> After he entered the shop [the Springfield foundry and machine shop of Hatch and Whiteley] he invented a breech-loading gun that was very successful, but he never patented it or tried to push it. In 1853, he made his first mower, but it was not of much force. His first successful machine, a mower, was made in 1855, and was tried when the state fair was here that year... He was then only 20 years old.
>
> Two years afterwards his machine took its first prize, a silver cup, at Nashville, Tenn...We all spent a great deal of time and study in bringing the machine to perfection, and by 1857 had a knife that has never yet been improved upon. The first big triumph for the machine, was before that time, at a field test on a farm [near Springfield].

With a unique dose of skill and imagination, young William Whiteley invented a revolutionary machine that was efficient, simple, durable and easy to use. Having christened his new device a "champion," he set out to prove he was right. From the start, he was bigger than life and his success came quickly. He was a born showman. His size, well over six feet tall and 250 pounds, commanded attention. At one of his memorable demonstrations, Whiteley unhitched the team of horses, strapped himself in harness and dragged his reaper across a field crying, "My Champion is the easiest pulling rig there is!"

The chemistry was there for a classic American success story. But time and circumstances made it much more. The salesman Whiteley hooked up with a talented machinist named Jerome Fassler. Together, they moved into downtown Springfield and rented a twenty by thirty-five foot shed on the edge of the Mill Run swamp. They banged out fifty of the innovative machines in 1856. The next year Oliver Kelly came to town looking for ways to spend the bankroll he had collected building houses for the California '49ers. Kelly's money launched the business and Civil War contracts grew the capital. Whiteley, Fassler and Kelly came out of the war riding a wave of expectation. Most of America was still farming and looking for ways to tap into a new farm industry that made work easier and yields greater. Restless war veterans were moving west and opening up vast wheat fields on the high plains.

The demand for reapers, mowers, cultivators, seed drills, threshers, any device that mechanized farm tasks, skyrocketed. The self-styled Springfield "Reaper King," a tireless promoter, was able to take full advantage. Unable to keep up with the orders, he and his partners contracted with Warder, Mitchell and Company and

A middle-aged William Whiteley (above) recalls the genius of inventions and marketing that made the "Champion" farm machine business the engine of Springfield's Golden Age.

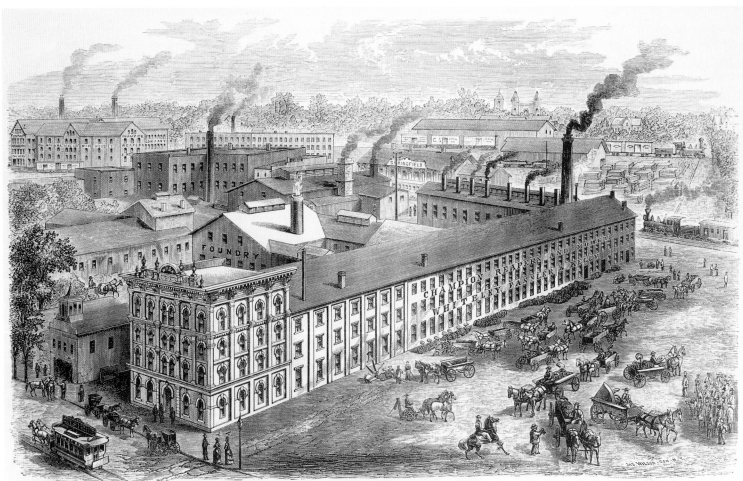

WM. N. WHITELEY.

JEROME FASSLER.

OLIVER S. KELLY.

SHOPS OF WHITELEY, FASSLER & KELLY,

Occupied exclusively in the Manufacture of Champion Reapers and Mowers.

created the Champion Machine Company to turn out more reapers. Soon they were putting together three other companies and a railroad to control the materials they needed to manufacture the machines. Only two decades after two men moved into a small shed next to Market Square, the Champion interests had red brick factories that stretched for blocks. In April of 1877, four trains, carrying over sixteen hundred reapers and mowers, left for the western markets.

Nobody had ever seen such numbers. Champion was on top of the world. Springfield became the "Champion City" and built a Golden Age on the company's success. For his part, William Whiteley became the charter member of a new economic aristocracy, self-made men with energy and ingenuity. They were pioneers just like their fathers and grandfathers, willing to take great risks on a new, uncertain business frontier. Their rewards were enormous, wealth and power reflected in the era's name, "The Gilded Age." Many now refer to the time as the "Brown Decades," but the so-called "robber barons" were proud of their smoke and soot-crowned factories. For them, replacing the virgin forests with industrial development was a natural and desirable part of human progress.

William Whiteley was born the year the National Road was approaching a rural and rustic Springfield. By the time he was fifty, his Champion Trust was moving to the forty-four acre East Street Shops, among the planet's largest, where two thousand workers labored to meet the worldwide demand for their farm machines. Soon, Oliver Kelly, concerned about riding into financial ruin with the flashy Whiteley, pulled out of the company and started his own very successful career. Kelly was right. Just six years later, a bad investment cost Whiteley his empire, but his indelible imprint on the "Champion City" lived on in hundreds of homegrown products and decades of prosperity. The Champion Company also lived on in other hands. The "Reaper King's" meteoric career was never duplicated by the hundreds of other local entrepreneurs who rode his coattails into the Golden Age.

continued on page 57.

The Champion Reapers and Mowers made Springfield famous. By the 1870s, Whiteley, Fassler and Kelly had a sprawling, downtown, brick factory adjacent to Market Square. After William Whiteley moved the business to the East Street Shops, his former partner, Oliver S. Kelly built the Arcade on the site. Today, the Springfield Inn occupies the spot.

Whiteley, Fassler and Kelly made their Champion Reapers a logo for the "Champion City." Along with the universal image of the plow, a farmer contentedly driving his team through the wheat crop became the symbol of the age.

Along with William Whiteley's desk, this ordinary cart (below) is all that remains from the giant East Street Shops in the Clark County Historical Society collection. Probably dating from an earlier era, the cart hauled pig iron in the Champion Factory yards.

A Champion City Enters a Golden Age

A somewhat romanticized image of Mr. Jesse Mead's prize bull "General Grant" decorates the pages of the 1875 Clark County Atlas. Mr. Mead might very well have been a Civil War veteran; hence the name of his champion.

John Bookwalter's 1869 Lagonda House was a big city operation with one hundred and forty rooms and a whole block of fine shops and restaurants. In just three decades, Springfield grew from rough and tumble country inns to sophisticated and elegant hotels.

There were subtle changes in the way Clark County portrayed itself to the rest of America after the Civil War. It was the age of the lithograph. Photography was still not a regular part of everyday life. The Springfield city directories had become just that, door to door lists of the shops and services that were multiplying year to year. The promotions had moved to the county atlases, bold and beautiful drawings of the orderly and bucolic life of city and country.

The new aristocracy was splitting its time between town and farm. There was symmetry to the equation. City factories supplied the machines to country farms and the farms fed the city in return. Factory chimneys were puffing, the new sign of prosperity. The elite citizens were building grand new townhouses and neat and tidy estates, featuring their prized livestock like a giant bull named for Civil War hero General U. S. Grant. Hard scrabble farms and the work-

ing poor were nowhere in evidence. This new pastoral mix of industry and agriculture that was sweeping the Heartland was not a lie to our ancestors. It was simply a statement of the palpable progress to a better tomorrow.

The prosperity was real. The population in Springfield tripled in twenty years. There were new banks, new real estate developments, new hotels and a new cultural palace. Scores of new buildings every year were totally

reshaping the community from decade to decade. In 1869, builder Alfred Raffensperger laid out East Springfield and demonstrated the true "goahead" spirit of the post-war era. His modern sounding promotion amazed the townspeople. Raffensperger used every sales device at hand, from a full page ad in the newspaper to brass bands and velocipede races and even carriage service to the home sites. The east end remained the place to build a home until the end of the century.

In the same year, another new-comer, John Bookwalter showed the same panache in putting together a business team that built a hotel worthy of the new Springfield. The five story brick Lagonda House filled most of a city block and featured one hundred and forty rooms. Only a few blocks away, Andrew Black opened his stately $100,000 Opera House with a thousand seat auditorium and conference facilities that he advertised statewide.

A year later, Springfield was a serious contender to become the home of the new Ohio Agricultural and Mechanical College. The wrangling with Columbus for the honor was almost as contentious as statewide fights over the National

Henry Stickney's impressive livestock placidly line up with a displaying peacock in front of his neat Clark County farm. The farms throughout Clark County fed the county seat at Springfield.

Messrs. Miller and Teagh may have used this wagon to collect country produce for sale in the Springfield markets (below).

working, staunchly Republican, fiercely pro-business, paternalistic toward its workers and generally civic-minded. It controlled the local banks that were the spigots of its financing. William Whiteley had been the first star of this fraternity, but many of his colleagues had longer and more successful careers. Whiteley's partner, Oliver S. Kelly (below), tamed the swamps that plagued the downtown, built the Arcade Hotel on the site of the original Champion factory and, as mayor, built the City Building which stands today as the

county's Heritage Center. Phineas P. Mast (top of opposite page) created his own empire building cider mills and grain drills. He served a stint as mayor, but is best remembered for starting a magazine, *Farm and Fireside*, to better sell his products. He gave his city, instead, a publishing empire that dominated the downtown for generations and then broke the community's heart.

Other influential members included the three banking and manufacturing nephews of city pioneer Griffith Foos; Ross Mitchell, who with John Thomas, gave the city its first true hospital in 1890; William Bayley, who found many ways to forge and cast iron; and the next generation of the Warders, a family that dominated Springfield throughout the 19th century. This group also had its headliners on the state and national political scene. During the 1850s and 60s, local Republicans had consistently elected radical abolitionist and free-trader Samuel Shellabarger to Congress. When Shellabarger retired and became an influential Washington lawyer, they turned to J. Warren Keifer, war hero and attorney to the Springfield busi-

Springfield's cultural life took a giant leap with the arrival of Andrew Black's five-story Opera House in 1869. The Mansard-roofed structure contained conference facilities and a thousand-seat auditorium. The premier performance, a syrupy Civil War melodrama called "The Drummer Boy of Shiloh," tugged at Springfield's heartstrings.

Road. Community prestige was at stake and civic leaders offered railway lines and cash to sweeten the pot. Governor, soon to be president, Rutherford B. Hayes put his considerable clout behind Columbus and it got the bid. The college later became the Ohio State University and the victory helped make Columbus the center for state institutions. Springfield did not soon forget the snub. In an attempt to retrieve their loss, community leaders tried to turn Wittenberg, with its liberal arts curriculum, into an agricultural school. They came close to losing Wittenberg to Mansfield, Ohio, in the process.

Many who returned to the village of their youth couldn't now recognize the place. James Cushman, former "Rover" fireman and Civil War veteran, returned after a seven year absence.

When I returned the train stopped...and I tell you I didn't

know where I was. I looked off south and the town was all built up where, before the war, had been largely swamps. I went north on Limestone St. and could recognize no landmarks...I went on to Main St. before I caught sight of a point by which I could right myself, so great had been the change in a few years.

Some of the old timers were upset with what industrial development had done to their hometown.

I think Springfield was a beautiful place when I first came here. There was such natural beauty that has since been destroyed. For example, where the Rogers Iron Fence Company works stands, was one of the most beautiful spots I ever saw. The waterfalls there, but a trace of which remain, were a great favorite and one of the sights of Springfield.

Those who were benefiting from the boom raced to see it grow and flourish. The inner circle of the business community was hard-

ness community. The former Union general served in Congress for more than a decade and was Speaker of the House of Representatives for one term. As the century came to a close, they helped elect wealthy industrialist and banker Asa Bushnell to two terms as Ohio governor.

While Springfield's political influence peaked, the city experimented with the latest inventions coming in from the east. Thanks to Oliver Kelly, a local plant was generating electricity only a year after the first power company in New York City. About the same time, two hundred and fifty townspeople were shouting into their new telephones, trying to hear and be heard over the primitive system. The city became a forest of poles and power lines when electric streetcars made their appearance just five years later.

All the trappings of a big city were in place. Multi-story buildings were going up all over the downtown. The county had put up a tall, Victorian courthouse in 1881. Not to be outdone, the city, led by Mayor Kelly, built its own even taller and more modern, block long building a decade later. Yet another gift of the Golden Age arrived in 1895. The two Snyder brothers, local farmers, donated over 200 acres of land for a park along Buck Creek. Springfield was not yet a century old, but the memories of a pioneer settlement had been buried by the wonders of the modern era.

A lady stands with two dandies in front of a hardware store. She may be the wife of the owner or possibly an owner herself. Note the thermometer at the front door and the straps for the awnings, an essential part of every Victorian storefront.

A thoroughly modern Victorian Springfield parlor sports the trappings of the Gilded Age. Ceiling high windows, an ornamental chandelier (possibly electrified but probably still gas lit), woodwork in the Eastlake style, curtains, rugs and wallpaper of widely different patterns, a collection of oriental pots and jugs, all of these features are the height of fashion.

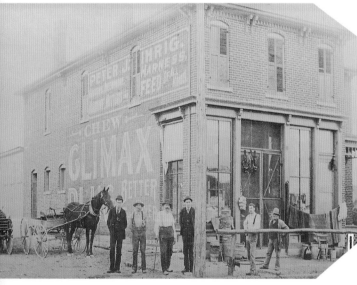

What is probably a family of barbers stands around a memorable, patriotic barber pole.

Harness maker Peter Ihrig poses with his workers and some customers who have their rigs nearby.

One of the earliest photographs of downtown Springfield shows the Brown Drug store and the Murray House Hotel. The tree-lined street sweeps impressively to the north. Note the old-fashioned sign on the left.

Tobacconist and old-timer David Cornor stands in front of his menacing cigar store Indian (opposite page). Mr. Cornor, who helped chronicle early Springfield, was old enough to remember the real Shawnees who had once lived in the neighborhood.

Construction on the street doesn't seem to be disrupting business at the Magruder Harness Shop (above). The Magruders' have chosen two horse collars to advertise their business. The baby carriage might be the work of the famous local Driscol Carriage Works. The carefully laid out fresh watermelons (left) are a featured part of the summer produce at a local shop.

Burly farriers stand in front of the Kearns Brothers "Horseshoers." Dozens of farrier shops kept the critical horsepower pulling and carrying through every kind of weather.

A local butcher shop hangs its daily allotment of meat on the front of the store for all to see. Hopefully, the weather is cool.

In a bold touch of Victorian excess, a Springfield furrier displays every type of animal pelt including a stuffed leopard. With no restrictions on hunting and trapping, President Theodore Roosevelt led the trend to put skins, mounted heads, even whole stuffed animals into American interiors.

A candy lover's dream is laid out in front of a Springfield tobacco and confectioner's shop. The owner probably lost some of his taffy, cream caramels and mixed candy, at ten cents a pound, to light fingered passersby.

Charles Wentz chose a life-sized horse to advertise his harness making skills (opposite page). He is also a leather maker, sewing together saddles, trunks and whips. The Springfield motto, "you want 'em, we'll make 'em," is partially visible in the window.

A dry goods and a drug store (above and left) demonstrate how neat and tidy store interiors were at the turn of the century. The service of knowledgeable clerks who knew their customers was a critical feature of neighborhood stores. Note the very modern looking seed display, the pharmaceutical bottles and the large collection of cigars, many made locally.

After the Civil War, America saw the end of one era and the beginning of another. This "last stagecoach" left Washington, Pennsylvania, with a very small ceremony, headed for Pittsburgh in 1867. Although stagecoaches continued to be used in the "Wild West," few were sad to see them go in the east. Travelers regularly endured long, bumpy rides on terrible roads until the railroad came to the rescue. As railroad tracks linked the towns of the eastern United States, the stagecoach soon vanished into history. *(Library and Archives Division, Historical Society of Western Pennsylvania, Pittsburgh, Pennsylvania)*

Dr. Russell's Horseless Carriage

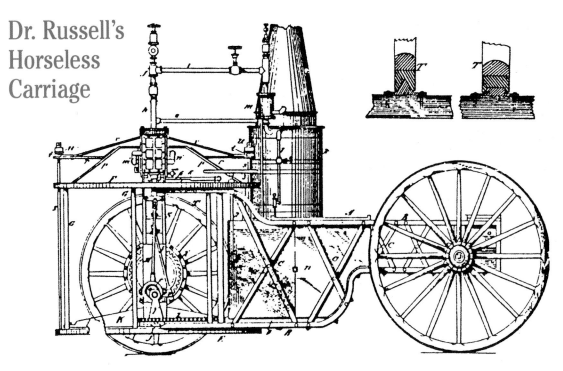

Dr. L. E. Russell submitted his drawings for a "self-propelling vehicle" in March of 1886 and received Patent No. 341,858. Note the single middle wheel on the left. The boiler has survived and the groundbreaking vehicle may one day be restored.

With all of the inventive energy churning in Golden Age Springfield, one major achievement was lost in the drama of its creation. The achievement was so far-reaching, so revolutionary that it frightened a community already geared up for innovation. Two backyard inventors tinkered together a steam driven "horseless carriage," then proved not once but twice that it could and would work. Were they a pair of crackpots or did they build and prove the first workable automobile?

The principals were L. E. Russell, a Springfield physician, and Henry Voll, a machinist who ended up in the automobile business. The year was 1886. Dr. Russell came to Mr. Voll with a design for his new device.

It was steam driven, with an upright boiler and engine mounted on a single wheel in front and two six foot wheels of a doctor's gig [buggy] behind…The engine was geared to the single front wheel, which was slung from a framework supporting the engine. The [horse] shafts of the gig were sawed off close to the body and hooked with bolts on the engine frame…When the steering wheel in front of the driver was twisted, the entire engine frame swung on a king bolt midway between the engine and gig. Expansion brakes, working on the drums around the axles of the high wheels of the gig, were worked by hand from the driver's seat.

Mr. Voll built the entire engine in his machine shop. Dr. Russell drove the "automobile," while Voll sat on a little platform under the driver's seat and served as chief engineer and fireman. Voll vividly remembered the vehicle's first trip.

We took it out first on the morning of Thanksgiving Day, 1886. There must have been five thousand persons around the shop when we started…The doctor was up in the driver's seat and I was down below, on the platform right under the gig. The doctor did the steering and I worked the engine and kept the steam up. We moved out of the yard into Linn Street and went south to Yellow Springs Street, turned down Yellow Springs and went down to High Street and then west to Shaffer Street.

There we had the first accident, for the grates of the fire box fell out and we lost all our fire. We had lost the crowd because we started off about twenty miles an hour, and they caught up to us again when the grate fell out. I had to go borrow some boxes and after fixing the grates back in, we started the fire again and went on.

The doctor turned north on Shaffer Street to Columbia…and then to Yellow Springs again. We went up to Main and turned east again to Plum Street.

There we had another accident. The wheels got in the car tracks and when the doctor tried to get out the machine got away and ran head on into Phillip Smith's grocery on the corner. It didn't hurt the machine any, so we backed it by pushing and took her back to the shop.

The advent of the 'horseless carriage' on the streets brought consternation and indignation in its wake. Horses reared and ran away when confronted by the snorting vehicle that rolled along with smoke trailing from the boiler and sparks and ashes dropping from the firebox. Hundreds of citizens protested the use of the machine that could roll along at twenty to twenty-five miles an hour and which they claimed endangered their lives and limbs. Many threatened to sue Dr. Russell for damages but never did.

The evening after the first try-out, Dr, Russell took the vehicle to his residence on east High Street. Henry Voll decided to drive the contrivance alone. He managed to get to the city building where he stalled.

The second appearance was the cause of another uproar on the streets. Horses ran away and pedestrians fled before it. After being stalled near the city building, I decided to send for Dr. Russell.

Steam was made again and with… Dr. Russell again in the gig, the automobile swung around the Esplanade and came down the eastside to make the turn on High Street. I believed we were about to see the finish of the whole affair as we attempted to make the turn at the Wren Store corner.

Vehicles were very thick. Horses were frightened and the owners not much better off. The doctor never lost his presence of mind, and avoiding all the traffic, he swung the right wheel of the gig onto the sidewalk and made the turn without stopping.

The final act…was played when sparks from the fire box set fire to the doctor's barn and required the aid of several volunteer firemen to save the structure.

America's first automobile was destroyed in the fire, but the doctor was not finished. He had patented his steam "horseless carriage" on May 11, 1886. Having spent another year experimenting with this design, he turned to the gasoline engine and turned out several models with Henry Voll. The brief appearance of the groundbreaking and quirky invention was too much even for "go ahead" Springfield. But, when the practical automobiles took to the roads a decade later, the Champion City embraced them with an enthusiasm that has never waned.

Rising Hopes and Rising Fears

The Golden Age came with a big price only slowly realized by the powerbrokers. There was a sea of workers behind the puffing smokestacks and the beautiful farms. Yes, there were opportunities for this blue collar community, but there were also frustrations and resentments.

Labor unrest was practically unheard of before the Civil War. As the work force grew, however, so did the attempts to organize against real and perceived wrongs. It was a time that preached anarchy and communism. The industrial revolution had made fortunes and had unleashed desperate measures to find a voice for the disenfranchised masses.

The first generation of Springfield business leaders was free wheeling and paternalistic. It had pulled itself up by its own bootstraps and expected everyone else to do the same. A chance to work and a regular paycheck were enough to give anyone a start. The rest was up to the drive and ingenuity of the individual. There was no free lunch and there were no guarantees in a Darwinian work environment. Questions about wage guarantees and safe workplaces were met with indifference and even disdain. Outside agitation was treated as unnecessary, subversive and downright lawless.

The workers' concerns could not be brushed aside. The supremely confident and optimistic generation of William Whiteley was ultimately shaken by the labor unrest in its own backyard.

After some confrontations that threatened to destroy the labor and management relationship, there was an uneasy truce that has held throughout most of the 20th century.

Clark County was upset by other social upheavals as growth and development changed the face of city and county. The community mirrored the changes occurring in the national fabric. Women, brought out of the kitchen and sewing room by the Civil War, began to lobby for permanent change in their second class status. African Americans, released from slavery by conflict and unimagined bloodshed, were still second class citizens struggling against nationwide bigotry. For all of its prosperity, the Golden Age also reminded leaders and ordinary citizens alike that America faced daunting challenges.

Temperance Leads to Suffrage

Clark County's battle with the evils of alcohol continued undiminished into the 20th century. It was a war against human vice where ultimate victory was mixed up in the never ending struggle against the seven deadly sins. Still, there were always crusaders ready to take up the cause. Springfield had its share, led by an indomitable leader who attracted wide attention. Eliza "Mother" Stewart's "Whiskey War," however, had unexpected consequences for the whole woman's movement.

A turn of the century postcard commemorates one of the many attempts to rid Springfield of alcoholic beverages. The battle for prohibition was waged for half a century. The city and police officials are smiling because they know this is just another skirmish in a long "Whiskey War."

The 1873 "Women's Whiskey War" in Springfield received national attention in *Leslie's Illustrated News* when Mother Stewart led her ladies in demonstrations at the front doors of local saloons. Note the expressions of the men surrounding the prayer meeting.

Sewing machines in the home were the first important symbols of increasing independence for women. They became popular in the decade before the Civil War because they gave mothers and daughters an opportunity to participate in the Industrial Revolution. Springfield industry built and assembled sewing machines but they never became a major local product.

Eliza Stewart was one of those "new" women who frightened the male population. At the beginning of the Civil War, wives and daughters were locked permanently in subservient roles. For centuries, the conventional wisdom had preached that women were merely reflections of their male counterparts. Nineteenth century social manuals, many written by females, taught a totally domestic role with no pretension to education or work outside the home. In fact, any thoughts about independence away from family and hearth were considered destructive to the long-established order.

The Civil War brought many changes. With thousands of men joining the fighting, women were needed to work in farm fields and offices. They also volunteered to assist in army hospitals and invented the nursing profession in the process. In short, they began invading the male dominated work and public spaces.

Once the war was over, instead of dutifully returning to hearth and home, women continued to search for new roles in a changing world. They found a cause in the ongoing crusade against free flowing liquor. Industrial Springfield, where workers often drank away their entire paychecks in the many saloons, was an easy target. The crusaders found an unlikely ally in 1870 when the Ohio legislature, in one of its periodic

bouts of conscience, made tavern-keepers responsible for the behavior of their customers. At the same time, they found a new champion named "Mother" Stewart.

Eliza Stewart was a middle-aged housewife who had earned her title "Mother" helping the wounded during the war. Never a shrinking violet, she even stood guard for Union soldiers trying to stop Morgan's Raiders in 1863. After the fighting ended, she traveled through the ruined south drawing attention to those she called the "war sufferers."

Mother Stewart saw the evils of liquor early in her life and was lecturing on behalf of temperance for the "Good Templar's Society" as early as 1858. But it was 1873 when she took up the cause in earnest. Joining and then leading the "Women's Whiskey War" against Springfield saloon owners, she spoke passionately and forcefully in any forum whether it wanted to listen or not.

> A horrible scourge is upon us…the time has come when a great effort must be made to exterminate this unequalled destroyer!

She marched into places no respectable woman was supposed to go. The Springfield city council was one of her favorite targets.

A contemporary photograph shows Mother Stewart in full battle gear for the "Women's Whiskey War." She was ready to pounce on any unsuspecting saloon-owner who sold her whiskey.

The "Women's Whiskey War" took on added importance when the ladies were reinforced by members of the male establishment. One of their biggest allies was the Reverend John Helwig, former president of Wittenberg College. After joining their ranks, the Reverend Helwig ran for governor on the prohibition ticket in 1889 and won 24,000 votes.

The mementos of the national movement for prohibition include the hatchets made famous by Carrie Nation, a temperance newspaper and Mother Stewart's memoir, *Memories of the Crusade.*

As the "Whiskey War" turned into a decades long effort to close down the saloons, there were temporary victories, but Springfield saloons managed to stay open most of the time. The Prohibition movement became a compartment in the community's life, but events like the 1909 Anti-Saloon Parade (opposite page) attracted thousands of participants.

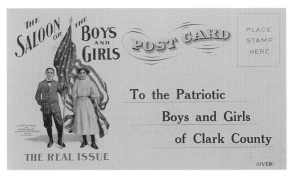

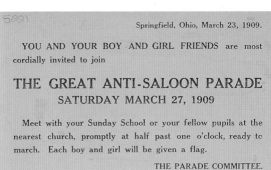

We propose you...prohibit the places of notorious tippling!...[The practice] is illegal...and ought to be suppressed! We have in Springfield seventy-five or more saloons, each doing its share of destruction.

Close them up and our beautiful city would become famous the country over as a temperance town! There are women in agony because of their sons who frequent these places. Some have proposed to execute summary justice by 'cleaning out' the pestiferous holes.

She appeared in a courtroom with a woman who had brought suit against a tavern owner and summarized the lady's case for the prosecution. Her appearance as legal counsel, the first by a woman in anyone's memory, so angered the defense attorney he told her to go home and stick to her knitting.

Mother Stewart soon became a star in the mounting international effort to stifle the use of alcohol. She hosted statewide temperance conventions in 1874 and 1877, both of which were important to the development of the national Woman's Christian Temperance Union. During that same period, she was lecturing in England and helping to form the British W.C.T.U.

During the Ohio conventions, the crusade reached a fork in the road when many delegates married their right to vote to the temperance issue. How could women get rid of alcohol if they couldn't vote? It was a logical question, but the two issues soon moved in different directions.

The temperance movement continued to gain steam as the 19th century ended. In 1889, the Reverend John B. Helwig, a local Lutheran min-

ister who had resigned as President of Wittenberg during the controversy over the school's curriculum, ran unsuccessfully for Ohio governor on the Prohibition ticket but garnered 24,000 votes. There were periodic attacks on the local saloons that continued to operate day and night in spite of the controversy. A male-dominated Springfield "Dry League" was lobbying to close the "dens of iniquity" in 1913.

At the same time, the woman's movement was growing because the lives of America's mothers, wives and daughters continued to change and new opportunities were available. In 1874, Wittenberg College, always a community innovator, welcomed women to the school. By 1900, a fifth of the 15,000 Springfield workers were female clerks, typists and secretaries. At the city's 1901 centennial celebration, local banker William S. Thomas was still trying to put the genie back in the bottle.

By 1900, women made up a fifth of the work force in Springfield. Many working class ladies were now performing the repetitive tasks in factories formerly reserved for men.

...It has come to seem natural for women to be employed...[but we are reluctant] to encourage too much employment of our girls outside of homes where they can do such excellent, natural and beautiful service as wives or mothers.

The clock could not be turned back. The early 1900s saw the debut of the pretty, free thinking and little bit naughty Gibson Girl. Women developed their own clubs, their own

The manual typewriter
became another great symbol
of the woman's movement.
Most women in the work-
place became clerks and
typists and the typewriter
became the major tool to
gain success and independence away from the home.

social causes and their own political issues. They even took to the streets to demonstrate for a revolutionary mission – full citizenship and the right to vote.

The supporters of prohibition and woman suffrage marched into the national agenda while the country was distracted by the "Great War" in Europe. The 18th and 19th Amendments to the U. S. Constitution were the result. The American attempt at social engineering, forcing the population to abandon its sinful use of alcohol, ultimately failed. Woman suffrage, on the other hand, was long overdue and the female population has never looked back with any nostalgia to the "quaint old days of hearth and home." Mother Stewart, a true Springfield original, continued to work diligently for both causes until her death in 1908. She had seized an opportunity when it presented itself. She moved ahead with courage and passion, never worrying about what others might think. Her memory survives because she made a difference when her country and her sex needed it.

Mother Stewart sat for her official portrait late in life. The ladies below, working at the Robbins and Myers Company around 1920, had Eliza Stewart and other women from the previous generation to thank for their new found successes. These women had recently captured the right to vote. One wonders how long the well-dressed and rather unhappy looking young lady in the front row will stay employed by Robbins and Myers.

The Roller Coaster of Race Relations

Clark County has seen the best and the worst in the long drama of American race relations. Because of its proximity to the slaveholding south, the county has experienced migration after migration of African Americans, fleeing slavery and seeking better jobs and improved lives for their families. It is a story mixed up with opportunity, heroism, tragedy and the grinding reality of racial bigotry.

From the beginning of settlement, the black population played a significant role in city and county. Virginia and Kentucky settler Simon Kenton brought ten slaves into Ohio when he settled on the Mad River in 1799. As the community grew, the division of Springfield between "Old Virginia" to the west and "Springfield," dominated by New England, to the east took on serious implications for any local African American, slave or free. The town reflected the growing national debate over the existence of slavery.

In 1824, the scores of black residents constructed the African Methodist Episcopal Church, showing the community they were here to stay. Having abolished slavery, the State of Ohio continued to give blacks mixed signals about their status. Most of the news was bad. Fugitive slaves were sent south, black civil rights were severely restricted and whites, across the river from slaveholding Kentucky, rioted regularly against blacks in Cincinnati. Colonization Societies, designed to take the American out of African American, were organized to send freed slaves back to Africa. The Warder family, filled with the north's growing resentment of slavery, brought a different attitude to east Springfield in 1832.

Soon there was a black school and an Anti-Slavery Society in town. Abolitionists began to speak their minds and pay the price so near the slave states. William Diehl remembered one unfortunate who paid dearly for his beliefs.

> When I came to Springfield, Chancy [Chauncey] Paul was the only milk man the town had...[He] was a great Abolitionist...some of the boys gave him an awful beating up. One of them blackened himself up one night and went to his house and told him there was a black man very sick down there, and when Chancy went with him the gang jumped on him and gave him a terrible beating. They found out who the boys were and prosecuted them, sending some of them to jail. Yes, they used to be pretty hard on the Abolitionists, and would egg them when they came around to make their speeches. But they gained their point...

Mr. Paul was remembered by many citizens as a true martyr for his cause. On another occasion, he made

> an abolition speech [in the old frame high school], and was mobbed by the good citizens of the town. They stoned the house, egged him, and afterwards rode him on a rail.

Other town abolitionists worked secretly to help the runaway slaves escape to freedom. For decades, Springfield was a major stop on the shadowy Underground Railroad. Fugitives crossed the Ohio River and came through Clark County on their desperate treks north to Canada and freedom. The issue of helping runaways stirred strong emotions. Daniel S. Morrow, a collector of stories about early Springfield and secretary/treasurer of the local Underground Railroad, gave his "final report" after the Civil War.

> In the year 1851, the traffic became so great and the vigor of the law so severe it became necessary to organize a perfect and safe-working company known as "The Springfield U.G.R.R." [Underground Railroad]...The membership was divided into two classes; first, all were contributing members, but a committee of five to seven were selected as a working force, whose duty it was to collect supplies and forward passengers. This committee never put on day trains – night trains always. They never had a smash-up or lost a passenger. An attempt was made about a year before the war to run a day-train by old Sheriff Layton, but he and his crew were captured by the enemy and the only passenger was returned to slavery, while the sheriff and his assistants were taken to Cincinnati and had to suffer much in time and money at the hands of Uncle Sam, who,

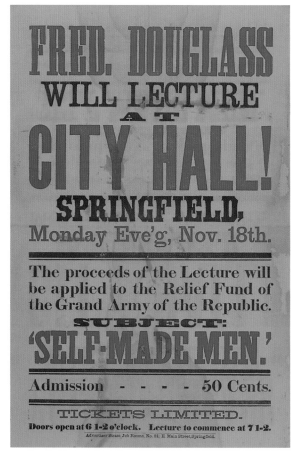

Along with her husband Jeremiah, beautiful Anne Aston Warder (seen above in an early miniature by Rembrandt Peale) brought the culture and sophistication of Quaker Philadelphia to Springfield. Late in life, she became a major figure in the supply and support of Clark County's Underground Railroad, winning the title of "Mother" for her efforts.

Former slave and national abolitionist leader Frederick Douglass returned to Springfield in 1867 (right) to lecture the community on efforts to help the freed slaves find a proper place in the post Civil War society.

at that time, was acting as the especial Attorney for the Slave-Holders.

Cincinnati was the main shipping point. There were two lines from there to Canada: One up the Miami valley, through Troy and St. Mary's, where many friends lived; the other line was a trunk-line from Cincinnati to Springfield, with many stations on the way. From here northward we had three branch-lines…one direct north through Urbana, under charge of the ever-loyal Peter Byrd, who for years ran a night train consisting of a covered wagon and a pair of strong horses. These different branches were used as circumstances required to transfer passengers so as to avoid the U.S. deputies. We had a supply store, where shoes, clothing, and many articles were kept to supply the half-clad fugitives. Well does the writer remember when that old-style roomy carriage of Mother [Anne Aston] Warder would drive up to his door, loaded with supplies when returning from the yearly meeting at Richmond [Indiana], not only supplies but the ever-needed ready money (that supply store may have been at Morrow's house on Limestone at the Public Square in downtown Springfield). …when the traffic was large the fugitives came in a wagon with two horses, having bought their time of their owner and paid for the same.

But for fear of being sold again they started and got this far north, expecting to leave the team here and foot it further north. But we found a friend of humanity in Mr. Buxton, the railroad agent, who furnished a box car to put them all in, and billed it through the lake [Erie], the freight being advanced here.

Another member named Boyd complained about the lack of support from the religious community.

In our long journey of twenty-two miles we did not know of a single family that would give any assistance to a fugitive to make his escape; and many of the preachers were hostile to any agitation of the subject of slavery; others were indifferent…You cannot find a pro-slavery clergyman in the United States. But while slavery existed they could be found in all communities…No wonder that men were under the necessity of travelling in the dead hour of night to free the fugitives, when the clergy, to a large extent, were advocating what they called the just rights of the slaveholder. Now, notwithstanding all this, there were three or four small churches in the midst of all this corruption that never held slaves, and they were the light in the midst of this surrounding darkness and distress; and how the slaves rejoiced to meet such firm friends…

The 1852 Springfield City Directory listed forty-two "persons of color" running businesses in town. When the Civil War came, these free blacks volunteered to save the Union and end slavery. At first the Union army was leery of raising colored regiments, but, by 1863, facing manpower shortages and seeing the bravery of the black 54th Massachusetts Regiment near

This photograph of an intense-looking Samuel Shellabarger was taken about the time he was elected to the U.S. Congress from Clark County in 1860. Mr. Shellabarger became a very influential Republican advocate for the Abolitionist Movement and later a lawyer to national figures in Washington, D.C. *(From the Collection of John H. Dickinson, Washington, DC)*

Charleston, South Carolina, the U.S. Government decided to recruit "United States Colored Troops." The muster rolls of the 14th, 16th and 44th "USCT" regiments, raised in Chattanooga, Tennessee, in 1863-64, all have soldiers from Clark County, Ohio. Frank Boyd, a painter, Samuel W. Bosley, Jeremiah Hannah and Charley Boss, farmers, Charles W. Williams, a hotel boy and Henry Charles Taylor, a porter, were willing to leave the relative security of their homes and risk their lives on the southern battlegrounds.

The promise of freedom was far better than the postwar reality. Having endured more than two centuries of slavery, African Americans faced a long, hard struggle before they could sit at the table with the rest of the country. They came out of the war with hopes and dreams and flocked north. By 1870, over two thousand, almost ten percent of Springfield's population, were in town to benefit from the booming prosperity. But local whites, many Union veterans

The National Guard was called in to stop the rioting in 1904 when a black man, awaiting trial for murder, was lynched in downtown Springfield. These soldiers are standing in a burned out black neighborhood called the "Levee." Riots and racial tension persisted nationwide through much of the early twentieth century.

OPPOSITE PAGE: The 1920s saw a strong resurgence of the Ku Klux Klan, here seen marching by the thousands down Pennsylvania Avenue in the Nation's Capital (top right). *(Library of Congress)*

Their special brand of prejudice was aimed at Roman Catholics and immigrants as well as African Americans. The Ohio Klan, twelve thousand strong, came to Springfield to burn crosses in 1923 (bottom).

home and in the workplace grew along with labor unrest and the increasing racial bigotry that infected America. Edwin S. Todd, a Columbia University sociologist and Springfield native, saw little contact and much mutual suspicion between the races.

> ...Animosity on the part of whites toward blacks is strong and growing, and on the part of blacks is a growing jealousy of rights, real or supposed.

It was an American compact with the devil that mocked the black race and worse. By the turn of the century, the country was descending into an epidemic of lynchings. Many of these terrible events, which went on for decades, were attended by a carnival-like atmosphere. Springfield had its own murderous episode in 1904. The victim, Richard Dixon, was far from a model citizen. Described by the newspaper as "a negro of dubious character," he had murdered his girlfriend and court bailiff Charles Collis during a domestic dispute. Collis was the first Springfield police officer ever killed in the line of duty. A mob gathered and took its revenge on Dixon.

> March 7, 1904 – The storm had been brewing all day. The town was out to get the lawless negro. From early evening the mob was collecting at the county jail...the jail was surrounded and the police were swept away as the doors were smashed with heavy railroad rails...the wretched negro was hastily dragged from his cell [and] almost instantly there were seven bullet holes in his body. His then lifeless body was strung up on a telegraph pole at Fountain and Main. Volley after volley was fired into his body. For the first time in Springfield, a human life was sacrificed to satiate the insane rage of a mad mob.

The mob went on to burn a black ghetto called the "Levee." The Ohio National Guard was called out. The mob melted away and no one was arrested. Within two years, the Guard was back to stop another race riot that destroyed whole black neighborhoods.

Unlike the deep south, Springfield did not adopt the full scale "separate but equal" lie that totally separated the races. The schools were desegregated in 1885, but blacks developed their own businesses, churches, movie houses and clubs in their own neighborhoods on Washington and Center Streets. Most local families abhorred the violence at the turn of the century, although violence kept erupting. In 1921, Mayor Burton Westcott drove into a black neighborhood in one of his "Westcott" sedans to negotiate with armed citizens who had heard a riot was headed in their direction. Mayor Westcott was shot at and ducked into a passing streetcar to make his escape. The Ku Klux Klan

who had fought to end slavery, could not yet accept blacks as equals. The country, having experimented with "reconstructing" the defeated south and giving the freed slaves true citizenship, compromised with southern leaders and fell back into old patterns. Slavery was replaced by "Jim Crow," and, for the better part of a century, the black population was treated as a separate and inferior nation, apart from mainstream America.

The frictions in Springfield started soon after the war ended. The first skirmishes occurred when African American families tried to send their children to white schools. The school board responded by planning a segregated black school. A particularly bright local student named Broadwell Chinn applied to Wittenberg in 1875 and caused a firestorm. Students and faculty rejected the application, but the college's president and board, remembering the militant abolitionism of the institution founders, reversed the decision. Chinn went on to become one of the first black lawyers in Springfield.

Black migrations continued and tensions at

FIRST OPEN CONCLAVE
SPRINGFIELD & CLARK CO. KLAN
REALM OF OHIO

INITIATION OF CLASS
OF
"SOMEWHERE" IN CLARK CO.

OVERLEAF:
Thousands of African Americans came north after the Civil War looking for industrial jobs. The black population more than doubled in the last half of the nineteenth century but remained at about ten percent of the total. Although racial tensions increased dramatically, integrated teams of workers, like the group posing in a quarrying or smelting factory, often labored in close harmony.

Springfield civil rights marchers braved cold and snowy weather in 1965 as they protested continuing discrimination in schools, public facilities and real estate. Local leaders, like Robert C. Henry, Dorothy Bacon and Hattie Mosley, captured national attention after World War Two as African Americans continued the struggle for equality.

After a century of turmoil, Springfield again became a leader in the civil rights movement. Robert C. Henry was elected mayor in 1966, the first African American to lead a major American city.

had a nationwide revival later in the '20s. Although most of the hate was aimed at Roman Catholic immigrants, the black community understood the message when the Ohio Klan, 12,000 strong, came to Springfield in 1923 and burned several crosses on the old fairgrounds.

The modern history of Springfield's African American community is chronicled in the 1983 Fifitieth Anniversary Issue of *Newsweek* Magazine. The magazine followed the fortunes of the older generation of the Bacon family, struggling to make its way through the Depression, World War Two and into the Civil Rights era of the 1950s and 60s. Dorothy Evans Bacon was raised in the separate and unequal black neighborhoods of Springfield. She married Jerry Bacon on the eve of the stock market crash and soon most small businesses, black and white, became victims of the Depression. A move to Columbus landed Jerry a WPA job but he was soon laid off. Dorothy summoned up her best letter writing skills and wrote directly to President Roosevelt. Within a few days, armed with a letter from the White House verifying that as a married man he could not be summarily dismissed, Jerry Bacon got his job back.

During World War Two, Jerry returned to Springfield and found a job at International Harvester that lasted 28 years. With that kind of security, the Bacons were able to step back and look at how little had changed for African Americans even with the prosperity of the 1950s. Filled with a dose of spirit from her ex-slave great grandfather and her friend Hattie Mosely, who had been campaigning for civil rights since the 1920s, Dorothy Bacon became a

middle-aged activist in the tradition of Mother Stewart.

Newsweek summarized the story of Dorothy Bacon almost singlehandedly mobilizing the black community to join the growing national civil rights movement.

> For a decade, embracing the great black awakening of the '50s and '60s, she was, in the words of the friendly competition at the Springfield Urban League, 'the spirit of the black community' – a public scold who obliged the city to examine its conscience and act on what it discovered there. 'Somebody had to get involved for things to be changed around here,' she said long afterward, and while she hadn't exactly planned it that way, [that] somebody turned out to be her. Her force of character became legend in the black community, and so did her growing influence with white men and women of power downtown...

Dorothy Bacon helped found a local chapter of the National Association for the Advancement of Colored People and then went to work on the still segregated movie theaters, the de facto segregation of the area schools and the discrimination in real estate that created segregated neighborhoods. By 1961, after months of unceasing doorbell ringing and canvassing, Robert C. Henry became the first black member of the Springfield City Commission. Within five years, Mr. Henry followed Springfield's first Jewish mayor, Maurice K. "Buddy" Bach, into office. He was the first black man elected mayor of a major American city. After a century, from Abolition to Civil Rights, Springfield was again a national leader in the arduous journey of African Americans to full U.S. citizenship.

The Prosperity Continues and the National Road is Reborn (1890-1929)

Now a century old, Springfield was ready to celebrate. From wilderness to major industrial center in a handful of generations, the growth and development had been non-stop. The city population was now almost twice as large as the county. No one could doubt that rapid improvement would go on indefinitely. A local orator, filled with the bombast of his time, proclaimed,

> We look and behold a city great, prosperous and beautiful, a home in the forefront of civilization!

Great and prosperous, yes, but beautiful? The present generation had built sprawling, grim, red brick factories all over the city. For them, the industry was beautiful because it stood for success. Their parents and grandparents had lived in a green landscape, managing subsistence farms where the backbreaking work never stopped. The progress, symbolized by modern, belching factories, was vastly superior to the "good old days."

So Springfield celebrated its centennial in a manner befitting its optimism. A week was set aside for parades, long-winded speeches and homey exhibits at the fairgrounds. It was all calculated to show a major success story. From August 4, 1901, when a religious service attracted 5,000, until August 10, a day devoted to the women and education, the Champion and Home City sang a long hymn to itself.

Event organizers took pains to praise their settler ancestors but also relegate them to the quaint past. They asked the Daughters of the American Revolution to build and furnish an old-fashioned, clapboard-covered log cabin. The brand new Clark County Historical Society displayed specimens from the art of prehistoric man.

> The utilizing of the forces of nature to serve man's wants, such as are used today, were unknown to him, and a life of mere animal force was about as much as he knew in his experience.

The Society also exhibited the

> methods and means used by the pioneers to supply their wants...Though these methods were far inferior to those of our day, yet those who used them were as happy as we, and wrought their work in gaining a livelihood and in building up the forces of society with great contentment of mind. Those who lived in those far-off days, and who have lingered long enough to experience something of the great improvements of our times, have kept pace well with the great strides that the last twenty-five years have made, showing that it is not the things that men possess that

make them great and noble, but their spirit and aspirations which lead them to adapt themselves to the times and circumstances under which they live.

Having paid their respects to the pioneers and pointed out how much life had improved, the festival committee spent several days extolling the veterans, the fraternal organizations, the press, labor, agriculture, women and education. One parade featured a mile long line of Springfield products and gaily decorated police and fire engines; another, all the city labor organizations and yet another the Clark County veterans. Civil War hero J. Warren Keifer, just back from the military campaign that captured Cuba from the Spanish, spoke for over an

About the time it celebrated its centennial, Springfield published this booklet cover, expressing the mood of the Golden Age. The community believed it could supply the world with anything it wanted.

continued on page 86.

At Home in Clark County

If you had some money, and most did, life in Clark County at the turn of the twentieth century was comfortable and secure. The country was spreading its interests overseas but had yet to face the major wars that mobilized millions. Locally, economic downturns and labor unrest had failed to dampen a pervading sense of optimism about living the good life. Springfield was turning out a world of products for waiting consumers. Factories were working long shifts. An inventive era of conveniences had made the hardworking lives of parents and grandparents part of a distant past.

As a flood of gadgets was designed to make life easier, George Eastman put photographic cameras into the hands of ordinary folks. It had become the era of photography. An art form for professionals became a chance for every family to record candid moments to cherish and remember. Photographic studios still produced studied portraits for the wall or mantle, but any cousin, aunt or uncle could now capture a family outing, a special dinner or a trip to somewhere with the homespun honesty of everyday life.

Middle and upper class Clark County families grasped this new opportunity with enthusiasm. The Historical Society archives have thousands of Gilded Age snapshots documenting picnics, vacations, marriages and graduations, work places, favorite horses, buggies and "horseless carriages," farmyards and manicured lawns, homes, parades, ball games, fairs, bicycle rides and plain old get-togethers with family and friends. Often with little or no background information, they still offer us a window on another time and another place.

Two families, the Pages and the Kellys, left us only their names and a small set of proud images of their Clark County lives. We can look and know that Mrs. Page was fond of dolls. We can see that the Kelly's had fun with "tableaux" in their backyard ivy and that their youngest daughter enjoyed "posing" for the camera. They have given us a gift of travel to those moments in time so long ago and left us to wonder what it was like to live in Clark County during its "Golden Age."

The prosperous-looking middle class Page family left behind two photographs. It appears that Mrs. Page is much more interested than her daughter in the impressive collection of dolls.

The Kelly family left a record of some shenanigans amidst the ivy in their backyard. Note the passage of years in the photos to the left and bottom. The younger Kelly daughter is putting on the charm as she perches precariously on the porch railing.

Bicycle Clubs Give New Life to an Old Road

Made just before the Civil War, this later model of the earliest successful bicycle has pedals to drive the front wheel. The early "veloci-pedes" shook their riders mercilessly and were called "boneshakers."

The late nineteenth century found Springfielders with more leisure time, enjoying the still unspoiled country-side in Clark County. Whether it was a camping trip to the gorge at Clifton (below) or fishing on a near-by creek (opposite page), it was proper to dress appro-priately for the occasion.

Prosperity brought leisure. For many, the drudgery of daily life gave way to time for recreation. As Springfield grew, the families with the sched-ules and means demanded a more sophisticated lifestyle. When Andrew Black built his Opera House in the 1860s, the community had a first class theater. The Champion City could now enjoy the most modern music and melodrama. Black chose *The Drummer Boy of Shiloh* for his premier production and there was-n't a dry eye in the house.

Three decades later, picnics were all the rage. The outdoors called as some sought the adven-tures of the gorge at Clifton while most enjoyed the merry-go-round, roller coaster and huge dance hall in the new amusement parks at the edge of town.

The natural life, exercise and athleticism were beckoning and the new city YMCA was suddenly the place to go for baseball, bas-ketball, tennis, track and bicycle riding. All of these sports were practically unheard of before the Civil War, but the bicycle was

something very new and very special.

It had started as the "velocipede." A Frenchman invented an ungainly collection of wheels and handlebars with no means to propel it except feet awkwardly pushing across the ground. For the next half century, it was a curiosity to see a gentleman in top hat and

The first great innovation in bicycles was the high-wheeled "Ordinary" or "Pennyfarthing." Without a bicycle chain, the rider used the pedals on the large front wheel to generate power and speed on the road. High-wheelers, often dangerous to mount and ride, were the adventurous realm of young males.

Male bicycle clubs took over the roads in the 1880s and ventured out on hundred mile "century" rides, often using the neglected old National Road. Recitation Hall on the Wittenberg College campus was a favorite starting point (below). The clubs attracted hundreds to social events and started a national movement that was determined to improve old roads (top right of opposite page). The 1880s saw the arrival of the practical, modern "safety" bike.

tails wobbling across the country-side in what came to be called the "boneshaker." Later, someone thought to add pedals that turned the front wheel, but the first practical bicycle didn't appear until the 1870s. The high-wheeled "Ordinary" or "Pennyfarthing" doesn't look very practical to modern eyes. Without a chain drive, the large front wheel gave the rider power as he rolled down the street. Young adventurers loved it because it was difficult to ride and more than a bit dangerous (when it was in use, the "ordinary" was the single greatest cause of injury to young men). A "header" over the handlebars was a bone breaker and a face masher. Still, this contraption gave exciting new freedom to a whole generation, and trouble for old-timers.

> Youngsters should be muzzled! A party of some half a dozen young bloods about town, made night hideous with their diabolical singing!

Bicycle clubs were created everywhere. The new League of American Wheelmen had local branches that sponsored "century" rides, hundred mile jaunts dodging the ruts and chuckholes on the old National Road. In 1885, the Champion City Bicycle Club held a statewide meeting that attracted

over 600 Ohio enthusiasts. The parades, featuring hundreds of high wheelers, must have been a sight to see and the highlight of the weekend was a dance at both the Opera House and Oliver S. Kelly's Arcade Hotel with a seven course meal after midnight. The Springfield Wheelmen held their own formal ball at the same hotel in 1888. The "excursionists" liked to meet in front of Wittenberg College's grand new Recitation Hall and "fly" the thirteen miles to Yellow Springs in just thirty-five minutes.

The now familiar chain-driven "safety" bike made its appearance in the 1880s and finally bike riding was practical for everyone. Ever enterprising, local businesses got into the act and the John H. Thomas & Sons Company manufactured innovative "safety" bikes for more than a decade. The ladies quickly took to these new bikes and began participating in the excursions. The outfits they wore outraged some.

> The scandal of it all! Young ladies of good breeding wearing revealing knee length Knickerbockers and Bloomer dresses in order to ride those contraptions!

We have not had a Broken Fork or Frame on '99 Season's Product.

PRICE $40.00. NEW THOMAS. MEN'S MODEL No. 27.

The bikers may have scared horses and offended the older generation, but they also brought new attention to neglected old roads. Some attempted to ride the whole length of the National Road and soon the League of American Wheelmen had another cause in addition to their cheerleading for the new fad. Sporting buttons exclaiming, "We Want Good Roads," and "Good Roads to Everywhere," they formed the National Committee on Highway Improvement and enthusiastically crusaded for better roads. The new movement would get a major boost from a transportation milestone that would revolutionize the lives of all Americans. The first practical "horseless carriages" were sharing the roads with bicycles as early as the 1890s.

There were innovative contraptions that allowed dignified ladies to ride along with their beaux (middle above), but the safety bike soon was adapted for female use. Bloomer outfits developed for bicycle riding scandalized many in the older generation.

Streetcars Roll into the "Home City"

Now vanished from the American scene, the street-car was once a convenient part of every large community's mass transit system.

At the turn of the 20th century, the American railroad was the transportation king. The statistics were amazing. Officials estimated that forty-four passenger and forty freight trains passed through Clark County every day. More than 135,000 local travelers took to the rails every year. It was an elegant and leisurely way to vacations in Grand Canyon, Yosemite and Glacier National Parks or to friends and relatives anywhere in the nation. In 1900, a government spokesman tried to put it all in perspective.

> One hundred years ago, the railroad was unheard of...now our railroad trackage would circle the world six and one-half times. Last year we moved sixty-eight billion tons of freight.

There was another railroad in everyone's neighborhood. Unless you wanted to saddle or hitch up the family horse, walking had been the preferred method of getting around town for generations.

About the time of the Civil War, inventors put horse drawn "streetcars" on the tracks above the ever-present mud and dust of city roads. The small mules pulling this Springfield car in the 1880s look resigned to their task.

About the time of the Civil War, some entrepreneurs in the eastern cities began to consider bringing the railroad into city streets. They laid tracks for the new "streetcars," but had to be content with horse-power because steam engines were too dirty and disruptive for the inner city. In 1871, Phineas Mast and George Spence brought this service to Springfield. By the early '80s, the Citizen's Street Railway began to make money and within a couple of years the mysterious energy force called electricity came to town.

The advent of electricity opened up a universe of possibilities. American cities were almost instantly draped with miles and miles of electric lines bringing incandescent lights to every home that could afford it. Why not hang more lines and figure out a way to bring electric power to the streetcars? With all the other heart stopping improvements going on, this idea didn't seem very farfetched and it soon became a reality. Within a decade, America had again conquered space with the electric railway. In the big cities, they put the

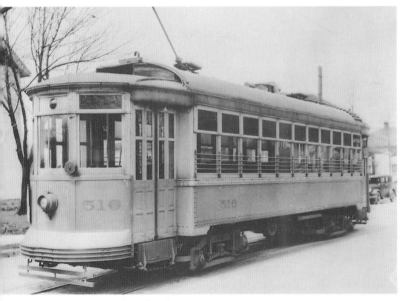

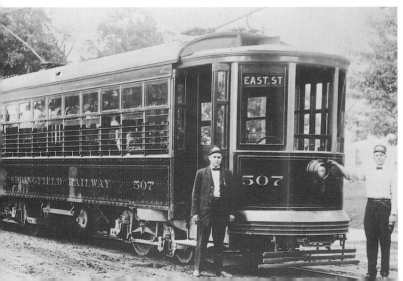

railway above and below ground to avoid making already impossible traffic jams worse. In places like Springfield, they simply hung the lines between the buildings and laid the tracks in the middle of the street. The Springfield Railway System purchased the electric lines already run by an enterprising soul named I. Ward Frey and the new system was in business by 1892. Everyone was soon at home with the clang of the trolley bell and the unnerving showers of sparks generated by passing cars. The whole system seemed right out of science fiction.

The next step was an Ohio Electric Railway, an "interurban" line linking all the cities in the Buckeye State. Electricity turned out to be a very effective power source, propelling the "traction" cars at high speeds over the countryside. It took huge amounts of coal to generate the power, but the country appeared to have an inexhaustible supply. Dayton, Urbana and Springfield had put a line together by 1895, and, after 1907, the Ohio Electric, financed by a Cincinnati financier, took over the local lines.

After electricity was introduced to Springfield streets about 1890, the Springfield Electric Railway flooded the city with clanging trolley cars. True mass transit had replaced the horse and buggy. This photograph shows the morning traffic jam at the Power Street Car Barn in 1905.

The Springfield Electric Railway cars, with their distinctive cowcatchers, were a familiar sight in Springfield for decades. The uniformed men who ran these noisy cars through the neighborhoods were heroes to local kids.

By World War One, the Ohio Electric Railway, or "OE," had almost three thousand miles of track running all over Ohio. Later, as the automobile era took hold, staged publicity "races" between the "interurbans" and airplanes, automobiles and even motorcycles (opposite page) demonstrated how quickly and efficiently the electric railway could move between cities.

Public accommodations in the interurban cars varied from the stylish, wood-paneled lounges to the typical bus and streetcar seats still used in urban transit systems.

This distinctive electric railway station built at the turn of the century still stands in west Springfield. After exiting the cars, travelers could cross a walkway and enter the brand new Snyder City Park for an afternoon outing.

A group of casually dressed Springfield ladies enjoy the freedom of the rails. The streetcars and interurbans gave everyone opportunities to travel easily to friends and family all over the Buckeye State. Surviving timetables and tickets (top right of opposite page) illustrate how inexpensive it was to ride on the electric railway.

By World War One, "the huge, long green cars of the 'O.E.' were a symbol of the interurban era at its zenith of perfection…" There were 2,800 miles of Ohio electric railway between everyone's hometown. The "O.E." was the largest system of its kind in the nation. The automobile, more flexible and convenient, eventually proved the streetcar's undoing. Except for a short revival in World War Two, when gasoline was short, the systems went into a long decline and have all but vanished from the American landscape and memory. Now only dimly remembered, the streetcars were once a ticket to everywhere. For only a few cents, you could step on the cars in Springfield and take an unhurried ride all the way to Toledo, Cincinnati and Cleveland.

The trolleys gave the Champion City a new nickname. Springfield, with convenient access to Ohio's other major cities, became the state's hometown. The turn of the century was an age when clubs provided fun and security from cradle to grave. Practically everyone belonged to one of the almost one hundred fraternal organizations. And women, now freeing themselves from the strictly home-based life of previous generations, also had clubs, many of which focused on the poor and indigent.

The biggest clubs built huge, rambling "homes" on hundreds of acres of farmland around Springfield. The homes could house up to 250 "widows and orphans and aged members of the order." The Pythians, Masons and Odd Fellows all competed for attention with social activities, elaborate theatricals and services like life and unemployment insurance. Each day, thousands stepped off streetcars from all over Ohio.

The many who came to these refuges now called Springfield the "Home City."

By 1900, the mammoth "homes" of the Ohio Pythians (top left), the Masons (above left) and the Odd Fellows (above right) ringed Springfield. They were designed to take care of the "widows, orphans and aged members" of the popular orders. The electric railways brought visitors from far and wide and gave Springfield the new nickname of "Home City."

Wealthy local businessman Asa Bushnell was one of two Ohio governors from Springfield (the other was more recent Governor James Rhodes). Two term Republican Governor Bushnell had a successful administration which brought the state into the twentieth century.

The Brain family, early settlers who followed the Quaker Warders from Philadelphia, still owns a lumber company that has been a thriving local business for generations.

hour about his army experiences. The children of the fraternal homes put on an exhibition of calisthenics. Asa Bushnell, Clark County's native son and Ohio governor, came from his state office in Columbus and proudly gave at least two speeches. It was an orgy of goodwill designed to make the residents appreciate all the city's success; past, present and future.

The truth wasn't far from the optimistic message of the anniversary. Clark County and Springfield were, indeed, good places to live. The so-called "Gay Nineties" had been a miserable decade for America. The country's unbridled industrial revolution was coming off the tracks. Labor and farm unrest, bigotry, financial panics, business abuses, pollution, even terrorists, all threatened the established order. Some of these problems would catch up with Springfield in the first decades of the 20th century, but the city had many of the attributes others were seeking. The answers to the concerns and the confusion lay in the small cities of the Heartland where big money, big industry

and big government had not lost contact with people and place. Wealthy community leaders like Phineas Mast, J. Warren Keifer, Oliver Kelly and Asa Bushnell all had a great sense of responsibility and duty to the community where they lived. That sense gave Springfield an anchor during the trouble and turmoil.

One of the Champion City's secrets was the diversity of its industry and manufacturing. Revolutionary farm machines had started the boom, but Springfield was never a one industry town. Other inventive entrepreneurs began selling their own products and, by 1900, hundreds of items from iron fences to electric fans and even caskets were sold all over the country. A community motto rang true, "You want it, we'll make it."

The continued prosperity, now approaching a half century, brought big city culture. There was a new "Grand" Opera House that attracted national acts. Full symphony orchestras and famous artists, including violinist Fritz Kreisler with the Philadephia Orchestra in 1916, were now regular fare. Vaudeville impresario Gus Sun opened a theater in 1904 and the Chakeres brothers came to Springfield in 1908, starting a family entertainment business that continues today. At eight stories, the First National Bank Building became the local version of a skyscraper and the community's skyline kept growing. Much of the stunning growth was the handiwork of Cyrus Kissell. After he opened his business in 1884, the world of real estate was

never the same. With an unshakable American belief in owning property, the Kissels, father and son, made home ownership available to the middle class and developed a national reputation as mortgage bankers.

Rapid growth had stretched an outdated city government to its limit.

> Springfield has reached the full stature of a city but still retains many of the characteristics of village days.

The comment was a gentle admonition that hid a troubling trend. The Champion City had simply grown too fast and government services were struggling to keep up with community issues. Most of the concern centered on the fire department. Over a three year period after 1900, the whole downtown seemed to be burning down. First a building on the Wittenberg campus was consumed. Then old William Whiteley was a spectator as the entire mammoth East Street Shop complex burned and all but one of the ten businesses in the shops were ruined. The climax came in the dead of winter, 1903, when a firestorm destroyed seven buildings in the heart of downtown, including the YMCA and Black's Opera House. The main culprit was low water pressure, but the antiquated fire department was inept and almost helpless when faced with these major conflagrations.

Other problems kept mounting. Beautiful Buck Creek was becoming a sewer. Garbage was piling up in the streets. Drinking and prostitution were out of control because local saloon-

On the bitterly cold night of February 19, 1903, the third of three catastrophic fires in three years killed three people and destroyed an entire city block, including the thirty-five-year-old Black's Opera House. Springfield was forced to modernize its antiquated fire protection.

The mail order rose and flower business thrived in turn of the century Springfield and made the city "the greatest rose producing center in the world." When pioneer businesswoman Miss Jesse M. Good sent out her "Famous Rose Collection" catalogue in 1927, she was calling herself "the Woman Florist and Seedswoman."

Springfield Firehouse No. 4 shows off its horse drawn steam pumper and ladder truck around 1900. Inept leadership, low city water pressure, old equipment and an epidemic among its horses tested the fire department to its limits and brought reform after the disastrous fires early in the century. The last surviving Fire Alarm Telegram Station (opposite page), one of twenty-eight fireboxes installed in 1876, served Springfield for a hundred years.

keepers were buying off city officials. Racial animosity was erupting into murderous riots. The National Guard was called in twice in three years. It was time for "Home Rule" and, in 1913, the state authorized Springfield to adopt a city charter. A new city commission wasted no time. The Champion City became one of the first in the nation to hire a professional city manager and local government began to act like a city business.

In the midst of the growing pains, another invention came to town. Ultimately, this new machine, marrying a motor to a carriage and sending the horse out to pasture, would change everything. The concept was simple but the race for a solution was not. Would the new motors on "horseless carriages" be driven by steam, electricity or internal combustion? Dr. Russell's experiments with steam in the 1880s frightened Springfield, but when the inventors started to find practical solutions around 1900, the old "goahead" spirit kicked into gear.

Soon a dozen local businesses, including carriage companies that feared for their futures and

gas engine companies that knew farmers were now not their only customers, were banging out prototypes and rushing to get their models on the market. The same frenzied attempts to cash in were being repeated in shops and backyards all over America. Rumors were flying that Henry Ford might want to open a plant in Springfield, but the "Westcott" and the "Frayer-Miller" were the only automobiles ever made in town that had any success on the market. The monopolies in Detroit eventually put Burton Westcott and practically every other would-be auto tycoon out of business, although the Kelly Springfield Company sold their massive, rumbling trucks for decades.

The automobile industry may not have been a success for Springfield, but automobiles quickly brought attention to the quality of American roads. The early adventurers who took their "flivvers" out on the National road soon discovered more dust and mud than road. They were not tourists but trailblazers, searching for good roads, precious gasoline, repairs, food and lodging, and, if they were lucky, their destination.

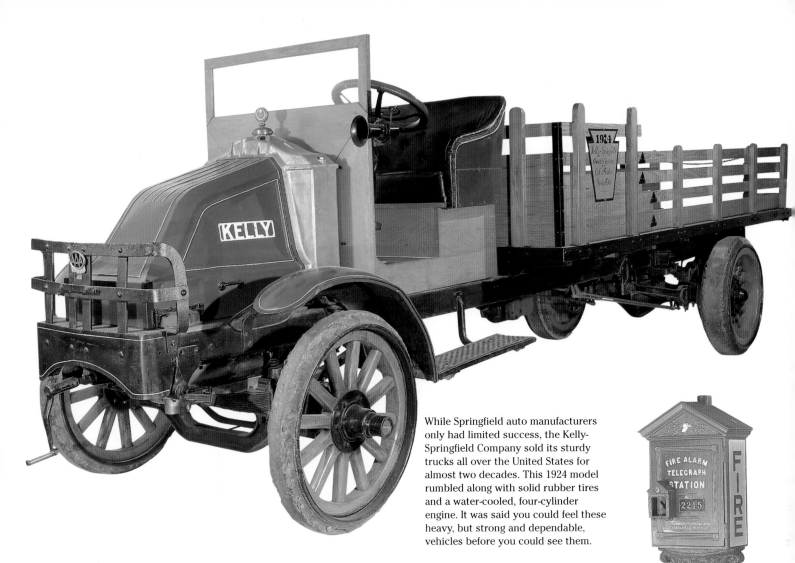

While Springfield auto manufacturers only had limited success, the Kelly-Springfield Company sold its sturdy trucks all over the United States for almost two decades. This 1924 model rumbled along with solid rubber tires and a water-cooled, four-cylinder engine. It was said you could feel these heavy, but strong and dependable, vehicles before you could see them.

Improved roads became a national issue as bicyclists joined the auto enthusiasts to demand federal help. Like the fight to get funds for the original National Road, the new struggle ran into federal versus state roadblocks. Another issue was road surface. The faster and heavier automobiles needed a more durable roadbed and the cement industry came to the rescue. In 1912, a twenty-four mile stretch of the road west of Zanesville was paved with experimental concrete using federal funds. After Congress passed the Federal Aid Road Act in 1916, more travelers than ever rolled onto the concrete highways as they became available.

Many Americans still saw the automobile as a needless, noisy and dirty nuisance. Others saw it as an opportunity. A new generation of businesses, catering to the "tourists" motoring on the National Road, developed on the roadsides. Tourist homes and camps provided lodging for travelers who often carried their camping gear on the tops and running boards of their Model T Fords. Gasoline companies provided guidebooks. Red, white and blue road signs were nailed to telephone poles and the renovated old historic roads got new names. Today, nostalgia for the two-lane Lincoln Highway and the National Old Trails Road has become a passion for those who feel the modern interstates are homogenizing America. Advertisers realized that billboards had a new audience, captive in their cars. The tourist industry, born of the need to pave old roads, eventually conquered America.

As the automobile turned everyone's backyard stable into a garage, Springfield entered its fifth and sixth decades of growth and prosperity. The new nickname was "The Best 60,000 City in America." There had been warnings, early in the 20th century, about industrial specialization and absentee ownership. Locally-owned business still turned out a sea of products. A flourishing nationwide mail order business in roses made Springfield "the greatest rose-producing city in the world," and yet the two giants in town had moved their corporate offices elsewhere. Using banker J. P. Morgan's money, seven reaper makers, including Champion, became the International Harvester Company, based in Chicago. Accused of being a monopoly by the government, "I.H." almost closed its Springfield plant in 1918, but saved thousands of jobs by switching production to a new line of trucks. The other giant, Phineas Mast's *Farm and Fireside* publishing empire, became Crowell-Collier when it purchased the *Collier's* Magazine in 1919. The editorial offices had moved to New

A farmer and his horses look on as a roadster glides past on a brand new section of National Road. Cement surfaces turned the old, muddy roads into real highways and launched the travel industry. *(Ohio Historical Society)*

With few services available along the highways, early tourists became adventurers. The 1920s couple, posing in their excursion togs in Zanesville, Ohio, have all their camping gear loaded up on the running board of their 1917 Overland Touring Car. *(Ohio Historical Society)*

York, but the printing plant in downtown Springfield now covered a whole city block and employed 2,000 people who turned out millions of magazines every week.

Wittenberg College, not yet seventy-years-old, flourished after its humble beginnings. It had won over the hearts of the community, growing into one of Springfield's biggest institutions. It received a major boost from several local philanthropists, as well as Carnegie and Rockefeller funds, and became a school nationally recognized for its academics and intercollegiate athletics.

By 1924, Springfield employed 26,000. It was settling into a conservative, middle-aged contentment with where it had been and where it was going. It had conquered many growing pains and was a mature city with a Chamber of Commerce, service clubs, even its own symphony and choral society. A crisis in prices was chasing county farmers off the properties their families had owned for generations. Race was still an explosive issue and thousands of Klansmen had rallied in town. Unsettling concerns had always simmered under the prosperity. There was no reason to believe anything would derail the progress of the last seventy-five years.

continued on page 102.

Cashing in on the "Horseless Carriage" Craze

The race to produce a marketable "horseless carriage" sparked the imaginations of American inventors. The key was finding a dependable and efficient source of power. Steam, electricity and internal combustion were all candidates for the prize. Steam engines were dependable but heavy, sluggish and slow to start. The science of electricity and renewable battery power was promising, but still in its infancy. The internal combustion engine was brand new, complicated and too heavy to be portable. Which power source would develop fast enough to win the prize?

Springfield, with all of its inventive talent, was soon in the hunt. Would-be inventors were scratching their heads in shops and backyards all over the city. Dr. L.E. Russell had proven steam would work in 1886, but had almost burned down his barn in the process. The same year, Clark Sintz patented a 2-cycle gas engine and formed the Sintz Gas Engine Company. Sintz was a third generation Springfielder. His father was a prosperous local farmer and miller, but young Sintz, like the older William Whiteley, was always interested in tinkering with mechanical things. He graduated from steam to internal combustion after a visit to the 1876 Philadelphia Centennial Exposition.

The secret for advocates of internal combustion was a truly portable engine that could be put on a carriage. Clark Sintz accomplished just that in 1886 and was lured to Grand Rapids, Michigan, the same year. By 1893, he had patented a 3-port, 2-cycle engine that became a standard for many early "gas buggies" including the 1894 Haynes-Apperson now in the Smithsonian Institution. Sintz went on to secure six more patents, but his greatest contribution was to the boating not the automotive industry. The Sintz-designed 2-cycle engine was and is a marine standard.

Meanwhile, no less than ten Springfield-designed automobiles entered the freewheeling race for the public's attention between 1900 and 1920. By that date, the

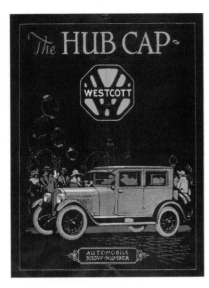

Detroit-based companies were shutting out individual entrepreneurs. Almost all of the Springfield models had short lives or never got beyond the prototype stage. Most utilized gas engines, but a few stuck doggedly to electricity and steam. The honor roll of failed, but undoubtedly inventive and well crafted, "gas, steam and electric buggies," includes:

- THE BRALEY (OR CLIFTON) (1900)
  Nothing is known about this short-lived and probably unrealized vehicle.
- THE BRAMWELL (1904-05)
  A refinement of the Massachusetts-made Bramwell-Robinson, it featured a single-cylinder, two stroke, eight horsepower, water-cooled engine fitted into a seventy-two inch wheel base chassis. It had a laminated wood frame reinforced with steel sheathing, planetary transmission and a left-handed steering wheel. Weighing in at a hefty 1,125 pounds, it sold for $800.
- THE BRENNING ELECTRIC (1901)
  The Brenning Brothers of Salem, Massachusetts, relocated their electric business to Springfield in 1900. They briefly produced and sold an electric car with a design from Dr. L.E. Russell, the father of the 1886 steam "horseless carriage."
- THE RUSSELL-SPRINGFIELD (1902-03)
  Dr. Russell built and marketed this gasoline-powered car on his own. It was powered by a single-cylinder, nine horsepower, water-cooled engine, mounted under the seat of the two-passenger runabout body. At a price of $1,250, it featured a three-speed selective transmission, chain drive, force feed lubrication and right-hand wheel steering.

- THE FRAYER-MILLER (1907-10)
  The Oscar Lear Automotive Company produced almost as many four and six cylinder, air-cooled "Frayer-Millers" as Westcott produced its "Lighter-Six" sedans. A few still survive.
- THE KELLY STEAM (1901-02)
  O. W. Kelly of the O. S. Kelly Company designed and built one prototype steam carriage with an engine of his own design featuring a rotary valve and positive cutoff. The prototype was adapted to a steam company delivery wagon. The Kelly-Springfield Company was famous later for a line of heavy, durable trucks.
- THE KROTZ ELECTRIC (1903-04)
  Alvaro Krotz built two electric cars with condensed storage batteries and solid tires in 1903. He then marketed several more the following year. Later, Krotz moved to Chicago and tried unsuccessfully to sell a gas-electric hybrid to Sears, Roebuck and Company. He returned to Defiance, Ohio, and produced the gas-electric buggy until 1911.
- THE KUQUA (1901)
  Springfield carriage-makers, Kuqua & Sons, announced they would go into the steam and electric carriage business shortly, but there is no evidence they ever did.
- THE McNUTT (1902)
  John McNutt bought the Springfield Brenning Brothers business and announced he would "take up the manufacture of automobiles." Nothing more was heard from Mr. McNutt.
- THE OWENS STEAM (1900)
  H. E. Owens, superintendent of the Thomas Manufacturing Company, built a steam carriage, called "a very neat piece of work," in the company shops.
- THE WESTCOTT (1916-1925)
  By far the most successful of Springfield automobile manufacturers, the Westcott Motor Company started in Richmond, Indiana, in 1909, and moved to the Champion City in 1916. Having sold 1850 sedans in 1920, the company went bankrupt in 1925, a victim of the Detroit monopoly.

Several Springfield companies manufactured tires, engines and car parts for the national market. Attempts to break into the vastly profitable auto manufacturing industry proved more elusive. While the industry was new and the door was open, the search for a profitable "gas buggy" was a gold rush. The entrepreneurs in Detroit used a combination of ingenuity and business sense to find the mother lode.

Practically everyone else fell by the wayside.

"A Westcott may be driven harder and farther because of the long life that has been built into it. 'Long life' of the right kind! . . . Stamina engineered into a fine mechanism as the watchmaker – and a few automobile engineers – know how to do it . . ."

Westcott *Saturday Evening Post* Advertisement

What's in an Old Photograph?

The "Spirit of '76" is revisited in this 1950s classic. Was this part of a parade or was it a backyard pageant?

Every household has stacks of photographs tucked away in boxes, drawers and on closet shelves. Snapshots, slides, books of photos, all have been a part of our lives for five generations. We record babies, graduations, military service, marriages, family reunions, even funerals and then put the memories away as an archive to be rediscovered in the future. There are those among us who avidly collect, catalogue and even publish memorable photo collections, but most family photos languish in some forgotten place.

During yard and estate sales and house cleanups, bunches of old photographs end up orphans on lawns and in trashcans. They are thrown out by the thousands, but are sometimes scooped up and taken to the archives of a local historical society. The society, a community's official attic, is left to look, ponder and speculate as it preserves these special moments in time.

Most of these images have lost their identity but not their meaning. They invariably raise more questions than they answer. They generally record important events in the lives of their subjects. Some archivists start with the theory that photographs are lies. As moments, almost heartbeats, in time, they cannot document what is truly happening both before and after the instant of the captured image. We are left with a false instant, when everyone has stopped what they are doing to pose for posterity.

Whatever limitations they have as windows to the past, these photographs have meaning because they record a specific action in a special time and place. We are left to do our own personal time traveling as we speculate on what is going on in an image that has lost its history. What occasion caused three kids in the 1950s to mimic the "Spirit of '76?" What event put together a group of beer drinking young men in suits and hats to pose on a farm with some rather unhappy looking ladies? Why have the ladies gathered (pages 94 and 95) in the yard of a handsome Victorian house and who are those two mischievous young characters at the fence in the foreground? Is the formal looking group (pages 96 and 97) a family or a special group of temperance supporters? The armchair exploration of anonymous photos from our ancestors' world is as much fun in the quest as it is in the answers.

A gathering features some beer drinking. The men look like they are having a better time than the women.

The group of ladies above has the look of a church group or a ladies aid society. The fine-looking group of young ladies on the left may be a graduating class from a finishing school.

FOLLOWING PAGES: The group with the bold young men at the fence may be getting ready for a church supper. The stern-looking, formal and prosperous gathering on the following page might be a family or a religious society.

THE NATIONAL ROAD 93

If the group above is on an outing, they are not exactly roughing it. Are they truly camping in the tent? Note the giant catch. The young men to the right, in turn, have the look of a crew on a serious outing. The gang on the top right look like they're having an old-fashioned good time. The "fat men" on the bottom right may have just won a baseball game.

The Gus Sun Era

Toledo native Gus Sun was a veteran of the national vaudeville and medicine show circuit when he arrived in Springfield in 1904. His success on the traveling stage is illustrated by the high quality posters to the right and on the opposite page. Sun found a profitable home in Springfield by marrying vaudeville acts to the newly-invented movies.
(Bruce Knight Collection)

The Gus Sun Booking Agency began booking vaudeville acts in 1906. At its height, the agency, which survived into the 1950s, was serving four hundred houses. Stars like Al Jolson, Will Rogers, the Marx Brothers, W.C. Fields and Mae West appeared in what came to be called "Gus Sun Time."

For a generation, Springfield was on the cutting edge of the national entertainment industry. A former circus juggler came to town in 1904 and brought a world of amusement with him. Gus Sun was born to be a showman and his career bridged the gap between old-fashioned vaudeville and the world of motion pictures.

In the era of "Buffalo Bill's Wild West Show" and the original "Barnum and Bailey's Greatest Show on Earth," Sun and his three brothers toured the midwest and then the country with their own "Largest Wagon Show on Earth." Starting in 1891, the brothers managed "over 200 Men, Women and Children, Horses and Ponies" for a decade. With the few months of extra time he had every season,

Sun, billing himself "America's Greatest Juggler and Equilibrist," had the energy to put together Indian medicine companies, minstrel troupes and old-fashioned melodramas. His version of "Uncle Tom's Cabin" was called "just about the best...that ever tore at the heartstrings of weeping audiences."

In the early 1900s, when an exhausted Sun returned to his home in Toledo, he was looking for something that might give him an edge. He discovered motion pictures. As primitive as one reelers like "The Great Train Robbery" look today, they mesmerized audi-

ences at the turn of the century. Sun decided to settle down and open a movie and vaudeville house in Springfield, a medium-sized city that had never seen the likes of what he had to offer.

With more pizzazz than funding, the Sun show came to town in 1904. Customers paid up to twenty cents to sit on old-fashioned wooden kitchen chairs in a storeroom. They were treated to three live acts like Glick and Bright and The Great Santell along with a reel of "flickers" projected on hanging sheets. It was magic and patrons couldn't get enough of it. Some stayed in their seats so long, Sun

had to introduce wretched "chaser acts," designed to chase out the entire audience. Always looking for new talent, he sponsored amateur nights for locals who competed for prizes.

Gus Sun took the Champion City by storm. By 1908, he had built a 750 seat theater he christened the New Sun. Building on that success, he opened a whole series of theaters including the Alhambra in 1913, the Fairbanks in 1917 and, finally, in 1920, the Regent, built on the foundations of the recently demolished Grand Opera House. With the houses he had opened in six other nearby cities, he had trouble booking enough acts for his special combination of vaudeville and motion pictures. Having started his own booking agency in 1906, Sun soon had control of bookings for most houses in the midwest and was handling bands as well as vaudeville acts for nightclubs, hotels, fairs and amusement parks.

Most of vaudeville's famous headliners were in the employ of the Gus Sun Booking Agency. Several future stars appeared on Springfield stages. Sun booked Mae West, Al Jolson, Will Rogers, Ted Lewis, Eddie Cantor, Bob Hope, Fannie Brice, Sophie Tucker and W.C. Fields. The Marx Brothers got their start on the New Sun stage. The famous columnist Walter Winchell began his career dancing on the Sun circuit. All of these stars spent time in Springfield before vaudeville was replaced by the talking motion pictures.

At its height, the Sun Booking Agency arranged acts for up to four hundred houses. It was a complex and unrelenting balancing act

and Sun was among the best at it. His agency stayed in business in the Regent Theater until the 1950s. Gus Sun's run in Springfield brought the community into the

20th century. It consistently got rave reviews from locals and brought some of the best talent in America to the Champion City.

This late 19th century vaudeville trunk belonged to the Lee family. Father Fitzhugh "Hughie" started with the Christy Minstrels after the Civil War. He later was joined by his wife Elizabeth Smyth who became "Oneida, Empress of Mystery," and a daughter Yetta, "Tulsa, the girl with the big black eyes."

Hard Times and World War (1930-1945)

Stories still circulate that somehow Springfield and Clark County escaped the worst ravages of the Great Depression. It is true that there never was a spectacular moment of economic upheaval. Both International Harvester and Crowell Collier, the county's biggest employers, weathered the storm and actually got bigger in the process. At seventy years of continuous prosperity, the community wanted to shake off the bad news from the rest of the country and simply get on with business.

But the trouble had been brewing long before the Crash of 1929. For almost a decade, Clark County farmers had been losing a battle to keep their property and their lives together. After the Crash, the Golden Age vanished. In just three years, almost one half of the jobs in town evaporated. The world economy had collapsed and nobody could escape the consequences.

The 1983, 50th Anniversary *Newsweek* Magazine recounted some of the mind numbing stories from that era. Howdy Weber's dad would get a dozen apples to sell if he couldn't find anyone to pay him cash for taking photographs. Matteo Cappelli bought a cake and couldn't find anyone who had the cash to break a twenty dollar bill. Nellie Zimmerman watched a young lady drop out of school, go to work as a clerk and then quietly starve to death trying to help feed the rest of her family. A crazy, reclusive local botanist named Walter Bree Evans put together forty scrapbooks to chronicle the coming apocalypse. Larry Cooper, who had the misfortune to graduate from Springfield High School in 1931, recalled,

The bottom just fell out, that's what it felt like, you couldn't find a job. You couldn't buy a job. You'd walk and keep walking, your clothes getting

Even as America struggled through its worst depression, the love affair with the automobile grew. A newly-renovated National Road, now U.S. Route 40, was flanked by Paul Deere's Bonded Oil gas stations and pumps and neon signs that welcomed tourists to motels and cabins.

more ragged, your shoes getting worn out, and you couldn't buy new shoes. You couldn't buy nothin'.

Nobody seemed to know how to get out of the mess. A new president arrived in 1933 promising to do something, anything to get the country moving again. Franklin Delano Roosevelt, the New York patrician, instantly became the champion of down-and-outers everywhere. "FDR" exuded confidence and America looked forward to his straight-talking "fireside chats." He was the first president to regularly use radio. In fact, he used it so effectively that listeners felt he was talking to them personally. Conservative Springfield wasn't sure it liked his big government, free spending approach, but it was soon confident he would work mightily to help the nation.

The decade of the 1930s saw a flurry of government programs all designed to prime the economic pump. The WPA, NRA, AAA and CCC, an "alphabet soup" of new agencies, put Clark County back to work. With salaries of $30 a month and ecstatic to have any job, nearly 5,000 in Springfield alone worked on roads, parks, schools, a new city hospital, a sewage treatment plant and a post office. They put together George Rogers Clark Park while the county commemorated the 150th anniversary of the 1780 battle that "helped make the Northwest Territory part of the United States." Larry Cooper, who couldn't buy a job, found himself working on the park along Buck Creek.

The federal government didn't carry the whole load. Wittenberg College built a new field house with private funds and two local housewives, Margaret Greenawalt and Fanny Winger, founded the Young Woman's Mission. The Mission pioneered birth control for struggling poor families at its health clinics, a concept that was still illegal in Ohio.

Money was always short, but people found ways to escape from the "Brother can you spare a dime" mood of the times. If you could spare seventy-five extra dollars, a radio would bring the whole world into your living room. Much of the news from elsewhere was frightening, but weekly national favorites like "Fred Allen" and "Fibber McGee and Molly" kept everybody laughing through the adversity. During the 1920s, some enterprising Wittenberg physicists had built WCSO, a pioneering local radio station. National acts, traveling on the Gus Sun circuit, often appeared on WCSO when they were in town.

For just a dime, you could enter a fantasy world at the downtown Regent or State Movie Palaces. The "flickers" had become the "silver screen" and triple features at the Chakeres-owned Theaters, now spread throughout the region, were the best bargain around. The elegant dancing of Fred Astaire and Ginger Rogers and the spectacular "follies" of Busby Berkeley lifted spirits everywhere and are still popular today. In fact, with "Gone with the Wind" and "The Wizard of Oz" among many other great films, the late 1930s are generally recognized as the best years in the history of the cinema.

With help from Henry Ford who produced the highly affordable Model T and then the Model A, the romance of the newly-paved National Road, now U.S. Route 40, returned. The car culture kept right on growing in spite of the troubles. It was another ticket to somewhere else for an always restless America. Consumers worshiped the expensive, beautifully-crafted classics they couldn't afford. Most chugged around in sturdy, black, stripped-down Detroit models now being sold by the millions. There were better roads and real gas stations, run locally by Paul Deer's Bonded Oil Company, replacing the old pumps at country stores. There were roadside diners and motorist cabins and motels instead of tourist camps. Some adventurous souls began to take the family car on vacations all the way across country. Around 1930, the auto makers married the automobile and the radio. Now families could take the world with them when they hit the road. The new freedom was exhilarating.

In the end, the country remained in economic decline for more than a decade. Nobody really figured out how to cure the nationwide malaise. FDR, for all of his radio skills and his many initiatives that reinvented government, remained a cheerleader hoping for the best. There was a certain homey, wholesome innocence to life in small town America during that era. For many who lived through challenging times, there remained a bittersweet nostalgia for simple pleasures and tightly-knit families.

The future held new prosperity for Clark County and the rest of the U. S., but it came from a strange twist of fate.

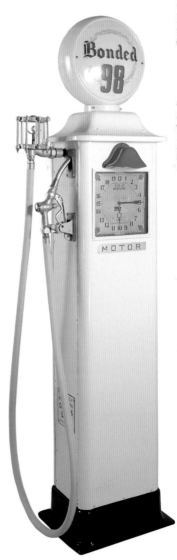

A 1943 "E" for excellence ceremony honors the Robbins and Myers Company at Memorial Hall in downtown Springfield. The "war-minded" R&M Company was a War Department favorite for its ability to produce technically-sophisticated equipment. Note the images of the four military services and several "Rosie the Riveters" in the audience.

The President of the United States desires to express his deep regrets that your son, Seaman First Class J. Richard Ward, was killed in action in defense of his country, Pearl Harbor, Territory of Hawaii, December 7, 1941...

Three telegrams of condolence were sent to Clark County after that terrible Sunday. Twenty-year-old Seaman Ward was on the U. S. S. *Oklahoma.* He had been a great baseball player in high school and had helped the crew of his battleship win the fleet championship. When the *Oklahoma* was hit by torpedoes, he helped his eighteen shipmates escape from a pitch black gun turret, shining a flashlight on the hatch. The ship was hit again and he disappeared forever as the giant vessel rolled over. A posthumous Medal of Honor was sent to his family in Springfield.

The United States had tried to stay on the sidelines and mind its own business while the rest of the world came apart. But neutrality was an illusion shattered by a Japanese sneak attack on the U. S. Fleet at Pearl Harbor, Hawaii. Thousands were killed and wounded. Suddenly the country was in a war to the finish. The world's future was at stake. Young men eagerly signed up to fight in places no one had ever heard of.

Before World War Two ended, 376 government telegrams of regret were delivered around Clark County. It was the same all over America.

A whole generation had joined the armed forces. Million man armies had been mobilized to wage war in both the Pacific and Europe. The casualties were staggering and each loss was a tragedy for a family back home.

It was the custom for the postman to ring the doorbell when there were letters from servicemen. The War Department telegrams were another matter. After months of missions, flying cargo across the English Channel to support the invasion of France, First Lt. Clyde A. Depuy crashed his C-47 just three months before the end of the war in Europe. The telegram was delivered to his in-laws, the Cappellis, in the early hours of January 26, 1945. Thirty-two years later, his son, born posthumously, found his grave among the over 5,000 white crosses near Epinal, France. David Gerhardt died in a prison camp in Tokyo. Francis Hogg was lost on Leyte, Reese Davis on Guadalcanal. James Marrah and George Winger were both killed in the same bombing raid over Ploesti, Romania. The telegrams kept coming right to the end. In April, as the Allies were driving deep into Germany, Rena Linson received two upbeat letters from her son Horace. She had received a telegram the night before the letters arrived.

It was the Civil War all over again. There was bad news arriving from the battle fronts but good news at home. Another economic boom had begun even before the war. American industry was gearing up as never before. Defense contracts skyrocketed. By 1943, the U. S. had enough war products to overwhelm any enemy. Old Springfield factories fired up and 18,000 found jobs, many working up to one hundred hours a week. There were new migrations of African Americans and Kentucky "hill" people, riding the railroad up from the south to get the new jobs. The thousands of immigrants would again change the face of city and county.

Springfield had military goods pouring out of its plants day and night. The community's giant, International Harvester, led the way. M-5 half-tracks, gun mounts, trucks and tractors came off the assembly lines by the thousands. Steel Products Engineering made propeller hubs and gun turrets for B-17 "Flying Fortresses." Springfield Metallic Casket made airplane doors. Oliver Farm Equipment turned out bomb crates. Others manufactured diesel engines for Liberty Ships, walkie-talkie antennas, artillery shells and calibration stands for the Norden Bombsights, the invention that made it possible for the U. S. Eighth Air Force to accurately bomb

its targets in Germany. The War Department came to Springfield to deliver "E," for excellence and efficiency, awards to several companies, including Bauer Brothers for turning out ten thousand 105mm artillery shells every day during the war.

The national emphasis on military equipment caused shortages and rationing at home. Practically everyone had money but nothing to buy. If a line formed anywhere, people joined it knowing something valuable was available. New cars and household appliances had to wait until the fighting ended. Families had to make do with one cup of coffee a day and a pound of butter a month. Every day items like laundry soap, facial tissue, thumbtacks and hair curlers disappeared. Nylon had "gone to war" and women had to turn to cotton and rayon for their stockings. Gas rationing reduced driving by the country's twenty-seven million automobiles a third, but the biggest scarcity was rubber for tires. After the tires got bald, travelers took to the trains, buses and streetcars.

The war brought a temporary revival to rail-

OVERLEAF:
Pages from an International Harvester newsletter list an array of war products (Springfield turned out half-tracks, trucks and gun mounts) and promote the "IH" men and women sent to military "Harvester Battalions" that fixed damaged equipment at the war front.

World War Two Springfield proudly displays its long lists of "men and women in military service" on a block long "Roll of Honor."

THE HARVESTER ARSENAL OF DEMOCRAC

Products of the Company for the Nation's Armed Forces

CARGO TRUCKS

MILITARY TRACTORS

TANKS

POWER UNITS

DUMP TRUCKS

PRIME MOVERS

HALF-TRACKS

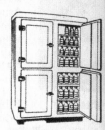

BLOOD BANK REFRIGERATORS

AMBULANCES AND MOBILE CANTEENS

GUN CARRIAGES

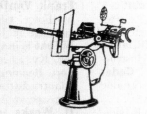

GUN MOUNTS

INVASION ICE CHES

HEAVY DUTY TRUCKS

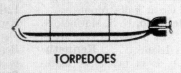

TORPEDOES

AUTOMATIC CANNON

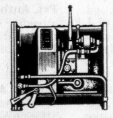

TANK TRANSMISSIONS

HIGH SPEED GUN CARRI

MILITARY FIRE TRUCKS

GEARS AND SPROCKETS

Equipment manufactured but not illustrated

SHELL PACKING STOPS	GENERATORS	FIRING PINS
BRAKE SHOES	FORGINGS	SLEEVES
SIGHT AND AMMUNITION BOX PARTS	CASTINGS	TRACK LINKS
ADAPTER BOOSTERS	AIRPLANE ENGINE COWLING ASSEMBLIES	BUSHINGS
BELLEVILLE SPRINGS	TANK TRACK PINS	VALVE GUIDES
HELICAL SPRINGS	TRACKERS	DIES
CASING BURSTERS	BEARINGS	GUN LOADERS
FUSES	HOUSINGS	BASE PLUGS

WHEEL TRACTORS

SHELLS

The Homefront at War

The Special Products Engineering Company received this "E" for excellence banner in 1944 after designing and building effective machine-gun turrets for B-17 bombers. Local leaders found innovative ways of selling government bonds to fund the huge war effort (below).

Like thousands of other American communities, Clark County went into World War Two prepared for the worst and hoping that the fighting would stay away. Springfield stood ready to "black out" in case of an enemy air attack. There was particular concern because nearby Wright-Patterson Air Force Base was a prime target for bombing. The government issued helmets, gas masks, handbooks and posters to local civilian defense teams. In the face of enemy assault, local volunteers were organized to watch for fires, decontaminate areas in case of chemical attack, carry messages, repair roads and give first aid so that the country's military machine would keep winning the war of attrition. Unlike other allies like Great Britain, the United States never faced the horrors of air raids. Still, the posters and the drills kept communities ready and morale high.

As the tide turned, Springfield worried about the safety of its loved ones and the fortunes of its overseas armies and navies, but it also faced the demands of a world war with ingenuity and discipline. Citizens studied government manuals on how to make do with less.

They stockpiled grease and tin cans, sent piles of care packages to the victims of war and regularly bought war bonds. They planted "Victory" gardens to make up for bothersome shortages. High School students were excused from school early to work part time in the factories. Local service organizations provided day care so more people could work for the war effort.

Wittenberg became an important center for Army Air Force training. The college's student population fell by half and lost sixty-five alumni in the fighting. Almost three thousand air force cadets, along with hundreds of women training for duty at the new radar stations, kept the school in business while fifteen hundred of its former students served in the military.

Local women served enthusiastically to help the country and fend off the loneliness of absent loved ones. Maria C. Livingston sent her son to war and served as a Red Cross "Grey Lady," rolling bandages and serving coffee and sandwiches to servicemen at Wright-Patterson Air Force Base. Ann Richardson was a public health nurse, trained and ready to help Springfield cope with the unthinkable if enemy bombers ever raided the Heartland.

Lulu Fay Shaw was proud that she was the first female employee of the Special Products Engineering Company. In 1940, the company was given the task of designing a new machine gun turret for the B-17 bombers, soon to be shipped to Europe. Within months, SPECO had developed a prototype and thousands of turrets were in production. A month after the D-Day invasion in 1944, General Orval Cook came to Springfield to present an "E" banner and an Army-Navy Production Award to the company. Three thousand attended the ceremony. Six employees, including Lulu Fay Shaw, were given an "E" lapel pin to wear "as a sign of distinguished service to your country."

The SPECO ceremony was an especially proud moment for Springfield. The community could thank war production for turning it into the fourth most productive city in America. The emergency had again unleashed the spirit that had dominated so many past generations. The old motto "If you need it, we'll make it" had helped it play an important role in developing the biggest war machine the world had ever seen.

Clark County braced for an air war that never came to the Heartland. Local civil defense teams put out posters and drilled for the possibility of enemy attack. Although the fighting stayed away, the efforts to stay prepared for possible emergencies, often marked by strong displays of patriotism (opposite page), kept morale high.

roads that had been declining because of the automobile. The trouble for civilians was that two million soldiers and sailors a month were being transported across country on the trains. The great railroad stations of Cincinnati and Indianapolis, and Springfield's own Big Four New York Central Depot, were the scenes of thousands of quiet dramas as G.I.'s daily came from and went to parts unknown. If you could get a ticket you had to endure conditions similar to steerage in the old immigrant ships. One railroad advertised, "You'll be more comfortable at home."

Most did stay in their communities and worked. There was another revolution made necessary by the millions of men in the armed forces. Unlike the Civil War eighty years earlier, women at home were eager not only to volunteer but also to work in any job where they were needed. They volunteered to roll bandages and serve coffee to servicemen and they went to work in the factories. By mid-war, they made up one-third of the work force. Doubters were brushed aside by the overwhelming need to win the war. "Rosie the Riveter" took on demanding tasks as a truck driver, welder and lumberjack. The ladies tucked up their long hair in bandannas, wore overalls, shopped after work and found ways to care for their families between shifts. Men who returned from the war found their women changed forever by the crisis.

Casualties mounted and there was fear that, having won the war in Europe, the allies were faced with an invasion of Japan that would kill hundreds of thousands of G. I.'s. Then two inconceivable blasts at Hiroshima and Nagasaki extinguished 200,000 Japanese lives and the war was over. Some predicted that the Depression would return, but Springfield had more money than before. The war had made the community rich and the servicemen returned to a new kind of prosperity.

Toward an Uncertain Future (1946-1980)

We had whipped the Germans. We had whipped the Japs. There seemed no end to the things we could do. The future seemed to belong to those who took it.

Robert Bayley remembered the mood of servicemen returning from a world war. There was a pent-up optimism that things would get much better now that they had stamped out the

Harley-Davidson had been making motorcycles since early in the century, but the 1947 WL Sport Solo, a model that had proved itself during the war, became a classic for the postwar generation.

tyrannies that threatened the world. Everybody had money to burn and an appetite for the things they couldn't have during the war. In spite of doomsayers, predicting a dire return to the past, the postwar economy took off.

Manufacturers were ready to feed the "Consumer Age." Suddenly there was a flood of electric conveniences for the home and fat, new automobiles with fins and chrome. The newest wonder of the modern age was television. It would soon dominate most American households. But, as the war ended, returning G.I.'s with government rewards for their service, were looking for a college education and new homes. A local ad announced, "We'll build a house on a hilltop…it's great to be young and dream and plan."

Springfield boomed in this new environment. Factories, primed by war contracts, continued to hum. Two local products, Parker Sweepers and Vining O-Cedar Mops, captured a national market. Ten thousand local babies, later to be labeled "baby-boomers," were born to seventy thousand residents in just one year. Wittenberg quadrupled its student body. Lots were ten times as expensive as they had been during the war. The newcomers moved into the north end, abandoning

much of the south and west sides of the city to the African Americans and Kentucky whites who had joined the work force during the war.

The city was determined to provide improvements for all of the explosive growth. Philanthropist Joseph Shouvlin led a drive to build the new Mercy Hospital. A new commercial airport south of town was soon eclipsed by Dayton and became a home for the Ohio Air National Guard. Dayton launched WHIO-TV in 1949 and, in just two years, increased its viewers from 2,500 to well over 200,000. Local viewers were soon hooked on "Howdy Doody," and "Uncle Miltie." The Greater Springfield and Clark County Association and Springfield Foundation were added to help improve the local quality of life.

But this wave of optimism was laced with disturbing problems. The country traded a hot war for a cold one, and, with a growing arsenal of indescribable destructive power, the world was fretting in uneasy truce between east and west. In Washington, the Truman Administration which had accomplished so much to insure a smooth transition from war to peace, ended in a brush fire war stalemate in Korea and a frightening, demagogic hunt for domestic communists. When war hero General Dwight D. Eisenhower became president, the country settled down. The 1950s became known as the "quiet, complacent" decade.

Springfield had its own demons to deal with. Too much money and not enough to buy were ingredients for significant inflation. Local labor unions, traditionally friendly to management, struck twice against International Harvester in four years as the United Auto Workers tried to make inroads into the trucking industry. The car culture was creating suburbs and the downtown was slowly dying.

Television brought a tragedy to Springfield that almost destroyed the city's notable spirit. One of the anchors of downtown for the better part of a century was Phineas Mast's gift to the community. *Farm and Fireside*, created to sell Mast's empire of agricultural products, grew into the Crowell-Collier Publishing Company, another empire that was turning out four million magazines a week by World War Two. The company had acquired *Lady's Home Companion*, The *American Magazine* and *Collier's*. These magazines became fixtures in American culture, as

Twelve-year-old Lawrence Nicholl became a Springfield hero when he defeated his fifteen-year-old brother Kenneth by one foot and became Soap Box Derby City Champion in 1951. He and his racer didn't win the Nationals at Akron, but Lawrence lived the dream of thousands who rolled hub to hub in competitions all over the country.

much as *Life*, *Look* and *The Saturday Evening Post*. A star-studded cast of writers, including Ernest Hemingway, Dashiell Hammett and Agatha Christie, contributed to *Collier's*. The magazines were put together in New York, but printed in the eight-story, red brick plant that filled a city block in west Springfield. The huge presses ran constantly, through depressions and world wars, for decades. The townspeople were certain that this giant, employer and security blanket for thousands, always had been and always would be a fundamental part of city life.

The advent of television gave the American public an alternative to reading magazines. The result was disaster for the time-honored magazine business. With television stealing its advertising revenue, Crowell-Collier sold more and more magazines but lost more and more money. By the mid-1950s, the three magazines were losing seven and a half million dollars a year.

The absentee New York ownership made a tough business decision that was heartbreaking for the Springfield work force. In a judgment worthy of Ebenezer Scrooge himself, the company board decided, with no warning, to close the operation four days before Christmas in 1956. Two thousand workers were sent home without so much as a handshake. The tragedy for a hardworking city, proud of its success and spirit, was palpable. Phineas Mast's empire ultimately broke the heart of the community that had nurtured its success. The huge, now empty building remained, unacceptable for a new use but too big to be torn down.

The "quiet, complacent" '50s became the "wild, rebellious" '60s. The decade began with a charismatic, young president who lifted the country with his style and intelligence. It ended with another "brush fire" war in Asia where victory became more and more elusive. In between there were public murders, urban riots and the "counter culture" shenanigans of a generation rebelling against their parents. And all of it was documented in excruciating detail on television.

Springfield no longer had a local culture. Like most American cities, it was a victim of what social scientists were calling "connurbation," the automobile-generated sprawl that connected suburbs but had no center. The Champion City and Clark County were in danger of becoming bedroom communities for Dayton and even Columbus. Regional planning became more important than local. The small towns out in the county, like New Carlisle, were growing because they were closer to the sprawl around Dayton. By 1980, for the first time in 180 years, the county's population outstripped Springfield.

In fact, the 1970s were not kind to Springfield. During the decade, the city's population

In a 1968 demonstration by America's largest truck manufacturer, almost one thousand International Harvester trucks, made in the new Clark County plant, were paraded down newly-completed Route 68 to dealers in southwest Ohio. The caravan caused traffic jams wherever it went. (Howard O. Weber, Jr.)

dropped ten thousand people. Young people were leaving town to live and work elsewhere. The locals were moving out of the corporate limits because the city center had died. The streets, where teens cruised with their souped-up Chevys and Fords, where families flooded the shops on weekends , where it was often hard to find a place to park, were now practically deserted. The downtown mom and pop businesses had lost the battle to the smart, new 800,000 square foot Upper Valley Mall on the far edge of greater Springfield.

Many community leaders were upset by the turn of events. Efforts began to bring the downtown back to life. It was a daunting task. Cities all over America were suffering the same reverses. Government programs only seemed to make matters worse. The suburbs continued to grow and urban neighborhoods were abandoned to the poor and down and out.

Plans for urban renewal began with reconstructing the city sewers associated with Mill Run, the now underground stream that had created swamps as it flowed through 19th century Springfield. That accomplished, a 1967 "Community Action Now" Committee started planning but was immediately frustrated by citizens against the renewal efforts and higher taxes. Other committees and other plans in the public sector moved in fits and starts while a Core Renewal Corporation, led by Paul Hellmuth and other business leaders, quietly concentrated on a good plan for a core block right at the

center of the city. With the spirit of America's bicentennial year, a voter approved income tax increase guaranteed a new city building in 1977. It was followed shortly by Credit Life's black glass, ten-story office in the same block. Whatever some critics said about the new buildings, Springfield had turned a corner and had started to do something about its own version of urban decay.

Back in 1968, a new National Road, created as a part of the Eisenhower Era national system, plowed through Clark County and headed west. The brand new Interstate 70 was the streamlined ticket to other places. It skirted the southern limits of Springfield and started dragging development and sprawl in that direction. International Harvester followed the tradition set by the old six horse freight wagons that had jammed the original National Road. The company put together 946 units built in their new plant north of Springfield and paraded them down the highway, causing traffic jams wherever they went. It was a show of power by America's largest producer of trucks, the last giant industry located in Clark County.

Chicago-based "IH" owned the old Springfield Champion Reaper works as a part of its huge farm machinery empire. Faced with anti-trust litigation with the federal government, it turned its Springfield plant to the production of trucks right after World War One. Sixty years and a million trucks later, the International operation was a mainstay of the Springfield and Clark County

This 1973 International Harvester "Travelall" Series 1210, featuring a four-speed transmission and all-wheel drive, was discontinued the following year. More than two decades later, these features were popular in Sports Utility Vehicles all over America.

Presidential Visits to Springfield

A merican cities and towns have always marked visits from presidents with great pride and reverence. It is as if the aura of the office has somehow brought special gifts for the community. Plaques are placed where presidents once stood. Potos and mementos of visits are lovingly preserved in local historical societies. Citizens remember with great solemnity how they shook the great man's hand. In short, visits of chief executives have a special place in American political and folk culture.

Springfield has a modest record in the presidential visit sweepstakes. Solid evidence exists that at least seventeen of the forty-two

Former President Theodore Roosevelt spoke at Wittenberg College in 1917. *(Wittenberg University Archives)*

Senator John F. Kennedy campaigned at the College in 1960. *(Dickerson Collection, Wittenberg University Alumni and Visitor Center)*

Large crowds came out to see their war hero Dwight "Ike" Eisenhower as he ran for president in 1952. Whistle stops on passing railroads were a standard campaign technique until the Big Four Station was torn down. *(Springfield News-Sun file photo)*

American presidents dropped in on the usually solidly Republican Champion City. All the visits were brief. They came through campaigning for office or they spoke for a particular cause both before and after they were in office. At least four sitting presidents, Franklin Delano Roosevelt, Harry S. Truman, Warren Harding and Gerald Ford appeared in the city.

The first eight presidents were all easterners with the exception of Andrew Jackson. There was little reason to make the long, difficult trip to the Ohio frontier. Would-be presidents, like perennial candidates Henry Clay and Daniel Webster, showed up on stagecoaches from time to time. The "Log Cabin" President, General William Henry Harrison, was the soon-to-be briefest of chief executives when he visited Springfield on two campaign stops in 1840. The 1812 War Hero was an old man. He caught a cold during a long and barely audible inaugural address in Washington and was dead a month later. His colorful "Tippecanoe and Tyler Too" campaign was a rip roaring success in the new western states and it changed American politics.

Abraham Lincoln almost, but not quite, got to Springfield when he stopped for a campaign speech at the Montgomery County Courthouse in nearby Dayton. Senator Andrew Johnson spoke to Civil War soldiers in 1861. After the Civil War, all seven of the Ohio presidents, Grant, Garfield, Harrison, McKinley, Taft and Harding, spent time in the region. Hayes, Garfield and Harding visited Springfield, but some additional digging may turn up another brief stopover. Rutherford B. Hayes must not have been too popular after he helped Columbus "steal" the Ohio State University from Springfield. There is a surviving photograph of Warren Harding standing on the steps of the then new Memorial Hall.

Former President Theodore Roosevelt came to Springfield in

1917 at the invitation of Harry Kissell and other local business leaders. Kissell was concerned that the city, caught up in the anti-German fervor generated by World War One, was turning against its significant German American community. Roosevelt gave one of his impassioned speeches at Wittenberg's Recitation Hall, preaching against prejudice and bigotry. The second President Roosevelt "FDR," told Springfield to avoid a "Model T" government when he passed through in 1936.

Campaign whistle stops at the Big Four Railroad Station brought many national leaders through Springfield after World War Two. Harry Truman stopped in 1948 and Dwight Eisenhower drew a crowd of several thousand in 1952. Senator and then Vice-President Richard Nixon stopped while campaigning in 1952 and in 1960. Another future president, John F. Kennedy, won many fans when he paraded through the Wittenberg campus sitting on the trunk of a convertible. He spoke to a large crowd during his close but successful 1960 campaign against Richard Nixon. George Bush stopped as vice-president and later as presidential candidate. William Clinton visited in 1992.

Springfield is justly proud of its presidential visits, but it is now off the beaten path. The loss of the Big Four Station all but ended the era of whistle stops. The new regional identification with the Greater Dayton Area has made visits to that community more effective for any national politician on the campaign trail.

economy. Almost 8,000 employees put together over six hundred vehicles a day. Even after the loss of Crowell-Collier, no one considered the possibility of losing "IH." The company had just built a forty-four acre, state-of-the-art assembly line and warehouse a few miles northwest of Springfield.

But the giant corporation was in trouble. It still had a huge share of the market, but it had lost its competitive edge and profits were plummeting. A new CEO, brought in to tighten belts and improve efficiency, instead engaged in mortal combat with the United Auto Workers. When a bitter six month strike ended, the country was in a recession, the truck business had dried up and International Harvester, having laid off thousands, was four billion dollars in debt.

Yet another CEO decided that one of the two American truck plants must go. Fort Wayne, Indiana and Springfield, Ohio, spent sixty days competing for the company's nod. It was a life and death struggle. Lives, economies and community prosperity were at stake. Both cities sweetened the pot with close to thirty million dollar incentive packages. In the end, Springfield won the contest because it had the newer, more efficient plant. But International Harvester was still fighting for its life and Springfield did not "want to get stuck with another empty building." The incentive package bought the plant and leased it back to "IH." Should the new partnership fail, the city now had the option of finding another tenant.

The Champion City was beginning to take back some of the prerogatives it had lost to absentee ownership. By 1983, nineteen of the twenty-five major businesses in town were owned and run by somebody somewhere else. It was another of those trends infecting most American commerce. There could be no return to the "goahead" days of a century ago. But there were still people who cared deeply about the place. As Springfield booster Paul Hellmuth said, "People like to have roots, to feel they belong someplace." Another observer, W. F. Austin, put his finger on the community's assets a century ago.

> The area has always been poor in natural resources but rich in people against whom misfortune and failure seem powerless.

In a recent book profiling the *Cities of the Heartland*, Jon C. Teaford began by briefly outlining the history of the industrial Midwest.

> From trading posts, pinpoints of habitation in the overwhelming wilderness, to industrial giants, with billows of smoke testifying to their manufacturing might, and finally to vast connurbations defying description...

Teaford's "vast connurbations" could be almost any large American city now losing its battle against suburban sprawl. But he also effectively depicts the midwestern communities that have their own special version of the American story. And Springfield can proudly take its place among its bigger neighbors Cincinnati, Indianapolis and Chicago. A 19th century meteor of industrial success and power with a worldwide reach, its decline in the last half of the 20th century has mirrored the frustrations of every city that has watched its business prosperity go somewhere else.

Super highways to somewhere else continue to define life in Clark County. Many travelers now pass quickly through the county and many local residents use the highways to commute long distances to work.

Portage

Town

Mineami

The Cross

V I N

PIQUES or

Tawichtwi or Pique Town

90

TAWICHTAWIS

Rocky River

Limestone

30

VINE AMIS or

MYAMIS

Salt

Asserenit or Gt. Rt. Myami

S H A W

Myamis without Falls

Little R.

Elk Creek

Salt Springs

Myamis Town

Ohio R. or Palawa Thepiki

Little Salt Lick

a War Path

Kentucke or Cuttawa R.

Warriors Branch

hants Bones
nd Here

the Ouasioto Mounts. Gap
is the only Way passable
with Horses from Ohio
3 or 400 Miles Southward.

Eskippakithiki

Ouasioto Mts. Gap

Rift

South Branch

R

Portage

Portage 10 M

Rift

Rift

Junguei idundeld

Wiandots

has no Falls

Sandusky R.

A M E R I C A N D O T S

Sandusky Fort

Wyandots

Bald Eagle Cr.

Guahadahuyi

Portage 4 M.

Big Swamp

Plains of Wild Rye

35

Delawares

Necunsia Skeintat

White & Red Bale

Hurric

Siota R.

Kiskeminitas

Lower Shawane Town

Wyanducholes

Salt

Salt
Coal

Little Totteroy

Big Sandy C.

War Path

E N E S E

Limestone

Great Salt Lick

Gt. Buffalo Lick

a Vein of thro. which

Cayahoga R.

White Womans Cr.

French Ho.
Mingoes T.

Whe

Porta

Mohiccons

White
Womans

Mt

30

30

12

3 o

Hockhocking or
French Margarets

A

6   12

14

Great Hockhocking R.

Magung

ne Tom

Salt Springs

Salt Creek

Free Stone

Little Hockhocking

Wanduchales old Town

Free Stone

Coals

15

Beaty's L.

old T.

Shawane Town

Le Tarts Falls

The big Bend

Rapid

Cuyandott R.

Gt. Kanhawa R.

Mountains about
there is not yet

O U A S I O T O   M O U N

Falls

Coals

30 or
any

Frederick R.

Louisa R.

Clinch's R.

North Fork

OPENING UP THE OHIO COUNTRY

The Springfield Pioneers

Shawnee Country

The Delaware and Iroquois called the Shawnees "grandfathers" and "elder brothers." They also, like everyone else, pushed them around. In the century before the Americans ran into the Shawnees in the Ohio Valley, the "chief of all tribes" was a refugee in its own land. It is difficult to follow Shawnee migrations into Maryland and then eastern Pennsylvania, leaving only their names, almost like graffiti, on landmarks as they were pushed west. The fierce Iroquois Confederacy dominated the whole region and it always had a love-hate relationship with the Shawnees, often treating them as pawns.

By the middle of the 18th century, the Shawnees were in western Pennsylvania and allied with the French. When the French lost their battle to control the continent, their allies, including the Shawnees, were forced further west into Ohio Country. In the 1760s, the Shawnees were in Ohio's Miami River valleys, west of the other refugees, the Delaware and the Wyandots. They had learned to hate the American colonists who were invading their hunting grounds like a rising tide. Peace treaties were always broken. The "Long Knives" brought new iron tools and cloth, but they also brought guns and alcohol.

By 1803, a Shawnee chief, beset by the troubles caused by white intruders, had changed his tribe's version of the Creation story.

The Master of Life…who was himself an Indian, made the Shawanoes [Shawnees] before any other of the human race; and they sprang from his brain; he gave them all the knowledge he himself possessed, and placed them upon the great island, and all the other red people are descended from the Shawanoes. After he had made the Shawanoes, he made the French and English out of his breast, the Dutch out of his feet, and the long-knives [Americans] out of his hands. All of these inferior races of men he made white and placed them beyond the stinking lake [Atlantic Ocean].

There never were many of them. The Shawnee tribes were widely scattered and never could muster more than a few hundred warriors. They were a classic Woodland culture, living in settled villages and raising crops, but also migrating to hunt for food on the land in the winter months. Their well-organized villages were the centers of their culture and were always named for one of the four tribal divisions. Two villages in the Miami valley, "Cha-lah-gaw-tha" (Chillicothe) and "Pec-ku-we" (Piqua), eventually gave their names to modern Ohio cities.

The frontier traveler David Zeisberger described how at home they were in the limitless woods.

On their journeys they are never in haste, for they are everywhere at home and whithersoever they wander they find sustenance in the forest… In the morning they do not break camp early, not

continued on page 119

A 1796 French drawing of a Shawnee warrior shows the traditional dress of a Woodland Indian at war. Note the tight leggings, breechcloth , painted face and ear lobes, cut and stretched to add to the ferocity. *(Bibliotheque Nationale de France)*

OPPOSITE PAGE: Detail of the Sayer-Bennet 1776 map of the Ohio Valley marks much of the area of what is now southern Ohio, along the Ohio and Miami Rivers, as "Shawnese" Country. *(Willard Hackerman Collection)*

117

Like other Woodland tribes, the Shawnees had a rich culture, highly adapted to its environment. They lived in settled villages and were already building log cabins when the Ohio settlers arrived. They migrated to find food during the winter months. *(Ohio Historical Society)*

The popular image of bloodthirsty, painted warriors carrying enemy scalps (top of opposite page) is only part of the Native American story. *(Private Collection)*

Only a few artifacts, a musket barrel and iron cannon balls dug up in the nineteenth century, remind us of the fierce 1780 Battle of Piqua. George Rogers Clark, painted late in life (middle of opposite page), was only twenty-eight-years-old when he defeated the Shawnees in the battle. A very rare Woodland "Walking Bow"(far side of opposite page), was picked up off the Piqua Battlefield and survived tucked away in the wall of a Kentucky log cabin.

A Clash of Cultures – The Battle of Piqua

The greatest frontier battle of the American Revolution was fought a few miles west of modern Springfield. It was only one episode in the long struggle between Native Americans, trying desperately to defend their way of life, and white settlers, equally determined to claim the land.

The Shawnees, after decades of fighting followed by migrations west, had settled in the Miami Valley looking for a permanent homeland. One of their villages was located near the Mad River on fertile land, covered by the long grass prairies so common further west. It was a sprawling complex of cultivated fields and clusters of buildings eventually spreading over five miles. As soon as the Shawnees arrived, there were white traders in their midst, continuing to supply them with the axes, trade cloth, guns and alcohol they now depended on. By the mid 18th century, many Native Americans, with new tools, were living in the log cabins so identified with the "Long Knives." The Shawnees named their village "Pec-ku-we," a standard reference to one of their tribal divisions. Without a written language, they left others to interpret their spoken Algonkian tongue. The result is a whole series of names for the village, including "Pekowi," "Pickaway" and "Peckuwe." Attempts to standardize the name in the nineteenth century, led to the now commonly used "Piqua."

Within a decade of their arrival in the Miami Valley, the Shawnees watched helplessly as a French against English struggle became an English fight with their former allies the American colonists. Never understanding the issues involved, they tried to pick their own allies who would support their lifestyle. At the beginning of the American Revolution, they bet their future on the British, now based at Detroit. The Americans were invading their hunting grounds in Kentucky. It would not be long before the "Long Knives" crossed the Ohio and overran the new Shawnee home.

Destructive Indian raids into Kentucky infuriated the settlers. The Americans warned the Shawnees, "If you continue your evil ways, the army will come into Ohio and trample you into dust." Never intimidated by the opportunity for a good fight, the warriors answered with more raids. George Rogers Clark, the talented twenty-eight-year-old commander in Kentucky, had already successfully attacked British forts in Indiana and Illinois and wanted to mount an offensive to capture Detroit, cutting off support for American enemies at its source. But the Kentuckians wanted revenge against the Shawnees, so Clark reluctantly put together a thousand man army and headed north in the summer of 1780. His objective was two Shawnee villages. He had learned that he could never stop hit-and-run Indian tactics unless he destroyed their villages and their critical crops of corn, beans, squash and "Irish" potatoes.

The strike force carefully protected itself from ambush as it crossed the Ohio and built a road, moving slowly north. The column was surrounding packhorses and a until they have eaten heartily... Thereafter they proceed very steadily until near sundown, when they go into camp. In rainy weather they peel bast from trees and speedily build a hut, that is, a roof supported by four posts, under which they remain comfortably dry.

Their culture was thousands of years old, had beautiful and intricate arts and crafts, and was a combination of personal affection, loyalty to tribe and friends and fierce violence toward enemies. The white settlers could not understand these paradoxes in Indian life and saw the Indians as brutal and ungodly savages. The Shawnees, in turn, with their own well developed sense of the holiness of the land and respect for the family, could not understand the white man's need to own the land and force his beliefs on both friend and enemy. It was a recipe for conflict that marched right across the American continent.

The Shawnees could never escape the spiral of violence that moved west with the settlers. First it was the French and English, then it was

single wagon, carrying slim rations and pulling at least two cannons, captured from the British a year earlier. The cannons were an important addition since they were weapons that intimidated the Indians. The march through dense wilderness was frightening, with imagined dangers lurking everywhere. But the Shawnees were nowhere to be seen. They had decided to abandon one village and concentrate their defense on Piqua, further north.

Hoping that he had the element of surprise, Clark discovered that a deserter had headed north to warn the Shawnee villages. Having found the first village recently deserted, they destroyed everything in sight. The Americans approached the second village in a violent thunder-

storm. On the morning of August 8, still looking for the elusive enemy, the invaders crossed the Mad River and found a large prairie ahead and tall limestone cliffs to the east. Three fortified log villages stretched over three miles. Clark planned to encircle the villages, sending three hundred around the cliffs to get behind the enemy and another three hundred into the woods to the west. He would march straight ahead with the cannons.

The Americans were met with heavy musket fire as soon as they crossed the Mad River. The Shawnees had massed at least three hundred warriors, with Mingo, Wyandot and Delaware allies, to fight off the assault. The fire continued for some time, "...with a savage fierceness on both sides," but the Americans were able to outflank and push back their enemy with larger numbers and concentrated firepower. The Indians finally retreated into a triangular log stockade they had constructed with a blockhouse attached.

A half-hour elapsed, as the Kentuckians brought up their cannons. Protected by a hollow square formation of soldiers nearby, the gunners began to dismantle the stockade with solid six and four pound cannon balls. Suddenly, almost a hundred fiercely-painted

warriors appeared in the prairie grass, chased the gunners from a cannon, and attacked the hollow square. The desperate assault could not succeed and the warriors were soon routed as all the village inhabitants fled for their lives. Clark's plan to cut off their retreat failed when his flanking force could not find a way to climb over the high limestone cliffs along the Mad River.

Casualties were high for a frontier battle. There were twenty-seven Americans killed and wounded and perhaps as many as triple that number among the Native Americans. The fury of the fighting led to atrocities as both sides tortured and killed some of their prisoners. The invaders burned the villages and destroyed miles of crops in the fields. They were surprised at how successful the Indians were at farming. Licking their wounds and running out of supplies, they could not continue north or east to attack other Indian and British settlements. Clark soon withdrew his force south to Kentucky. After a difficult winter caused by the destruction, the Shawnees were back in Kentucky looking for revenge. The bloody Battle of Piqua turned out to be yet another incident in the long struggle between Native Americans and white settlers.

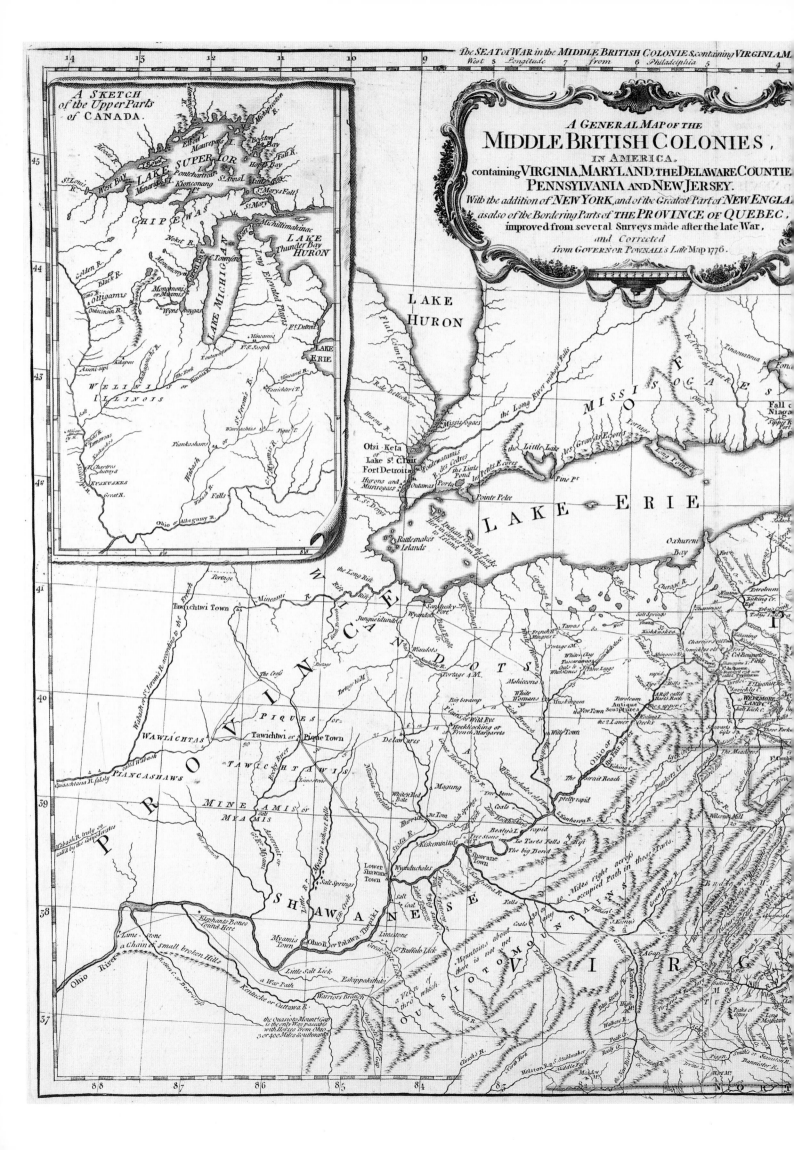

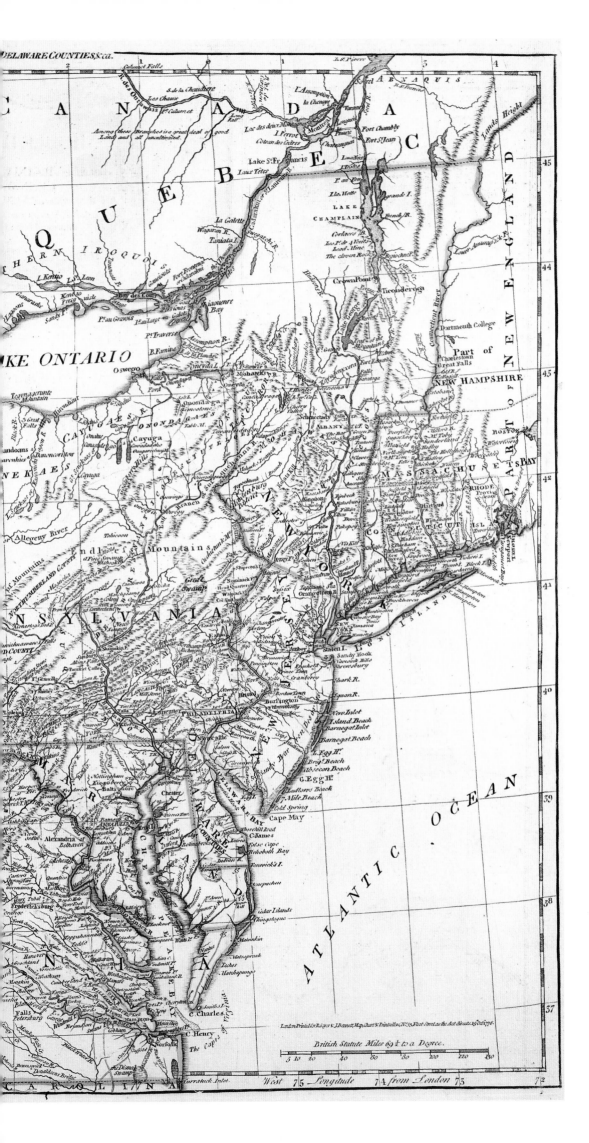

The Robert Sayer and John Bennet 1776 *General Map of the "Middle British Colonies"* was included in a pocket atlas for British officers fighting in the Revolutionary War. It defines what the American colonists knew about the interior of North America at the beginning of settlement in the Ohio Country. The Appalachian Mountains are the fierce impediment that keeps the Americans hugging the Atlantic coast. Adventurous settlers have already moved west up the Potomac Valley and north to the Forks of the Ohio at Pittsburgh. Others have moved southwest through the gaps in the Virginia mountains into the still ill-defined "Kentucky" country. The Ohio River and the Great Lakes provide the easiest access to the frontier and British Fort Detroit looms in the upper left corner of the map as the key for British hopes to control the west. Within a generation, the National Road will cut a path due west from the Pennsylvania and Maryland frontiers. *(Willard Hackerman Collection)*

121

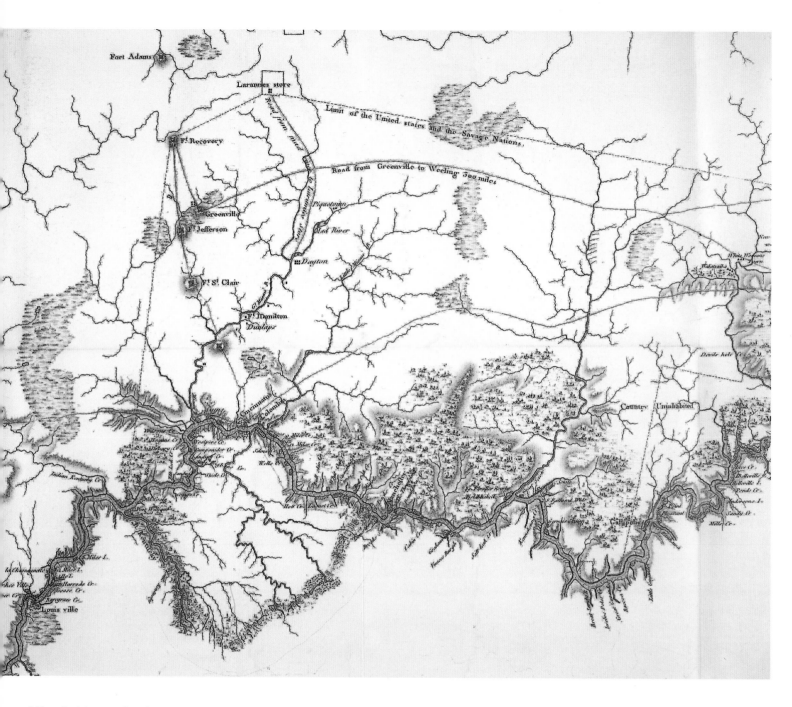

Labels on map: Fort Adams, Larames store, Limit of the United states and the Savage Nations, F.t Recovery, Road from Greenville to Weeling 300 miles, Piquatuwn, Greenville, Mad River, F.t Jefferson, Dayton, Little Miami, F.t St Clair, F.t Hamilton, Dunlaps, White Wopanc Town, Wakatomika, Devils hole Cr, Cincinnati, Columbi, Country Uninhabited, Louisville, Gallipolis

A French visitor produced an up-to-date map of Ohio Country in 1796. The recent Treaty of Greenville had divided up the land in the soon-to-be State of Ohio. Note the Mad River and the Shawnee villages in the area. The French tried to understand and adapt to the Native American culture and several lively drawings of "Sauvages" (see page 117) are included. The *Collot Carte l'Ohio* was reprinted in English in 1826. *(William L. Clements Library, University of Michigan)*

the English and Americans and, finally, it was the Americans alone, intent on taking over their traditional hunting grounds. A Native American negotiator had commented during one of the many conflicts, "We are the cloth and the French and the English are the scissors." A brutal style of hit-and-run warfare embraced the frontier for generations. The Shawnees were very good at it and they made the most of their small numbers.

Shawnee warriors, almost naked with the traditional woodland topknots of hair, slashed and looped ear lobes and red and black body paint, descended on small frontier enclaves in lightning strikes that terrified the settlers. The Prophet, brother of the great Shawnee chief Tecumseh, declared that he and his tribe "have never been in the habit of suing for peace themselves, but of receiving the propositions of their

enemies." They were ruthless with captives, forcing prisoners to repeatedly run gauntlets and sometimes even engaging in ritual cannibalism. But they might also, without rhyme or reason in the eyes of their white enemies, adopt captives and make them full-fledged members of the tribe.

It was easier to hate these seemingly primitive Native Americans than it was to understand and live with them. At every turn, for a whole century, the native population was caught in a desperate middle ground. By the 1770s, the Shawnees were on the edge between the eastern forests they knew so well and the great prairies they did not. It was a last stand, both fierce and futile. The rising tide of European invasion could not be stopped.

Discovering a Rich and Empty Land (1750-1800)

The French had been in Ohio Country long before, but one of the first Englishmen to cross the Appalachians and explore the Ohio Valley was Christopher Gist. A Maryland native, Gist spent years risking his life in the backwoods to find business opportunities for the collection of Virginia frontier land speculators called the Ohio Company. Before there was a United States, the individual colonies were planning to expand their domains to the Pacific Ocean. In his travels, Gist found a river brimming at flood stage and christened it the "Mad" River. He also discovered an old white woman living among the Wyandots. She had been kidnapped and then adopted by Native Americans in some long forgotten frontier war. She told Gist that she remembered "they used to be very religious in New England, and [I] wonder how the White Man can be so wicked as [I] have seen them in these woods."

The wickedness of white men would be a theme that would vex natives for generations. But, when the bloodletting of intermittent border wars stopped, there was a remarkable amount of friendly contact between Indians and whites. The tribes loved, and soon came to depend on, the wondrous wares, good and bad, that traders brought on their packhorses. The tough men, who led the Europeans west, learned to appreciate an unspoiled way of life. They married native women and adopted Indian customs and dress. People further east were often appalled by these wild "go-betweens" who were an ever present part of the western movement.

The next wave that arrived, determined to settle the land, openly threatened native claims to their ancestral lands. The hostility that ensued was a battle to the death, for one side or the other had to claim total victory. Numbers and technology made an Indian defeat inevitable.

The early settlers, women as well as men, were a rough lot. There was no safety net for failure on the frontier. The warfare was no holds barred and a whole family could be butchered in a moment. The work was ceaseless and back-breaking. The rewards, freedom and land for the taking, kept the pioneers coming.

Simon Kenton was one of those roughhewn characters made for life on the frontier. Kenton was a robust six-footer with red hair and a wild temper. He first fled to the frontier from Virginia when, at sixteen, he mistakenly thought he had

Simon Kenton, a frontier hero in the mold of Daniel Boone, sat for this portrait in 1836, the year that he died. In spite of his advanced years, one of the original Clark County settlers still has fire in his eyes and grips his walking stick with determination. *(Ohio Historical Society)*

killed a rival in a nasty fight. He soon became a legendary scout, helping George Rogers Clark during the 1780 campaign, and was noted for his first hand knowledge of the Indians. His biographer and descendant, Edna Kenton, traced the source of that knowledge to a ten month captivity in 1778-79.

> While in southern Ohio on a spying mission, he was captured and accused by the Indians of horse-stealing. An extraordinary series of torments, insults, and indignities followed, the first of which involved being bound tightly and strapped to the back of a horse that was driven through tree branches and underbrush. Painfully bound at night, he repeatedly was forced to run the gauntlet as his captors traveled to various villages. His upper arm was broken and left unset for days. Sentenced to burn at the stake, his execution was delayed [twice]…[and he was] finally ransomed by an emissary from British Detroit. Kenton spent the winter there, but eventually escaped…

Simon Kenton earned well-deserved fame as a skilled frontiersmen, in a league with Daniel Boone. But his real passion was land and he became a Kentucky "squire," eventually owning almost a half million acres in four states. In the late 1790s, still filled with the itch to claim new land, he moved his family and slaves up to the

The Book of Virginia Military Lands, dating from the end of the American Revolution in 1784, is a survey of about four million acres of land reserved by the Commonwealth of Virginia for its settlers. Virginia agreed to relinquish its historic claims to the interior of the continent, in exchange for a large tract of land north of the Ohio River and between the Miami and Scioto Rivers.

branches of trees and how young boys sent out to get pigeons for a pie knocked as many birds as they wanted out of the trees with sticks. They recounted how there were deer, elk, bear and buffalo in abundance and how settler David Lowry killed a thousand deer in the area. They remembered that there was water, pure and delicious, cascading down Buck Creek to the Mad River. They told of the nearby undulating, high-grass prairie, covered in summer with grass, mixed with the greatest variety of flowers, and how the horse's legs were stained by the wild strawberries and the cattle often ate the grass and flowers to the point of bursting.

The wilderness was beautiful but it was an unforgiving paradise. The settlers sometimes noted the astounding sights they saw, but the task at hand was the harnessing of wild places for agriculture and settlement. It was not work for the faint of heart, but as soon as the question of who had the right to the land was settled, there were pioneers lining up to take on the challenge.

The American Revolution had been one more chapter in the conquest of Indian lands. The British would maintain an interest in the Ohio frontier for another generation, but the Shawnees and other tribes in the region were now on their own against an onslaught of American pioneers. The new United States saw the settlement of the Ohio Country, part of the Northwest Territory, as a high priority. In exchange for new land available to war veterans, the nation would benefit from a bounty of goods produced in this newly-developed Heartland. The presence of the Indian nations obstructed the country's progress. The U.S. military, laboring under a prejudice against standing armies left over from British rule, was under funded and poorly-led. The Native Americans had proven themselves a worthy foe and were fighting to defend their own land and their own survival. Several campaigns were launched against the Ohio Indians. All were defeated and one was annihilated. The doomed tribes, however, could only win battles not wars. After Revolutionary War hero General "Mad" Anthony Wayne defeated a force of Indian allies at the "Fallen Timbers" in 1794, the entire Ohio Country was opened to settlement.

David Lowry and Jonathan Donnel were quick to move into the prime land on the Mad River. In the fast and loose era of "Ohio Fever," they joined a survey party and picked out some land for themselves. By the fall of 1795, both Lowry and Donnel were raising cabins on land that would become Clark County. John Ludlow,

Mad River Valley. After serving briefly as a brigadier general of Ohio state militia, he had a series of business reverses and spent time in the Urbana debtors' prison. Late in life, he recovered his dignity and became something of a celebrity, reminding the community of its frontier past. A contemporary called him "the master spirit of the time…He was looked upon by all as the great defender of the inhabitants…" In 1832, a traveler ran into "General" Kenton in a coach. As they left Springfield and approached Urbana,

> [he] gave me sundry snatches of detail as to his early hardships in the backwoods, and adventures with the Indians…All the time I did not take any hint as to who he was…When we landed at Urbana…the people collected pretty freely around the hack, all anxious to see…who I now became convinced was a man of eminent distinction. On eager inquiry I soon learned that I had been travelling with him whom I had, till then, known only in history – the celebrated pioneer Simon Kenton…

The occasional 18th century visitors to the Mad River Valley, including Simon Kenton, were struck by the fertility and the beauty of the area. The Shawnees had discovered the nearby prairie and had planted miles of crops at their village of Piqua. Legends about the unspoiled land grew as Springfield became an industrial center. Old timers liked to talk about how passenger pigeons were so thick they broke the

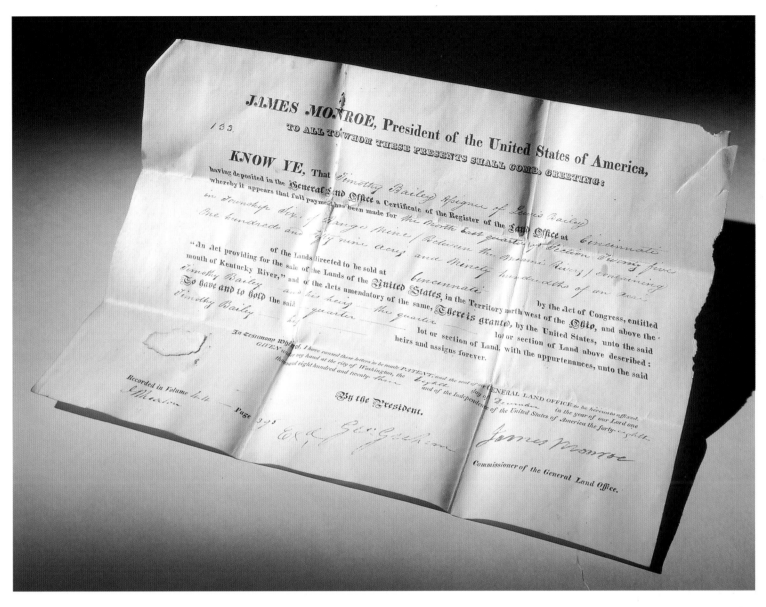

chronicler of early Springfield, was born in the new settlement only fifteen years later.

> David Lowry killed seventeen bears [near his cabin during the winter of 1795.] The new settlers found themselves in the midst of the Shawnee... and they managed to live with them on terms of friendship...Lowry spent much of his time in hunting with them..[He] would sometimes get lost in the great wilderness, they would convey him to his cabin again... On one occasion, they took offense because of his superior skill in their favorite sport of wrestling. [They] loaded a gun with the seeming intention of shooting him, Lowry displayed so much courage at their threats, that their wrath was turned into the most extravagant demonstrations of admiration, while they took him up in their arms and carried him about the camp, exclaiming "Brave man! Brave man!"

By 1796, Lowry and Donnel had neighbors. Two newcomers, known to history only as Kreb and Brown, raised a first crop of corn. In 1799, Simon Kenton, newly-married after his first wife died in a house fire, arrived from Kentucky with his wife and five children along with six other families. Having had previous close encounters with the Shawnees, Kenton and his party built a fortified blockhouse station with fourteen cabins nearby. The next year, Kenton and his partners John Humphrey and James Demint had scattered to separate locations in and around what was soon to become Springfield.

Next to Simon Kenton, David Lowry was the most interesting and enterprising character in this hardy group of settlers.

> In the year 1800, David Lowry built a flat boat upon the Mad River, for the purpose of navigating the Mad River and the Miami to the Ohio, and thence to New Orleans, with a cargo of pork, and venison hams. The venison was taken aboard, and the boat navigated down as far as Dayton, where Lowry stopped for the season, and...made the barrels necessary for the pork. These barrels were put aboard the boat and floated down the Miami to the Ohio River, and thence rowed up to Cincinnati. In the meantime Lowry's hogs were driven on foot from his farm to Cincinnati, where they were slaughtered–the pork salted in the

This official looking 1823 federal land grant, signed personally by President James Monroe, gives one hundred and fifty-one acres between the Miami Rivers to Timothy Bailey on behalf of Lewis Bailey.

Surveying the Northwest Territory: The Ludlow–Symmes Compass

Artist Charles Willson Peale painted New Jersey native John Cleves Symmes on the eve of his adventures in Ohio Country. Land speculator Symmes was able to claim millions of acres in southern Ohio, but his "Miami Purchase" soon became a nightmare of creditors and litigation. *(Miami University Art Museum, Oxford, Ohio)*

John Cleves Symmes had Israel Ludlow survey his Miami Purchase (opposite page) in the 1780s. The huge tract, north of the Ohio River, contained land between the Miami Rivers that became Cincinnati and Dayton. *(Cincinnati Museum Center)*

This precision surveying compass was made by Dean of Philadelphia and sold to Israel Ludlow in 1771. A national treasure, it belonged to nine men between 1771 and 1880. All scratched their names into its lid. It surveyed large tracts of the old Northwest Territory and ended up in the Clark County surveyor's office.

John Cleves Symmes and Israel Ludlow are forever linked to the "Ohio Fever" at the end of the 18th century. Son of a New Jersey clergyman, Revolutionary War veteran and Congressman, Symmes was sucked into the frenzy by a neighbor who had returned from a 1786 trip to the Ohio Valley. After visiting the frontier himself the following year, he became an enthusiastic real estate promoter. Having obtained a grant from Congress for a million acres between the Miami Rivers, he advertised "soil that was equal to any part of the federal territory," a "moderate" climate, farms that were "generally level" and "well watered," "several fine" navigable rivers, stone for building, "clear and certain" land titles, "wholesome laws, and the wisest regulations for promoting emigrants to that country, protecting and rendering happy all those who become peaceable settlers therein." He was on his way to live there and he welcomed anyone interested to join him.

Symmes did indeed relocate to the Northwest Territory and his dreams of becoming a land baron soon turned into a nightmare. His Miami Purchase was much better in concept than it was in application. He laid out settlements along the Ohio River, but soon faced Indian wars and the petty politics of territories on the frontier. Trying to administer the details of his land grant himself, he was a victim of sloppy surveying and ignorance of the land inside his Miami Purchase. He was a land speculator hounded by creditors, including the national government, and sued by settlers who found they didn't own the land he had sold them. Although he played a major role in the settlement of southwestern Ohio, his reward was bankruptcy.

Israel Ludlow, another New Jersey native, came to Ohio by way of South Carolina. He was hired, by national geographer Thomas Hutchins, to join four other surveyors in laying out the "Seven Ranges" district of eastern Ohio. From there, Ludlow floated down the Ohio to John Cleves Symmes and the survey of the Miami Purchase. By 1789, he was part owner of eight hundred acres on the Ohio, laying off four-acre and half-acre lots for settlers. The new town of Losantiville, protected by the blockhouses of Fort Washington, was soon re-christened Cincinnati by Governor Arthur St. Clair. Ludlow went on to own the settlement named Hamilton, survey the original plat of Dayton and lay out the Ludlow line in Clark County, separating, as prescribed by the 1795 Treaty of Greenville with the Indians, the Congress Lands to the north and the Virginia Military Lands to the south. His descendants were influential in the early history of Springfield.

The national surveyors had brought a new, more scientific type of surveying to the Ohio Country. On September 30, 1785, Thomas Hutchins and his survey team stood on the north bank of the Ohio River and recorded a reading of 40"38'02" above a post that had been pounded into the ground. It was a mark that would guide the location and sale of public lands across the continent. The traditional method of survey throughout the colonial period had been the old system of metes and bounds, finding a memorable tree or rock at the edge of a property and laying out the survey from that point. The new system, using the invisible mathematical lines determined by the surveying instruments, could still be sloppy by modern standards. Hutchins missed his mark by about a half mile in his original survey. But the new systematic survey promised a less frustrating process for the settlers seeking accurate property lines.

The whole idea of surveys and property ownership was befuddling to Native Americans. They believed they were trustees, not owners, of the land. Treaties, raids, even victories over whole armies, could not stem the flood of immigrants seeking land they could "own" in the new territory.

There is no greater symbol of the "clash of cultures" in Ohio country than the Ludlow-Symmes Compass. On the one hand, the compass was a symbol of opportunity. A true national treasure, it belonged to the men who opened up the Northwest Territory. Israel Ludlow bought it in Philadelphia before the American Revolution and carried it out to the frontier. It was used to help start the survey of the Northwest Territory. From there, it laid out the Miami Purchase, Cincinnati, Hamilton, Dayton and Springfield. Passing through several owners to the Kizer family, it was used proudly in Clark County until 1880. For the Native Americans, it was the symbol of the end of their freedom to live on the land. The surveys that carved out the new boundaries of Ohio destroyed their way of life.

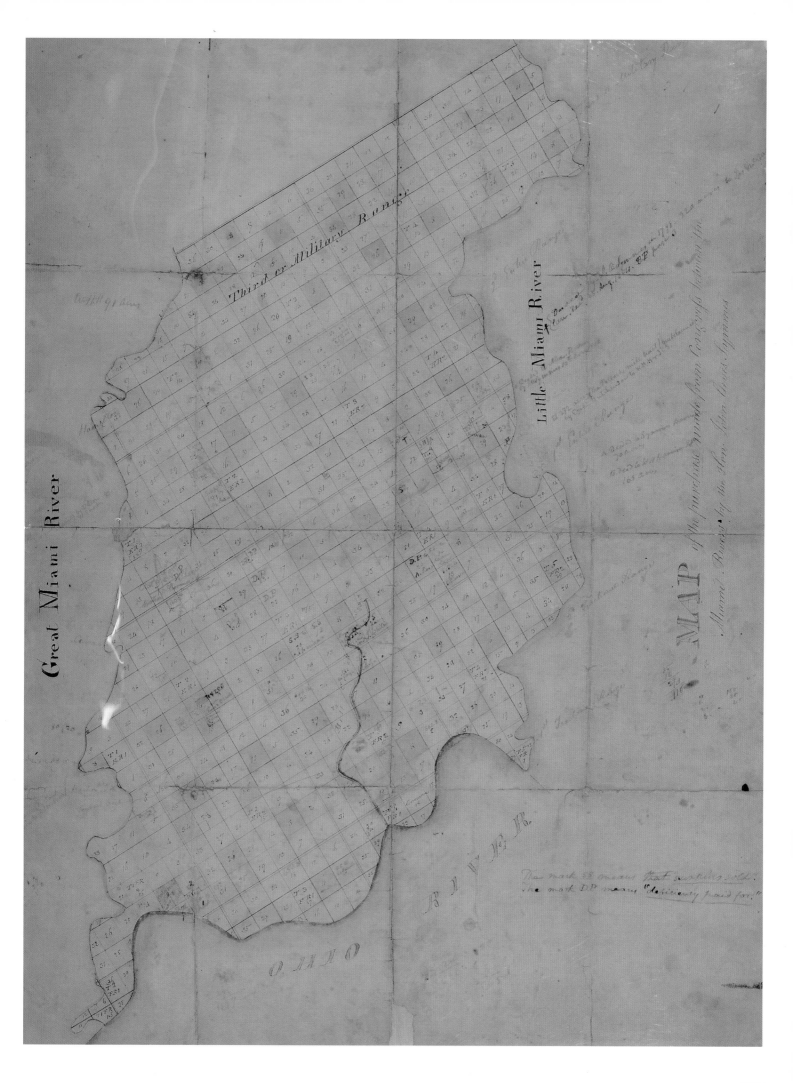

Blue. Entered
Yellow. Reserves.

Fourth Township - ninth ran

36	30	24	18	12
35	29	23	17	11 East Bran
34	28		T: A	10
			R:9	
33		21	15	9
32	26	20	14	8
31	25	19	13	7

Mad River
Road to Dayt
Road t

John Daugherty used the Ludlow-Symmes Compass to lay out Springfield in 1801. This plat of the surrounding land (above) dates from 1809.

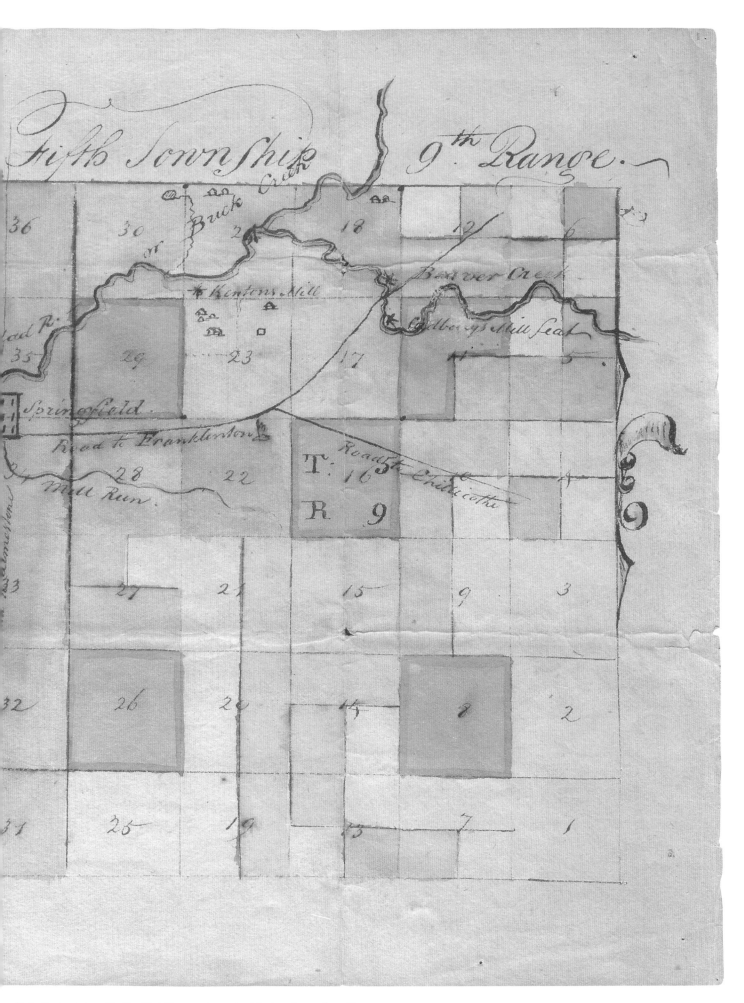

Note the large bend in the Mad River, an important feature for early settlers.

barrels, and started for New Orleans, at which place he arrived after a tedious journey, attended with many mishaps and hardships. For want of a sufficient supply of salt in packing, Mr. Lowry found that his pork was slightly damaged, and yielded him but twelve dollars on a hundred pounds–a sum less than he had anticipated, yet upon the whole, he found himself very well rewarded for his bold and laborious enterprise.

The "goahead" spirit was present in Clark County and Springfield even before they existed. David Lowry, known to his friends as "By Grimany" for his constant use of the term, was the first in the county to grow grapes and make wine. He died at 92 and probably saw more changes in his community than he could have ever imagined.

Drovers herd pigs to a slaughter house down the streets of Cincinnati. David Lowry's adventure in 1800, driving pigs from the Mad River Valley to Cincinnati, began a business that earned the Ohio River community the early nickname of "Porkopolis." *(Cincinnati Museum Center)*

The Rough and Ready Pioneers of Early Springfield (1801-1820)

James Demint is remembered as a gambling and drinking man. Like all the settlers who came to the Mad River Valley with Simon Kenton, he was rough and ready for trouble. You had to have the heart of a gambler to move into the middle of Indian country. Demint picked a spot in the woods a little north of the cascading waters of Buck Creek and put up a log cabin. Being a profit-minded man, he next put together a still so he could trade and sell corn liquor to his Shawnee neighbors. He was soon looking for someone to help him stake out a new town. Mrs. Demint suggested the name Springfield since the place had springs bubbling out everywhere.

The new proposed town got a boost when Griffith Foos and some companions came up from Kentucky by way of the Columbus area in March of 1801. After running into a giant spring where the center of Springfield now stands, Foos and his companions wandered west to the Mad River, up the valley as far as present day Urbana and finally south along Buck Creek, past a "pretty" prairie, until they found Demint's cabin. They had originally been a quarter of a mile from the cabin, right across Buck Creek, but the deep woods caused a twenty-mile detour.

Foos and Demint were soon working with a young surveyor named John Daugherty. Mr. Daugherty, by some unknown deal with Israel Ludlow, appears to have now owned the famous Ludlow-Symmes Compass. We assume he used that compass to lay out eighty-two lots in March and April of 1801, although the plat was not registered in Greene County until 1803. Foos and

his party returned home with their wagons, hacking the first wagon track through the woods and running into a swollen Big Darby River. It took a whole day to transport the goods, horses and wagons across the rushing water. But Foos was soon back, raising the first house in Springfield, a double log cabin that was half tavern and half residence.

Clark County and Springfield are blessed with a first hand account of those early years. John Ludlow, born near Springfield in 1810, grew up with the frontier settlement. A well known town pharmacist and amateur historian, Ludlow delivered four papers on the early settlement to the Mad River Valley Pioneer and Historical Association in 1871. Reverently reprinted in 1963 by the Clark County Historical Society, the papers, drawn from personal experience, are as close to being there as possible. Ludlow traces the town development, follows the town's adventures and describes a whole cast of colorful characters.

The big events of 1803 were a wagon road to Dayton and James Demint's new grist mill grinding five bushels every twenty-four hours. Farmers no longer had to go all the way to Lebanon to grind their flour. A storekeeper named Charles Stowe came up from Cincinnati in 1804, but he soon had competition from two unnamed Frenchmen down the street. That year brought the Smallwoods, he a coarse blacksmith and she a pious Christian who introduced the first attempts at peace and morality to a "vice-ridden" town. There was now a post office and a frame house. Eleven log homes, a couple with stone chimneys but most with mud and sticks, lined the muddy streets of the budding metropolis.

There was trouble in 1807. A man named Myers was killed by passing Indians and a rifle ball passed through the bonnet and grazed the throat of Mrs. Elliott. The Shawnees, now led by Tecumseh, the "Meteor," were asked to give reason why they did not commit the crimes. The neighborhood had reason to fear the Indians. The charismatic Tecumseh, along with his strange brother "The Prophet," who was having trances about white men who were great crabs rising up from the east to take their lands, would soon lead the last great rebellions against the white settlements. An ally of the British in the War of 1812, Tecumseh was eventually defeated and killed ending all local Indian attempts to prevent the invasion of settlers. For the moment, however, Tecumseh agreed to a council in Springfield. It was the most memorable event in the community's early history.

They assembled in a sugar maple grove across from Foos's tavern. All weapons were left behind except Tecumseh's combination pipe and tomahawk. When he was given a clay pipe to replace his own, he disdainfully threw it over his shoulder so the townspeople yielded on that small matter of policy. During the discussions, it was learned that the Shawnees meant the whites no harm and that the murder was the act of one individual. Everyone present had an opportunity to see Tecumseh in action. When he spoke, "rapid, animated and fluent," they were impressed. He was thirty-eight years old, five feet, ten inches tall, straight, erect and very muscular. "The Indians remained three days in town, and at times amused themselves in jumping, wrestling, and other feats of activity and strength." No one soon forgot this last great meeting with the doomed Shawnees and their great leader.

The Reverend Saul Henkle, Springfield's first resident preacher, arrived in 1809, another ally for Mrs. Smallwood against the drinking and brawling. Maddox Fisher erected a gun powder mill at the mouth of Mill Run. The "New Lights," an old-fashioned religious revival, brought the first church in 1810. In 1812, Pierson Spining started a new store with fine goods imported by wagon and flatboat from the east. The first brick house, a Methodist Church and a woolen factory, on the first floor of Fisher's mill, followed in 1814. Mr. Fisher started a two-story brick house in 1815. It took two years to finish it. The first printing office started turning out *The Farmer* in

No contemporary likeness of the famous Shawnee Chief Tecumseh is known to exist, but this Benson Lossing composite is thought to be accurate.

The finely-decorated combination pipe and tomahawk belonged to Tecumseh and may have been the one he was carrying during his 1807 meeting in Springfield. (*Ohio Historical Society*)

1817. It wasn't much in the beginning, "a piece of foolscap, printed on coarse and dark-colored paper." The printers were still using the same style press that Ben Franklin knew so well a century earlier.

The year 1818 brought the birth of the "county of Clarke." When the "gratifying intelligence" arrived, the citizens gathered at a local tavern and "celebrated the occasion by the burning of tar-barrels in the street, and the free use of apple-toddy, with the other accompaniments belonging to a great jollification of that day." The honorable Maddox Fisher had long fought for the creation of the new county.

> Joseph Vance was…the representative of Champaign county in the Legislature, and therefore the representative of the people in Springfield, but he opposed with great violence the measure of Mr. Fisher; but Mr. Fisher continued his efforts as a lobby member of the Legislature, year after year, at his own expense, until he finally succeeded…

The same year brought the first jail with a black bear chained to a stake nearby.

> I remember a black man named Johnson being confined in this jail, and who, in contempt for such a jail, pried off the door, pitched it down a steep bank into the run, and went away about his business.

When the 16' by 16' log structure was replaced in 1824, William Wilson bought it for twenty-four dollars.

A young married couple took a wedding tour in April, 1819.

Thomas Wharton drew this earliest view of downtown Springfield in 1832. Looking out from Werden's National Hotel, he saw the first county courthouse dominating the townscape. *(Cincinnati Museum Center)*

[Their tour] was made on horseback, both riding one horse. After they left the paternal roof of the bride they forded the Lagonda [Buck Creek], and after a short and pleasant ride they halted at their newly prepared residence at the corner of Main and Plum Streets, where they spent several years of their happy lives.

In 1869, the couple, Mary Christie and Louis Bancroft, celebrated their Golden Wedding Anniversary.

Hotel Keeper "Billy" Werden came to Springfield in 1819 and local hospitality was never the same again. That year, forty prominent citizens chipped in over two thousand dollars to build a county courthouse. The town was already divided by the formidably marshy Mill Run, with "Old Virginia" to the west and another settlement to the East around the Public Square called "Sleepy Hollow," "on account of the lack of enterprise in that part of town."

The west bank of [Mill] Run was exceedingly muddy, and in crossing the Run on a foot-log, to go to the eastern part of the town, it was necessary to wade through the deep mud and mire until you reached the foot-log, and when you had ascended the east bank of the run it was quite steep. The land along the south side of the Run…was a continuous quagmire, in which cattle would often become swamped. The extension of Limestone Street through this quagmire, was first accomplished by throwing in brush, and placing logs upon them in the form of a corduroy bridge, before it could be covered with gravel or

dirt…The town was destitute of pavements, except a small one of brick in front of Mr. [Maddox] Fisher's store. Firewood was deposited and lay in the street in front of the houses, where it was cut up with an ax, there being no wood-saws then in use. Wagons were driven close up to the front doors of the houses, and the town was more noted for mud than anything else…

Clark County had its first census in 1820. Springfield then contained:

510 inhabitants, 285 males and 325 females, embracing 8 mercantile stores, a good supply of lawyers, doctors, and tradesmen, a flouring mill, a woolen and carding mill, a cotton mill, several schools, a printing office, and a post office; at which 'the mails were received in elegant four-horse coaches.' At this time the only villages within the limits of Clark County were Springfield, South Charleston, Monroe (now New Carlisle), Lisbon, and New Boston. The total value of all property in these villages was $57,657, the mercantile capital in the county was valued at $32,500, the whole number of houses subject to taxation was 94, and their value was fixed at $22,486, all other houses in the county being appraised at less than $100 each, and, therefore, exempt from taxes. The value of horses and cattle was put down at $133,072, and the total value of the property in the county, including the lands, was $773,830.

Property values aside, Springfield and the county were filled with engaging characters right out of a Dickens novel. There was Dr. Peter Smith, grandfather of Civil War General J. Warren

Keifer and the "Indian Herb Doctor." Educated at Princeton, he was fascinated by herbs, roots and other remedies known to the Indians and frontier folk healers. His 1813 *The Indian Doctor's Dispensatory*, was the first medical book published west of the Alleghenies.

Mr. Maddox Fisher was a "true gentleman of the old school style." He strode about town with a silver-headed cane and a silver snuff box, "from which he frequently indulged."

Surveyor and politician John Daugherty was tall and slender,

> with a large head thickly covered with black bristly hair, with black eyes and long heavy eyebrows. He chewed tobacco to great excess, and the copious flow of saliva left his mouth wherever he went…His manner of electioneering was to visit each voter in the county and make his appeal to him in person. On these occasions, he rode on horseback and carried a jug of whiskey on each side of his saddle, contained in a bag. His quick perception of character enabled him to reach every class of voters, and the contents of his jugs were brought into requisition as his judgment dictated, which was very frequently in those early times.

"Granny" Icenbarger was a "portly, good-natured and motherly-looking person," vexed with a "wild and drunken husband" who was "extremely noisy, and danced and hopped about in the wildest manner." Granny was a "regular attendant at all the military musters and other public gatherings where her cakes and beer were made part of the programme; and many a hungry and thirsty soul was replenished at her board."

Merryfield Vicory was the resident Revolutionary War veteran. Rumors were that he had lost his drum "shot from his side by a cannon ball at the siege of Yorktown." He was a "little

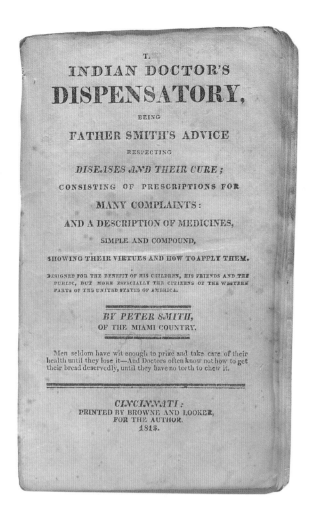

round man with a jolly face, and went by the name of Little Daddy Vicory." Little Daddy once caught a thief stealing bacon out of his smokehouse. He tied him up and "drove him down Main Street under the threatenings of a large club, with two sides of bacon swung about his neck."

The schoolmaster, and sometime justice of the peace, was Englishman Samuel Smith,

> a stout, square man, he was rough in the government of his school, in which he thought flogging an indispensable part of the discipline…and full grown men and women were often compelled to stand up and receive the savage strokes of his ferule upon their hands. He had a nickname for nearly every boy in school such as, 'Lucius Pelly,' 'Mark Anthony,' 'Julius Caesar ' and 'Pompey.'

Another justice of the peace, Robert Renick, killed an Indian in cold blood. A man "a little above the ordinary size, with a dark complexion, an erect body, with a long neck, and a remarkable amount of corpulency," Renick was hauled into court. One jury member was heard to say he would never hang a white man for killing an Indian and Renick was acquitted.

The hundreds of frontier characters in Springfield and Clark County, made it a lively and sometimes frightening place in the early days.

Congressman Samson Mason, one of the shakers and movers in early Springfield, used this carpet bag in his long stagecoach travels to and from the national capital in Washington.

AGRICULTURE AND INDUSTRY

The Seeds of Revolution

From Family Farms to an Industry of Agriculture – Three Innovators Help Create a Revolution

For more than half a century, Clark County had a window on the world. The three revolutionaries who primed the pump of progress not only looked back to a world of pioneer family farms. They also helped rural America face a future of belching factories that reverently proclaimed the "gospel of wealth" and used the quaint image of an old-fashioned plow as their symbol of success.

The settlers of Clark County were farmers. It was the opportunity to own fertile land, no matter how wild and remote, that drew them to the frontier. In the beginning, a would-be farmer in the wilderness had three tasks; clear the land, plant some seed and put up a log cabin. Labor was the rarest of commodities in these isolated settlements, so shortcuts were sought after.

Trees had to be removed so fields could be cultivated. Fertile prairies and Indian "old fields" were ready made for planting, but they were harder to come by. There was a "Southern" style of tree clearing and a "New England" style. Southerners cleared the brush and "girdled" the trees which made them die. They then worked around the trees as they rotted. A big, dead tree with falling limbs could be an occupational hazard and a danger to livestock. New Englanders, accusing southerners of laziness, cut the trees down and dragged the wood into a pile for burning. Both methods left stumps in the fields where they were left to rot. Axes were readily available for the work but saws were rarely used. A hardworking farmer could clear no more than two to three acres a year, and the more he cleared the more he had to cultivate. An industrious settler could clear enough land, using the

trees to build his shelter, to raise a big enough crop of wheat and corn to survive the first, and often the toughest, winter. The "Reaper King's" father, Andrew Whiteley, remembered that nothing about any of it was easy.

> Farming was hard work then. This county was largely overgrown with hazel brush, and to break up the ground the first time, three, four or five yoke of oxen were usually used. But there were a good many horses owned too; I should say about three horses to one ox. In my earliest recollections of our farm we had no fenced-in pastures, and an hour or more would be required every morning to find the stock. My father would get up every morning and listen for the bell on his work horses, and by the time he would hunt them up, he would be as wet as water, from walking through the weeds that grew as high as this ceiling.

General J. Warren Keifer also spent his childhood on a farm.

> [Starting] at the age of seven years…I performed hard farm work, hauling, ploughing, sowing, planting, cultivating corn and vegetables and harvesting. I was never idle…the rough marks of the [sickle] are still on the fingers of my left hand.

Pigs were the only livestock that could thrive in the wild and they were favored for their inde-

135

This charming scene from another age depicts the back-breaking labor that meant survival for a frontier family. Some men clear and burn trees in the background as two others plow the cleared fields, possibly for the first time. Farmers needed the strength of eight oxen to plow on virgin land filled with roots and stumps. As the mother milks the family cow, the only one who seems to be enjoying herself is a daughter feeding a pet sheep. *(Anonymous, "He that by the plough would thrive. Himself must either hold or drive," c.1825-50. Purchased as the gift of Mrs. Evelyn L. Roberts. ©Addison Gallery of American Art, Phillips Academy, Andover, Mass. All rights reserved)*

pendent ways. Allowed to run free and fend for themselves, they could be a neighborhood menace, called "razorbacks, elm peelers, land sharks, alligators and prairie rooters" by their human neighbors. When it came time to butcher them for bacon and ham, the farmer often would shoo them into an old cornfield to fatten them up and then head out with his gun to shoot them and dress them in the field rather than chase them to kingdom come. Hogs could get easily lost and mixed up with other herds, so ear marks, notches and slits, would be registered with the county recorder's office. Stock found in the woods without a brand or recorded mark belonged to the finder. Anyone who wanted to market his hogs had to gather them up and drive them to the nearest market. At the beginning, that might be the budding "Porkopolis" of Cincinnati, more than a week of hog driving away.

It was easier to drive cattle. As the settlers raised bigger herds, they considered driving the animals to eastern markets. The first big drive, sixty-eight head, plodded from the Scioto Valley to Baltimore in 1805. The price at market was right so drovers from the eastern cities started coming out annually to purchase cattle, bringing the markets to the settlers' front doors. It was the best way to earn ready money in the early days. There were riders with the eastern drives, but most of the work was done by "drove hands" walking alongside the hundred to two hundred head herds, cracking a long, loud, "black snake" whip.

Dairying was always part of daily life on the farms, and, by 1815, extra milk found a ready market as cheese in Pittsburgh. Every farm also had sheep for wool and mutton, but most were "native" breeds, brought with the settlers, and interest in the higher quality "Merino" breeds grew slowly.

The first Clark Countians had bittersweet memories of the hard work that went into daily chores amidst the crops and kitchen gardens.

Before going to the field the housewife set a lunch of butter, bread and tansy bitters, at seven o'clock the horn blew for breakfast; and ten o'clock lunch is sent to the field; at twelve o'clock, dinner; at four o'clock, lunch in the field, and supper at dark. Thus there were many meals to prepare – on an open fire or in the bake oven.

As soon as sufficient clearing was made, a picket fence was put up to exclude scratchers [chickens] as well as stock...people were dependent upon their own resources for food...the old time garden had a very complete variety and a succession of all kinds of vegetables then known, from the onion to the artichoke...potatoes, cabbage and early corn...for early potatoes we had the kidney, or six weeks, small, cream-colored, hard fellows, good when boiled with early peas...for late...a medium sized red or calico...called Scotch; Mc Donald and Shaker blues. The place for the currant bush was along the fence, unvexed by caterpillars, it flourished like a green bay tree and its loads of fruit...was one of the sights of old times. The garden was the place for medicinal herbs, rue, garlic, sage. Saffron and lastly that which was not food nor

A drover, armed only with his "black snake" whip, walks nonchalantly ahead of a herd of long horned cattle on their way to market. Some mounted men ride in the background, but large herds of cattle were often driven hundreds of miles by groups of drovers walking alongside the lumbering animals. *(Courtesy of the Virginia Historical Society, Richmond)*

Described as a "very quiet, methodical, patient man," botanist George Harrison Shull revolutionized corn production by proving that breeding hybrid varieties would greatly increase crop yields. (Antiochiana, Antioch College)

The "father of hybrid corn" published his groundbreaking findings in the American Breeders Association Proceedings of 1909 and then quietly went back to his work on primroses. The findings were rediscovered in the 1930s and corn yields were increased six fold by the 1990s.

From these humble, and often poetically beautiful, beginnings, the farms of Clark County became a major industry. Sometimes resisting the changes that made their lives easier and their work more productive, local farmers helped move America into a major agricultural revolution.

Three homegrown geniuses made that revolution possible. The first stayed in Springfield and made and lost a fortune. Before he was twenty years old, William Whiteley jumped into the highly competitive national race to produce simple, efficient and cost effective machines for harvesting crops. He called his mowers and reapers "champions," and proved it. For almost three decades, his company manufactured machines for the world market. When he left the scene, that company was a future important ingredient in the formation of International Harvester, the largest producer of farm equipment the world had ever seen.

Armed with the equipment to make a revolution, farmers needed better more productive crops. Born on a tenant farm northwest of Springfield, George Harrison Shull and his five talented brothers all became university professors, teachers and scientists.

Shull taught school for a couple of years and then decided to attend nearby Antioch College. There he discovered the long neglected pioneering genetic research of the monk Gregor Mendel. He had found his life's work and, after winning a doctorate in botany at the University of Chicago in 1904, he was lured to a new experimental evolution station on Long Island.

Mendel had postulated the existence of dominant and recessive genes. When asked to demonstrate how Mendel's work applied to American maize or corn, the preferred food of millions for humans and livestock, Shull abandoned his experiments on primroses. Farmers had traditionally tried to improve their corn crops by picking the best looking corn for seeding the following year. Building on the work of others before him who had scientifically experimented with crossing different corn strains, Shull discovered that inbred strains of corn actually purified a "mass of very complex hybrids." By carefully crossing inbred strains, good qualities could be emphasized and subsequent generations could show a fixed "hybrid vigor." After presenting his findings to the American Breeders Association in 1908-09, Shull went back to his work on primroses. Described as a "very quiet, methodical, patient man," his revolutionary discoveries, designed only to show that Mendel's genetic theories applied to

William Whiteley's Champion Reaper Empire helped create a farming revolution by making crop harvests a more efficient and less laborious task. This poster depicts the East Street Shops, largest in the world next to the Krupp Works in Germany.

medicine but which glows in the memory like a paradise of quiet happy hours.

The Flowers which filled the eye with pleasure by their simple breaths, and delighted the eye with their beauty. Whatever might be forgotten in the many years of toil, anxiety and sorrow, the pinks, the blue bottles, daffodils, jump-ups, tulips and peonies of the old time gardener, linger in the memory as a joy forever. Then there was the rosebush which, after a shower, had roses, like the one 'Mary to Ann conveyed'…Later in the season came the morning glories and marigolds to tone up the autumn scenery of the departing year, the marks of which were already depicted in the gold and crimson forest, where still hung on the partially denuded boughs the walnuts, the butternuts, hickory nuts, black-haws, wild grapes, etc, all of which gave that peculiar charm to the woodland of those days and can never be seen again.

Turn of the century Ohio agricultural students inspect corn with an aim toward improving the next year's crop by picking the best examples for seeds. Picking the best seed corn by eye was the only method used to improve yields before Dr. Shull demonstrated the important value of cross-breeding and hybridization. *(Ohio Historical Society)*

Two Clark County agricultural revolutionaries came together late in life to receive well-deserved honors in Springfield. 4-H Founder A. B. Graham is second from the left and Botanist George Harrison Shull is third from the left.

Springfield Township School Superintendent Albert Belmont Graham poses with a group of bright and attractive young graduates who have benefited from his innovative and imaginative approach to teaching in rural schools.

Students are busy testing soil samples as part of Superintendent Graham's attempt to demonstrate that "all of learning is not in books."

Turning Flax into Linen

...Flax for homemade garments was raised, pulled by hand, spread, rotted, broken, skutched, hackled, etc.

– J. Warren Keifer

General J. Warren Keifer was describing one of the most difficult and time-consuming tasks for a frontier family. In the early days, with little access to any manufactured cloth, farmers raised sheep for wool and a patch of flax for linen.

"They made nearly all the textile material they used...They sheared the wool...grew hemp and flax... they would card the wool, break and hackle the flax and hemp, spin into thread and weave it. The finer cloth was made of flax and the coarser of hemp and wool.

"Every farmhouse had its spinning wheel in my childhood, and nearly every farmer's daughter learned to spin. Many of them would go to work by the day at spinning and there was great opposition to laying aside the spinning wheel for more advanced methods, on that account. They thought there would be no way left for young girls and women to earn money, but they were mistaken."

"The raising of flax was not an agreeable task by any means. It was first pulled, then laid out to rot. After the pulp was fully separated from fiber we had to break it, that is we hammered it until the body was broken into small pieces; then we 'scutched it' – that was my work. With a hickory [wood] knife I would rub the pieces of stock off the fiber. Next it was 'hackled;' every farmhouse had its hackle. It was a piece of wood about a foot long and six inches wide driven full of spikes. The fiber was drawn over this until it was torn into strings and long shreds. Then it was ready for spinning, and after the thread was made it was woven into coats and trousers and shirts. I didn't know what a cotton shirt was until I was a grown man.

Silk dresses among the ladies were very rare; if you saw one on the street, you knew the woman surely belonged to quality...

Self-sufficiency meant constant labor and turning flax into linen was one of the most laborious tasks of all. When cotton and wool, along with blends called "jeans cloth," became commercially available, farm families abandoned linen making with no regrets. The old style flax disappeared from farm fields and the shorter variety, yielding flaxseed for oil, was all that remained to remind old-timers how much trouble it had been to put a shirt on a family member's back.

The specialized tools needed to prepare flax thread for a linen loom are assembled above. A spinning wheel is flanked by a wooden "scutching" board and knife and a device used to measure and wind the linen thread. Two types of "hackles," used to finish stripping off the harder outer layer from the flax fibers, are in the foreground.

OVERLEAF:
Boring, repetitive tasks on early farms often became reasons to get the whole neighborhood together for a good time. This romantic painting of a frontier settlement portrays a community in their best clothes gathering to "scutch" flax. The wooden "scutch" knives are very much in evidence although most of them are being used for tomfoolery rather than work. *(Linton Park, Flax Scutching Bee, Gift of Edgar and Bernice Chrysler Garbisch, Photograph © Board of Trustees, National Gallery of Art, Washington, DC)*

Most turn of the century American rural schools were old-fashioned and plain. The German Township High School was built in 1874.

The Springfield School District No. One school bus (below) is horse drawn and well-ventilated. Note the muddy road, a regular part of travel until concrete was introduced to American roads.

The Springfield Township Boys and Girls Club exhibited the results of their experiments at the Clark County Courthouse in 1905 (bottom). Note the collections of corn cobs, mounted insects and dried leaves. The exhibits first mounted in Clark County have since become a standard part of agricultural fairs all over the country.

corn, took the agricultural world by storm in the 1930s and 40s. George Harrison Shull, the "father of hybrid corn," proved to the world that it could raise its corn yields from twenty-one bushels per acre in 1930 to one hundred and thirty-five by the 1990s.

In 1900, the children of farmers were still learning in ancient one-room schools. They spent large parts of the school year helping their families with the endless chores. In the fall of that year, one of the greatest teachers America has ever produced, became the superintendent of Springfield Township schools. His five hundred students were scattered over many miles in seventeen small country schools.

During the several years that he worked with the Springfield students, Albert Belmont Graham began a rural school revolution. There were no magic secrets. Graham brought energy, imagination, patience, curiosity and compassion into the dull and old-fashioned classrooms. He understood that his students were living in a time of great change and they could not succeed in the new century unless they could be helped to find out what life was all about. He had simple questions and comments that were radical for the status quo.

> Will you not help the children to see some of the most interesting things around them? All of learning is not in books.
>
> Why should children be compelled to be surrounded by bare walls?
>
> Won't you please give the children your everyday problems?
>
> Agitation is the beginning of everything. If you never open your mouth you may trot along in the same old harness.
>
> One may live in perfectly still air but I prefer the exhilarating effects of a good stiff breeze.

Graham nurtured out-of-the-classroom projects that helped students apply in real life what they learned in school. He instituted traveling libraries so the classrooms would offer the students more knowledge. He called himself an "educational heretic," asking probing questions and opening young minds. In the process, he taught his students self-respect, pride in community and, ultimately, improved citizenship.

A. B. Graham took his teaching revolution first to Ohio State and then to the U. S. Department of Agriculture. His passion for helping the students from American farms turned into a worldwide movement now known as "4-H." After a long career, he came back to Clark County to recognize and thank the wellspring of his inspiration.

Working the Fertile Land –
Plowing, Planting and Harvesting

Clark County is part of the glaciated land in Ohio. Glaciers covered most of the state, but did not get to the Appalachian foothills in the southeast. The farmland of Ohio was much more important to American agriculture before the great agricultural areas of what came to be called the "Corn Belt" were opened up to settlement. Much of the arable soil is "glacial till" and there are layers of underlying limestone that have been weathered over millennia. The Miami River Valley, fed in part by the Mad River, seasonally was, along with the Scioto and the Muskingum, one of the most flatboat-friendly river systems in the young Buckeye State. But having a major river nearby was both a blessing and a potential curse. A flood could be expected to cover the rich bottomland every few years. The nineteenth century saw seven major floods on the Ohio and its tributaries and four of them were devastating. The 1832 flood left behind piles of dead livestock and a thirty-foot wall of

> ruins of buildings, fences, trees, rafts of boards, rails, barrels of flour, pork, furniture, farming utensils, carriages [and] store goods…in short, everything that had been in use by the inhabitants…

Clark County had many "patchy barrens," dry rather than wet most of the year. Some of these areas, fifty to two hundred acres each, resembled the prairies further west, "apparently a perfect level having neither tree, shrub, stump, or stone, and the soil the deepest black I ever saw." Others still had small clumps of oaks and hickories. But most of the county, like the rest of Ohio, was covered with thick, old forest.

Once the forested land was cleared, the annual cycle of raising crops could begin. "[Often] they would take what they call a 'jumping plow,' scratch the surface and sow buckwheat. That would put the soil in condition for next year's crop." When plowing began in earnest, the farmer walked behind his horses or oxen as they pulled a simple machine that had been used practically unchanged since the days of the Old Testament. The only improvement added to the old-fashioned plow was a wrought-iron share, attached to the wooden moldboard, that helped the plow cut furrows without the "clogging" that often forced farmers to stop and clean off the dirt. By the 1840s, plows were made of durable cast and wrought iron, but the process remained the same until the internal combustion engine made mechanized plows possible.

Planting also was a straightforward, time-consuming task. Farmers either "cast" the seeds around the field or "dropped" corn seeds by

Even after the introduction of dozens of different mechanized farm implements, the old-fashioned plow, practically as old as civilization, remained the agricultural symbol of choice.

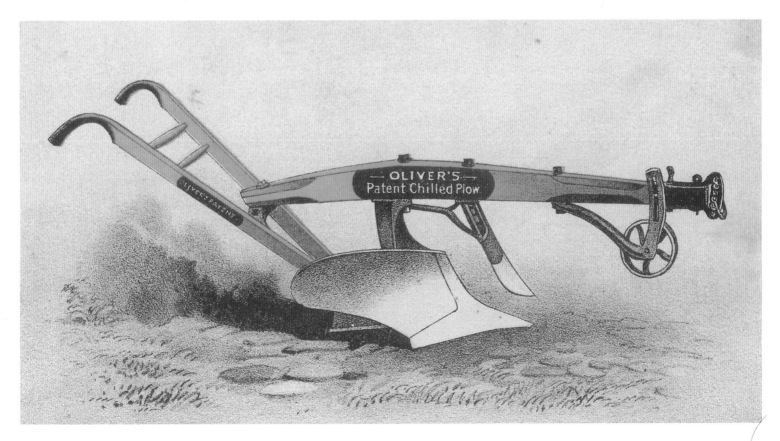

The wooden plow (top below), with an attached wrought-iron share to cut more efficiently into the earth, was a standard piece of equipment for the early settlers. Note the old ramrod from a musket reinforcing the broken right handle, a genuine field repair. The brute strength of a pair of oxen was needed to pull this plow. The wrought and cast iron plow of similar design but much greater sophistication (bottom below) cut through the earth easily. Its design pushed the dirt away and prevented "clogging." Larger draft horses, popular in farmyards after the Civil War, could pull the new plows and quickly replaced the slow, plodding oxen.

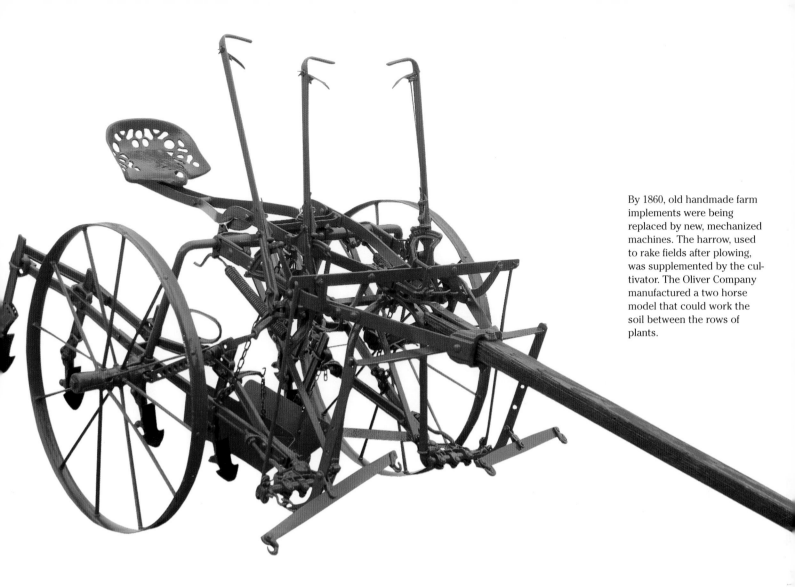

By 1860, old handmade farm implements were being replaced by new, mechanized machines. The harrow, used to rake fields after plowing, was supplemented by the cultivator. The Oliver Company manufactured a two horse model that could work the soil between the rows of plants.

hand, covering each with a hoe. "Boys got ten cents a day for dropping." Sometimes a horse-drawn harrow was used to cover furrows where the seeds were dropped. By mid century, mechanized seed drills were introduced and they were all but universal by the 1870s.

Harvesting was a much more complex process.

Prior to 1830 all the small grain was cut with the sickle. The cradle was at first regarded with suspicion, not favored even if it did save hands as it would deprive an army of skilled reapers of their employment and wages. It took twelve to fifteen reapers to make the work go lively. When the "Through" was cut, the binding was done by the same men as they went back carrying their sickles on their shoulders. Then the water and whiskey were passed and fun indulged in while resting up.

Often hay was harvested from untilled fields.

A meadow of three or four acres was considered quite a field in the 1830s – the runs and wet places that could not be tilled furnished the greater part of the hay. With wooden forks the [cut] swathes were spread by women and children, when dry on one side it was turned and the windrow thrown in…after still more drying it was forked and raked by hand to a full wind row, ready for hauling to the barn.

Threshing of the small grains was the next step in harvesting. The oldest method, called "flailing," beat the grain from the stalks after they were placed on the threshing room floor in a barn. A good flail thresher could process between seven and fifteen bushels a day, depending on the type of grain. After threshing, the grain was "winnowed" by tossing the grain in the air and letting the chaff blow away. Another method of threshing was "treading."

Some ten or twelve sheaves with bands [holding them together] cut were thrown upon the barn floor, with heads up…as many horses and colts were turned in as would work well in pairs – a boy riding the leaders and then the process of going round and round, throwing in and throwing out, turning over and shaking up, was continued until it was clean or tramped fine enough…The wheat was then…cleaned by being run through a fanning mill [an artificial breeze to clean the grain]. Before a floor was made or the fanning mill came, the bare ground was used for tramping and a sheet to clean with…

Ears of corn were shelled by hand at communal "shelling bees."

Farmers were experimenting with machines

The source of the Champion empire, a restored 1870s combination mower and reaper, stands majestically alongside a field ready for harvest at Carriage Hill, a preserved 1890s farm near Dayton, Ohio. Following the monumental success of Champion, at least twenty other Springfield companies began making a wide variety of farm machinery. The Superior Company was noted for its grain drills and grass seeders. A one horse model stands next to a poster advertising a two horse model that had won sixty-three "first premiums" at sixty-five fairs.

A colorful 1870 McCormick poster depicts an almost totally mechanized wheat harvest. As a mower cuts a field in the background, two reapers work the front field. The only manual tasks are binding the sheaves on the bottom right and loading the hay wagons for the trip to the barn. On the left, young ladies, who would have been helping in the fields a generation earlier, enjoy a picnic. *(McCormick Collection, State Historical Society of Wisconsin)*

to help with these tedious tasks as early as the 1820s. Old-time Clark Countians remembered these experiments because they were so innovative.

The Crofts used a machine for threshing as early as 1828. They brought it from Pittsburgh via the Ohio River to Cincinnati...and it was the first in the state.

...Late in the 30s...Mr. Samuel Snyder commenced running a portable machine...The cylinder was armed with wooden pegs about eighteen inches long...with a master wheel a rod or more in diameter and could thresh one hundred bushels a day.

A creative explosion came in the 1840s and 50s. The revolution started with the horse drawn machines that mowed and reaped the crops. After developing devices that made the scythe, sickle and cradle obsolete, the inventors went after the task of binding the sheaves. The stationary "separators" or threshing machines burst on the scene at the same time. Run with steam engines, the amazing mechanical threshers used an ingenious system of pulleys, cylinders and conveyor belts to thresh or shell the wheat, separate the straw from the grain and chaff, separate the grain from the chaff and the dirt and deliver the straw to one point and the

grain to another. The sight of a whole neighborhood, gathered amidst the noise and dust to thresh a farmer's wheat crop, was a special moment for generations of Americans.

Once the revolution gained momentum, there seemed to be no task that defied mechanization. By the 1890s, there were close to twenty companies in Springfield alone manufacturing mechanized reapers, mowers, binders, plows, manure spreaders, cotton seed planters, hay rakes, disc and spring tooth harrows, seeders, grain drills, feed mills, two and four horse sweep mills, corn shellers, cultivators, sowers, cane mills, corn and potato planters, saw mills and hay tedders.

A farmer could spend a good part of his profits trying to keep up with the latest labor saver. When steam and then internal combustion tractors came in, there was yet another quantum leap forward. The image of today's gas combine, with one driver doing the work that in the past demanded dozens of laborers, would amaze our ancestors. One of the great revolutions of human history took hardly more than a century, about four generations, to accomplish. Much of it took place right in Clark County. As one writer said, "Man, bowed for centuries over his hoe and sickle, stood erect and rode to work."

continued on page 160.

OVERLEAF:
At the beginning of the Golden Age, the staff of the Springfield Agricultural Works surrounds its handiwork, an elegant grain drill and a cider press. The photograph was taken before 1872 because the original owners, Ferrell, Ludlow and Rogers, became Thomas, Ludlow and Rogers after that date.

Springfield
AGRICULTURAL
WORKS

An Age of Craftsmen

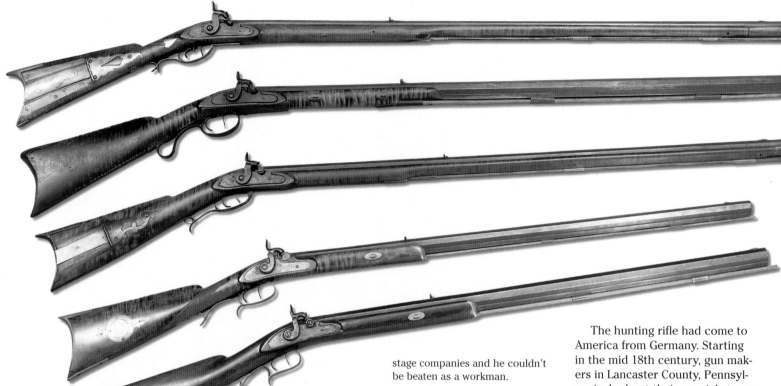

Clark County participated in one of the most honored of America's historic crafts. Handmade hunting rifles, unique combinations of carved wood, wrought iron and brass inlays, came west from Pennsylvania, Maryland and Virginia. Local gunsmiths picked up the craft and put their own special stamp on it.

The monogram at the corner of this 1845 "Jacquard" coverlet (right) permanently identifies the maker, his community and the buyer. The brightly-colored and highly-decorated bedspreads were very popular in pre-Civil War homes.

The J. Driscol & Sons Carriage Manufactory was a landmark in downtown Springfield for more than four decades (top of opposite page). Their three dozen workers could turn out "almost anything that runs on wheels," and they were noted for their attention to quality detail.

Clark County settlers brought craftsmen with them when they moved to the Ohio frontier. Practically every family brought the skills to build houses and make clothing. Other crafts, like coopering, blacksmithing, milling, furniture making and gunsmithing, were simply too specialized for the average household. Until the big mills and factories started arriving just before the Civil War, county craftsmen worked in their houses and on their farms to supply goods that were too expensive to order from the east. These artisans, with skills passed down from a previous master, took carefully wrought quality for granted. Their love of craft survives in the artifacts left behind for present generations to collect, enjoy and preserve. David West, an old-fashioned carriage maker himself, respected his generation of craftsmen.

> …They don't make things now like they used to. The blacksmiths in those days could do any kind of work at all in iron. There are a few of the old-timers left, but the new ones don't learn the trade the old way. Grove Green was one of the good mechanics when I came here. He had a shop…and used to build a great many stage coaches for the

stage companies and he couldn't be beaten as a workman.

No craftsman is more honored than the early American gunsmith. A hunting rifle or "fowling piece," ancestor of the modern shotgun, was an important possession for a frontier settler. Springfield mayor Oliver S. Kelly remembered,

> In 1830 there was hardly a man or woman in the county who could not handle a rifle. I had an aunt who was an especially good shot; she could bring down a deer or anything else that crossed her path, any day."

The hunting rifle had come to America from Germany. Starting in the mid 18th century, gun makers in Lancaster County, Pennsylvania, had put their special stamp on it. Every rifle became a unique blend of carved wood, wrought iron and brass inlays. Settlers took these long rifles, exquisite in their simplicity, west to the Ohio and Kentucky frontiers. As time went on, the "Pennsylvania Rifle" was more identified with Kentucky, but Ohio makers also put their stamp on the craft. Clark County could boast several quality gunsmiths who worked into the 1870s.

Even everyday objects, like barrels and iron tools, were elegantly

handcrafted. Handmade items bore the homespun art of their makers. Some of the new cottage industries, imported from the east, showed signs of the industrial revolution to come. A French-designed "Jacquard" weaving system allowed home looms to weave coverlets with predetermined patterns. A collection of punched cards attached to the loom, gave a weaver the opportunity to weave a rainbow of colors and special designs, including the place and date of origin, into the fabric. The punched cards used an open/shut method similar to the system used in computers a century and a half later. The blue, red and yellow "Jacquard" coverlets, sporting eagles, floral designs, even houses, along with the names of makers and owners, were a highly prized addition to 1840s bedrooms.

The Springfield craftsmen began catering to a rising middle class. Furniture makers, like William Coles, found ways to put their own touches on simple chests, tables and chairs that the previous generation could not afford. Townspeople, who had once walked or ridden on horseback to their destinations, were now seeking buggies and carriages to go out in style. Andrew Whiteley remembered when the town discovered "riding vehicles."

There were no carriages…of any kind here in my boyhood. I was a grown man before my father got a carriage and it was one of the first in the county. It was a great heavy affair, more like a hack [a horse drawn cab], and cost him $200.00, although it had been used in the East, and $200.00 was a great deal more money than it is now.

Elias and James Driscoll [later Driscol] came to town in 1843, determined to build the finest "riding vehicles" Springfield had ever seen. For the next half century, the E. & J. Driscol Carriage Works was the best carriage maker in the region.

The 'good times' will justify the indulgences of the best to be had, which is always a 'Driscol' carriage. Phaeton, Barouches, Open and Top buggies, Side-bars, Rockaways, Spring Wagons – almost anything that runs on wheels, turned out at short notice by the Driscol boys.

As a factory-based culture developed in Springfield, old style craftsmanship remained a critical feature of the Driscol operation. James Cushman, a city fire chief, once worked for the carriage maker.

The Driscol shop was famed far and wide for its first class work. A man who could hold a job there being counted an A-1 workman. They worked about twenty-five hands and ten or a dozen apprentices… We all boarded at James and Elias Driscol's, and high old times we young fellows used to have, too.

Those "high old times" included some radical politics in the 1850s. The Driscols demanded that all their employees belong to the "Rovers" Fire Company. The "Rovers" were Radical Republicans and believed fervently in the abolition of slavery.

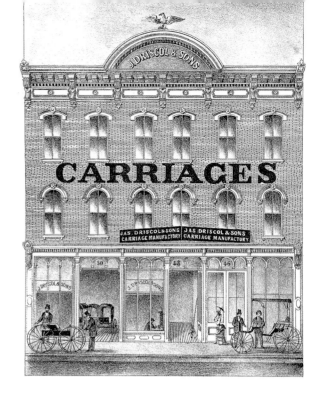

Springfield furniture maker William Coles produced this solid cherry Empire Style chest of drawers in 1854 for a growing local middle class that could now afford store bought furniture.

The "Cunning Handicrafts of Man"*

Sketches of Springfield, 1856

The design of the sails or "buckets" of the Mast-Foos Iron Turbine Wind Machine, an early water pumping windmill, are a study in engineering elegance.

Sometimes the most ordinary of nineteenth century artifacts become, on close scrutiny, art objects. The manufacturers and craftsmen of the era took great pains to add special color and flair to their wares. Reapers, pumps, steam and gas engines, fans and sewing machines; all are decorated and designed to be pleasing to the eye.

One great example, demonstrating the art of craft, is the "Iron Turbine Wind Engine" manufactured after the Civil War by the Mast-Foos Company. Clark County has some claim to being a pioneer in the windmill business. In 1845, South Charleston became the site of the first water-pumping windmill in Ohio. The idea of saving farmers from endless hand pumping was welcome, but the "unsteadiness of the power [wind], and the liability...of the machinery being torn to pieces by too great speed during a gale" were still deterrents. After the Civil War, windmill inventors, measuring the water needs of western farms on the high prairie, were competing for a share of a big new market.

Never willing to lose a business opportunity, Springfield entrepreneurs hastened to develop their

The Driscol Carriage Company put the same high quality craftsmanship into all of its models from a baby perambulator (left) to a closed carriage for the family of Springfield businessman and governor Asa Bushnell.

own model for the windmill sweep-stakes. Phineas Mast and John Foos joined forces to manufacture their "iron turbine." Today, as familiar as windmills have become on American landscapes, they still have a simple, elegant fascination. They are skeletal perpetual motion machines, usually sitting in the middle of nowhere. When Mast and Foos were designing and build-ing their "wind engines," the wind-mill business was still young. The "Iron Turbines" may not have been as practical or efficient as the com-pany's later more traditional "Columbia" models, but they were excellent examples of the consum-mate artistry and craftsmanship that went into everyday objects in the Victorian Age.

The Driscol Carriage Works built "fancy rigs." James Cushman commented on a special job the shop did for the "Rovers" Fire Company.

One of the best pieces of work ever done at the shop was the building of a fancy hose-reel for the 'Rovers.' They paid $1,000 for it, and I remember hearing Driscol saying he didn't make a dollar on it...an old colored man named Sam Rouse, who had a great reputation for origi-nal designs, did the fancy iron scroll-work. 'Old Sam' had been a slave, but bought his time, and came north to Dayton, where he had made almost a state reputation in blacksmith work. Driscol heard of him and would not rest until he got him.

Any vehicle that came out of the Driscol shop, whether a full scale buggie or a baby carriage, had the same first quality iron fit-tings, wheels, paint and striping.

James Leffel and the "Best Wheels in the Known World"

Springfield inventor James Leffel unveiled his "improved turbine" during the Civil War and revolutionized the use of waterpower.

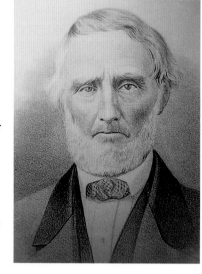

Squire and Mayor J. J. Snyder once bought a downtown Springfield property from James Leffel.

He was a very nervous, gruff man… When we began to dicker [for the property] he wanted $13,000 for the place and he wouldn't take less. I was in his office an hour and a half, I guess, and started to leave two or three times before we closed the bargain [at $10,000].

Snyder also commented that Leffel was "energetic," "a great talker, and a person who would undertake almost anything." After his foundry made good money inventing and selling an innovative "Buckeye" stove, Leffel turned his fertile mind to the water that was cascading through the center of downtown Springfield.

Never, perhaps, did a man pursue a fixed purpose with more devotion, patience and industry. Day after day, and year after year, the study of hydraulics, and experiments connected therewith, occupied his leisure hours.

James Leffel was obsessed with using the abundant water to power Springfield mills. His controversial millrace tapped Buck Creek and then fell twenty feet as it ran for about a mile and a half. The race had the power to run twenty wheels. By the 1850s, there were twelve new factories just north of downtown, with churning belts and pulleys turning out cotton and wool fabrics, oil, flour, wood planks and sash and cast iron.

The efficient local water mills shut out other potential power sources. Charles Rabbitts brought his woolen business to Springfield in 1847.

We ran our mill by an overshot wheel. When we came here, I think there were not more than two or three steam engines in the county, all the mills and factories, being on streams so as to have water power.

Leffel was not finished dreaming about using that waterpower. He began work on a revolutionary water "turbine," bringing the water not over or under the traditional vertical wheel but straight into a double horizontal wheel that had adjustable louvers to control the water flow. After years of tinkering, he was ready to demonstrate his extraordinary new invention.

It was the second year of the Civil War. In April of 1862, the Battle of Shiloh had raised the bloodletting to a new level and there were calls for more men and war supplies. A month later, Leffel unveiled his device in a highly publicized contest. His opponent was Dr. Tobias Kindleburger, another well known local inventor. The newspaper was enthusiastic about the competition.

People gathered from across the state to view the exciting 'Battle of the Wheels.' Leffel put up his reaction type double turbine against the…Kindleburger wheel. Leffel's model cranked at 125 revolutions and put up twenty-one pounds of pressure. Kindleburger lagged behind at one hundred revolutions and sixteen pounds of pressure.

James Leffel was certain he had a winner. Every water-powered mill in the world would be interested. The story goes that the inventor-salesman carried his patent model

A simple but ingenious water gauge (above) from a Springfield mill measured that all-important water flow.

The patent model of the water turbine (right) illustrates how the water was forced through a horizontal wheel. The louvers around the outside of the wheel could be opened and shut to control the amount of flow.

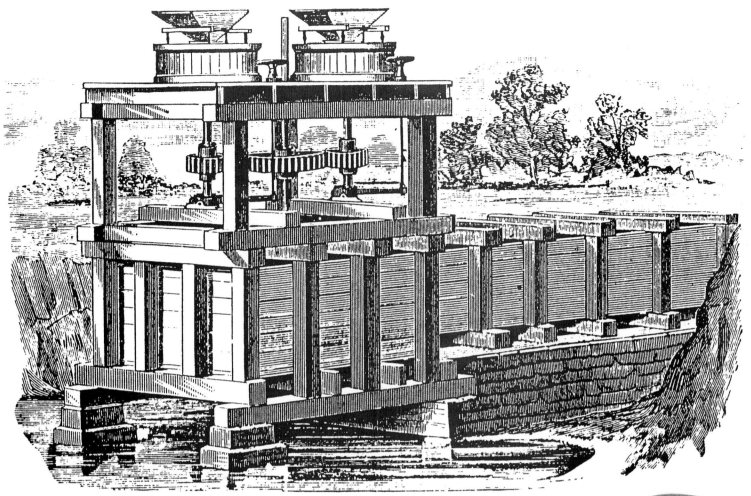

around under his beaver hat just in case some one might inquire.

The Leffel contribution to the American Industrial Revolution was enormous. In 1864, the new company was turning out one hundred and fifty of the "best wheels in the known world." Leffel himself was gone a couple of years later, but his company prospered, selling thousands of the turbines for decades. Ironically, James Leffel and Company went on to manufacture the steam engines and boilers that Leffel had helped Springfield overlook. A century after the company's founding, a Finnish company was still interested in the products of Leffel's unique genius. It purchased the Leffel interests and one more company that had contributed to Springfield's Golden Age passed into history.

The story goes that Leffel carried his patent model under a beaver hat so he could have it handy just in case some one inquired about his invention.

Detailed diagrams from a Leffel Company booklet demonstrate how a sluice can bring water to a turbine (above) and how a turbine can run a sawmill.

An Explosion of Manufacturing and Products

"Uncle" William Reid was looking back from the "Gay Nineties" on the incredible run of business successes that Springfield had seen since the Civil War. The city had two hundred companies on the books and a whole universe of manufactured products unimaginable a generation earlier. The innovative atmosphere had been feeding on its own success. Champion City companies believed in their "You want it! We'll make it!" slogan.

Manufacturers sought products that would give them an edge in the consumer market. Hay rakes were turned into bicycles and reaper castings became electric fans. There was so much creativity in the workplace that the U. S. Patent Office opened a branch in Springfield. Some local people wondered if everything anyone needed would be invented by the turn of the century. If that happened, the patent office would have to close.

Patent attorneys came with the patent office. One of them, Harry A. Toulmin, had a national reputation and was recruited by the Springfield manufacturers. Toulmin turned out to be a real

credit to his adopted community, but he is best known as the Wright Brothers' patent lawyer. After their 1903 flight, the brothers applied for a patent on their "flying machine," but the U.S. Patent Office couldn't figure out what they had invented. In 1904, Wilbur Wright got on the interurban streetcar in Dayton and came over to visit Mr. Toulmin in his downtown Springfield office. Two years later, Patent No. 821,393 was granted to the brothers for their flying machine. Toulmin had guided them through the rigorous and time-consuming process of legally defining their world-changing invention. The relationship continued for the next six years as the Wright Brothers received three more patents for stabilizers, vanes and rudders that gave their machine stability and maneuverability in the air. Wilbur and Orville Wright were beset with claims that they were not the true pioneers of flight. Thanks in part to the intelligent counsel of Mr. Toulmin, they received the worldwide recognition they deserved.

Besides the flood of farm equipment manufactured in Springfield, the biggest Golden Age

A sample of the universe of cans, jugs, boxes, bottles that contained Springfield products illustrate what was available to local consumers for generations. A fifty-pound can of lard from the Springfield Abbattoir, bottles of Lagonda Club Rye and Whiskey, milk from Mill Creek Dairy, beer from Springfield Breweries, even "Superior" California Wine for "family and medical use," all were stocked on the shelves of local stores. *(John Bartley Collection)*

A colorful poster (left) advertises the Globe Lawnmower, so easy to use that a young lady, sporting a somewhat immodest short skirt, can push it across the family lawn.

companies produced steam and gas engines, lawn sweepers and mowers, electric fans, washing machines, cast iron fencing, bicycles, pumps and windmills, horse drawn carriages and motor cars, pianos, caskets and embalming fluid, movie theaters and vaudeville acts, floor weaving looms, magazines and sewing machines. The companies simply saw opportunities and grabbed them. The city business environment was so dynamic that anyone, with drive, business sense and a good, marketable idea, had a fair chance to find resources and turn a concept into a successful company.

Agricultural machines weren't the only Springfield products that found a national market. The developing funeral business came to town after the Civil War. Before the war, a local cabinetmaker, William Coles, was also an undertaker.

Why was it that undertaking was always carried on by cabinet-makers? Why, because it took a cabinet-maker to make a coffin. You see there were no coffin factories in those days. There was no supply kept on hand in anticipation of the demand. It was a common sight to see some man come into a shop from the county with a long cornstalk in his hand – a measure of the length of someone just dead...

The Union Motor Company manufactured efficient washing machines from 1908 to 1937. This model with a copper basin has only five moving parts and can be operated from an ordinary faucet with city water pressure.

Get into business for yourself, no matter how poor you may be. Be honest, never taking what does not belong to you. Keep up your credit. Never help a man who won't help himself; never go security for any one; never take a partner with no money, where you have to furnish all the capital. The other fellow has everything to gain and nothing to lose, and he is saucy and independent. Never do business with a man who never made or saved a dollar himself, and let his wife wear the breeches – with such a man you can never prosper. Keep out of bad company; let wine women and gamblers alone, but get married and raise a good Republican family. Then, I assure you, you will get along in the world. All of the above is no hearsay for I have been there too often myself.

—David Miller
"Advice to a young man," 1890s

The first hearses were drawn by but one horse, and they had no glass about them, the sides being hung with black draperies…What was the cost of a funeral? Well, the usual price, including the service of a hearse, was $15.00 or $20.00. A great many funerals were held without any hearse or undertaker, either. The neighbors simply came to town and had a coffin made and conducted the funeral themselves.

… At the time of the cholera visitation – in 1849, I think it was…a man died alone in [a] little temporary shed…I went out for him, but on account of a fallen tree could not get the hearse near his door. I could get no one to help me, either put the body in the coffin, or get the coffin into the hearse, and I had an awful time of it before I got the job finished.

After a time, my father tired of being called at any time of day or night…to make a coffin, and began to make a stock of them. People who came into the shop looked at the coffins in the wildest astonishment, and wanted to know how it hap-

pened that so many people died at once! I remember we had a new servant girl who as soon as she saw the room of the shop where the stock of coffins were kept, immediately packed up and went home, saying that she would not stay with people who would do such a thing.

In my first experience in caring for the dead we had small means of preserving the bodies; a little ice placed upon them in a pan, and a little solution of saltpetre on the face was the best we could do. Frequently bodies had to be buried immediately and the funeral services held afterwards. Later we had the 'ice box,' with which bodies could be preserved some time.

The Civil War brought grim changes to the world of funerals. With 620,000 dead, the country faced an emergency that President Lincoln said "carried mourning to almost every home, until it can almost be said that the heavens are hung in black." American undertakers, who had been experimenting with intravenous embalming and metallic coffins, suddenly had a ready market for their services. Families descended on battlefields looking for wounded and dead loved ones. Enterprising morticians, both greedy and honest, offered their services to get a dead son or husband home to the family graveyard. The modern funeral business was

162   HEARTLAND

launched by the overwhelming need of Victorian families, touched by a cruel war, to have some tangible closure for their grief.

Mr. Coles lived through major changes in the business of burying people.

> ...Wholesale factories started up all over the country and the whole manner of conducting the [funeral] business locally changed. I think the first coffin factory in the country was started by Hamilton, Lemon & Arnold, in Pittsburgh, and the second, so far as I know, by Gabriel Albin and his son, Joe, in this city [Springfield]. They had a factory for a year or two on Main St...they afterwards moved to Cincinnati...

Dr. A. A. Baker built a major business on those beginnings. The Springfield Metallic Casket Company (1886), followed by the Champion Chemical Company (1888) which produced embalming fluid, burial vaults, funeral supplies and cemetery equipment, were national players in the funeral industry for more than fifty years.

Springfield foundries found eager buyers for the decorative "cast" iron that graced buildings and yards in Victorian America. In the world of "conspicuous consumption," the homeowner with the most cast iron on his property was generally the envy of his neighbors. Once common

in the inner city, most of it has fallen victim to the elements, collisions with automobiles and scrap drives. Starting around 1880, a dozen companies poured molten iron into sand casts for four decades. The results were highly prized for their ornate decorations and relatively light construction. Fencing, railings, crests, supports and brackets, stairs, urns, fountains, statues, garden furniture, fire escapes, light fixtures, prisoner-proof jail cells, fire hydrants, even manhole covers; anything cast from metal was fair game.

Mast, Foos and Company was the biggest purveyor of its justly famous "Buckeye" fence. In 1892, a single shipment to Virginia was three thousand feet long. The Texas State Government decided to fence its state capital in 1890 to

The Buffalo-Springfield Company produced a wide variety of steam and internal combustion street rollers for decades. Faced with the challenge of showing customers a hefty piece of equipment, salesmen took models like this one on the road when they made calls.

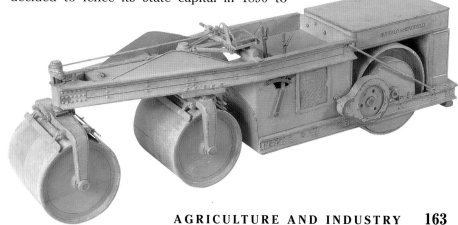

Until the Civil War, the funeral business belonged to cabinetmakers who could build wooden coffins. The appalling casualty lists from the fighting helped create the modern funeral industry. With the introduction of intravenous embalming and metallic caskets, even small businesses like J. Moll & Sons (above) could now provide important new services for grieving customers. Taking their place with other successful local operations, the Springfield Metallic Casket Company and the Champion Chemical Company (which produced embalming fluid) became national players in the funeral industry for fifty years.

"keep out the cattle and horses." The Lone Star State paid $22,000 for fencing sporting "Texas Stars" decorated with gold leaf. The William Bayley Company was the last to make cast iron products, finally abandoning the business in 1923.

Chandler Robbins and James A. Myers ran a foundry that found success in another arena. Civil War veteran Robbins purchased the Lever Wringer Company for five hundred dollars in 1878 and was soon joined by teacher turned retail grocer Myers. Along with many other local foundries, they were providing castings for Springfield's major farm implement market, but, by 1884, they had moved into bicycle parts to take advantage of the new American love affair with the "velocipede."

Next seeing opportunities in the new era of electricity, they began to manufacture electric fans that soon became the standard around the country. Building on this major success, they abandoned the foundry business and continued to produce their distinctive fans along with a new line of efficient, large and small electric motors for everything from washing machines to industrial machinery. One of the only major Golden Age companies that still survives in Springfield, Robbins and Myers has again changed directions and now builds the "Moyno" pump, an ingenious device that can pump a huge range of hard to move substances like oil, radioactive waste, peanut butter, pickle relish and toothpaste.

Business creativity continued after the 1929 stock market crash ended the Golden Age. The Chakeres Family built a regional chain of movie houses with smart marketing and customer service. Paul Deer saw a future for chains of gas stations when he opened his first Bonded Oil facility in 1932. After 1939, the Leventhal Brothers turned the Vining Broom Company into a successful national business, marketing the self wringing O-Cedar Mop. Springfield's astonishing record of manufacturing innovation and efficiency is unique even among diverse American cities many times its size.

The World's Columbian Exposition of 1893

When Americans began considering the idea of honoring Columbus four hundred years after his famous voyage, four major cities jumped at the idea. Chicago, St. Louis, New York and Washington, D.C. all petitioned Congress for the honor, but Chicago won the prize. Fairs were big business and the 1893 World's Columbian Exposition promised to be the biggest. Given Victorian America's thirst for biggest and best, Chicago did not disappoint. More than a century later, the statistics that astonished our ancestors still have the power to amaze us.

The Exposition was an exercise in Gilded Age excess. Forty thousand workers labored for three years at a cost of $28 million to construct fourteen "main" Beaux-Art buildings and 65,000 exhibits on 633 acres. Anxious fair watchers spent twenty-five cents to see a preview as the workers used 75 million board feet of lumber, 18,000 tons of iron and steel and 120,000 incandescent lights on the fair construction. It took 20,000 "tons of staff" to man the pavilions. The Exposition opened with great pomp and circumstance.

The spirit of the nation is at its highest. Its triumph…has chased away all fears, justified all hopes, and with universal joy we greet this day…We have not proved unworthy of a great ancestry; we have had the virtue to uphold what they so wisely, so firmly established.

Between May and October, 1893, 27 million visitors (one quarter of the American population) paid fifty cents to see the "Olympics, DisneyWorld, the Superbowl and the National Gallery all rolled up in one."

A visit to the Exposition was an overwhelming and exhausting experience. Forty-three states and territories and twenty-three foreign countries sent exhibits. Visitors spent weeks exploring national treasures like the genuine Liberty Bell and a book brought over on the Mayflower, reproductions of Mt. Vernon and Pompeii, almost 6,000 speeches and lectures by scholars and politicians, a map of the United States made entirely of pickles, a 22,000 pound cheese and the Fair's power plant of forty-three steam engines and 127 electric dynamos. In addition, they were introduced to a midway with ice cream, hot dogs, hamburgers and the shocking "hootchy-kootchy" belly dancer, Little Egypt.

Standing proudly amidst the sea of goods and products exhibited in the 400,000 square foot Agriculture Hall and the Ohio State Building were the impressive fruits of Springfield's labors. The Champion City was able to hold its own in this competitive climate because its products were being used throughout the entire world.

Fairs were a part of Clark County life from the beginning. "Uncle" William Reid remembered

Two highly successful local products found national markets. In 1900, the Robbins and Myers oscillating fans were the standard for the industry. A few decades later, the Vining O-Cedar floor mop again set an innovative standard.

The 1893 Columbian Exposition in Chicago was the giant of Victorian fairs. Visited by a quarter of the American population in just five months, it featured exhibits and treasures from around the world. Springfield and Clark County proudly exhibited their products in the Ohio and Agricultural Pavilions. The spectacular view above looks across the entrance and the Court of Honor. *(Chicago Public Library/ Special Collections and Preservations Division)*

the first Clark County Fair at South Charleston, the county's "cow town."

The fair didn't amount to a great deal; the thing that interested me most was an educated pig, exhibited by the late William Foos, then a young man. It was a clever pig, indeed, performing such tricks as spelling words by picking cards from the pile, and it could play cards, too, and played a very good hand.

Every fair had its medicine shows and acts of prestidigitation. Fairs were also old-fashioned get-togethers. But the exhibitions and contests

This handsome stained-glass window was front and center in the Springfield exhibit at the 1893 Columbian Exposition.

Springfield businessmen knew the value of fairs and showed their equipment to the public at every opportunity. The rather gloomy "Machinery Hall" exhibit at an 1899 Industrial Exposition is a combination of barnyard and patriotic flags. Evidently visitors are taking exhibitors up on their sign "give it a whirl." Two farm machines have "sold" signs.

were serious business for an agricultural society. The competition was keen because new machines and quality livestock could be shown and sold to an interested audience. Everyone stood to gain from a prize stud bull or a new machine that gave a farmer the edge during harvest. On the eve of William Whiteley's meteoric rise as the "Reaper King," Springfield held an 1852 trial of reapers and mowers and the Ketchum model beat both of the better known Hussey and McCormick reapers. Within a few years, young Whiteley found out, when he put

himself in harness to show how easy his "Champion" reaper was to pull, that a lot of money could be made with a good machine and some showmanship.

County fairs evolved into state fairs and finally the giant national and international expositions that exposed millions to the agricultural revolution. After the Civil War, a booming Springfield put in a bid to be the permanent home of the Ohio State Fair but it was not to be. The economic stakes were just too high for the competition at the state capital in Columbus.

One of the featured machines at the 1893 Exposition was an immaculate Superior two horse Grain Drill (left). Three drills were presented for the Exposition exhibits. One of them went to the Shah of Iran.

continued on page 178.

Marketing an Agricultural Revolution

Advertising was an understated affair before the Civil War. Produced on old-fashioned presses, the spreads sometimes had primitive illustrations but always featured long pronouncements in a wide variety of type styles.

Before the Civil War, advertising was polite and understated. Since most of the neighborhood already knew where you were, literally "hanging out a shingle" or painting your awning would suffice. A chummy print ad in the newspaper or annual directory would feature a variety of ornate typefaces and an occasional hand pointing at an important announcement. There was always a clutter of copy about "stoves of the latest style," or "in fact everything that a man can wish to make him comfortable and happy," or "miniatures for children, taken in two seconds, by the celebrated Quick Working Camera Obscura."

Then young William Whiteley burst on the scene.

That Whiteley is really something! He stopped a reaper contest,

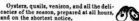

The 1875 Clark County Atlas (above) depicts a lively Springfield Fairgrounds. Fairs became big business as manufacturers found a ready audience for their wares. After the Civil War, Clark County lost a battle to make Springfield the site of the Ohio State Fair.

"Harvest Interrupted" This McCormick Poster (left) demonstrates the type of advertising that sold reapers and binders to tens of thousands of Civil War veterans. Here a McCormick machine has turned up on the Battlefield at Gettysburg (center of poster). Even the violence of a fullscale battle could not damage an indestructible reaper! *(McCormick Collection, State Historical Society of Wisconsin)* unhitched his horses, strapped himself in harness and hauled his own machine, exclaiming, "My Champion is the easiest pulling rig there is!" He was panting like a dog in July, but he made his point!

No one had ever seen a stunt like that. Clark County had a real showman on their hands and an advertising revolution had begun.

After the Civil War, the new Champion Company had national and international markets to consider. It was a brave new world practically unknown to a rural community like Clark County. But a born promoter like Whiteley warmed to the challenge and used it to sell millions of reapers, binders and mowers. The new color lithography was a perfect tool for Champion's promotional blitz. Along with romantic images of smoking factories, proud workers and confident farmers gliding through wheat fields on their rigs, there was often an over the top sales pitch showing chickens pulling reapers. Some of this showmanship made traditional Springfield uneasy, but, even after he lost his company, Whiteley's peculiar influence remained. In 1889, Champion produced one of the Gilded Age's unforgettable ads when it convinced President Benjamin Harrison to mount a mower on the White House lawn as his entire cabinet looked on.

The marketing of Golden Age Springfield went a step further when Phineas Mast began publishing the *Farm and Fireside* Magazine in the 1870s. No less a promoter than Whiteley in his understated way, Mast wanted to use his magazine to sell more of his products. He got more than he bargained for when he hired talented and ambitious editors like John S. Crowell and Charles E. Thorne. In editorials that criticized the state university for not paying more attention to agriculture, *Farm and Fireside* became the voice of midwest farmers. Soon its circulation had mushroomed to a million readers. After moving to a new building in 1881, the Mast, Crowell and Kirkpatrick Company acquired new magazines and grew into the Crowell-Collier publishing empire which dominated downtown Springfield for the first half of the twentieth century.

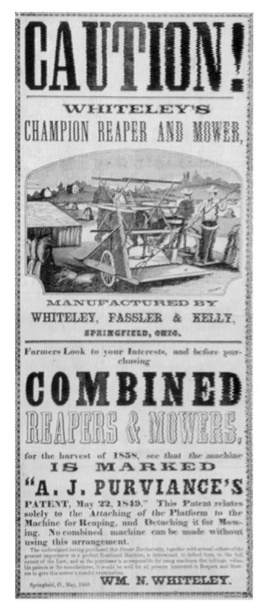

THE IMPROVED CHAMPION MOWER

CUTTING GRASS ON THE SOUTH LAWN IN FRONT OF THE WHITE HOUSE AT WASHINGTON.
PRESIDENT HARRISON IN THE DRIVER'S SEAT AND THE MEMBERS OF HIS CABINET LOOKING ON.

WANAMAKER. RUSK. TRACY. BLAINE. HARRISON. PROCTOR. WINDOM. NOBLE. MILLER.

THE WARDER, BUSHNELL & GLESSNER CO, SPRINGFIELD, OHIO, AND CHICAGO, ILLINOIS.

Entered at the post-office at Springfield, Ohio, as second-class mail matter.

VOL. VII. NO. 24. SPRINGFIELD, OHIO, SEPTEMBER 15, 1884. TERMS {50 CENTS A YEAR. SINGLE COPY 5 CENTS.

FARM AND FIRESIDE.

ISSUED FIRST AND FIFTEENTH OF EACH MONTH.

MAST, CROWELL & KIRKPATRICK,
PUBLISHERS AND PROPRIETORS.

The Circulation of Farm and Fireside is far greater than any other Agricultural Journal or Political Weekly in the United States, and equal to 400 average weekly papers.

TERMS OF SUBSCRIPTION:

One Year, - (24 Numbers), - 50 Cents.
Six Months, - (12 Numbers), - 30 Cents.
INVARIABLY IN ADVANCE.

The seventeenth annual report of the Ohio State Horticultural Society is a pamphlet of 232 pages, which contains, in addition to the proceedings of the Ohio State Society, brief reports from several of the county societies, and from the Mississippi Valley Horticultural and American Pomological societies. Throughout the pamphlet are scattered numerous valuable hints gleaned from the discussions of the practical fruit growers who compose the society, and for the first time these hints are rendered accessible by a copious index. It is placing but a moderate estimate upon the value of this index to say that it doubles the practical value of the report. We have yet one criticism to make upon the index, however, and this applies

FARM AND FIRESIDE worthy to enter every rural home in our land, and though we have not yet attained our ideal, and are by no means ready to fold our hands and say " it is good enough," yet we are willing that our work shall be compared with any that is being done in similar channels, for we sincerely believe that no other journal gives so much in real value for the money received as FARM AND FIRESIDE. That we are not alone in this belief is evidenced by the multitudes of commendatory letters we receive from subscribers, and which have never been more numerous, nor expressive of more earnest approval, than during the past few months. With regard to the future, we have only to say that there shall be no

combing produced by a cross of the Merino upon the Liecester, the medium by the Merino on the downs—now command a higher price in our market than the finest Merino wool, while the sheep which are calculated to produce them are just those best adapted in other respects to the circumstances of farming on high-priced lands, being probably the closest approximation to the ideal of a wool-and-mutton sheep.

It is true, we have not yet succeeded in producing a cross of this kind which will perpetuate itself satisfactorily, the third generation seldom being equal to the second; but the experience of those who have formed the various breeds we now possess, by years of careful and patient

By the time Whiteley had lost his empire, Champion had the solidly Republican President Benjamin Harrison sitting on a reaper (above).

OPPOSITE PAGE: Thanks to the showmanship of William Whiteley, the Champion Company became a marketing giant. As early as 1858, Champion was already starting an advertising revolution (top left of opposite page). *(McCormick Collection, State Historical Society of Wisconsin)*

The Lagonda Plant offices were decorated with stained glass windows that proclaimed Champion's success.

Phineas Mast's Springfield-based publishing empire included the *Farm & Fireside* Magazine which became the voice of midwestern farmers and later *Woman's Home Companion* and *Collier's* with millions of readers.

A Tale of Failure and a Tale of Success

Albert Krell came to Springfield, eager to produce "Lagonda" upright pianos. He set up shop in a portion of the old Champion East Street Shops. His dreams were shattered by a 1902 winter fire that totally destroyed his business. A few years earlier, the O. S. Kelly Company began making piano plates (top of opposite page). A century later, the Company is still producing plates for Steinway pianos.

Albert Krell came to the Champion City from Cincinnati eager to take advantage of the community's industry. Krell was in the upright piano business, the mass-produced, affordable musical instrument, in "player" and regular styles, that was the rage in American parlors. It was the age of "Tin Pan Alley." New York songwriters were turning out mountains of sheet music. Songs, like "Bicycle Built for Two" and "In Your Merry Oldsmobile," were designed to be first heard on the Edison Phonograph or at a vaudeville show and then played on the family piano. It was state-of-the-art entertainment for American households in the early 1900s.

In 1901, Krell brought his Krell-French Piano Company to Springfield. He had purchased and extensively renovated a part of the massive forty-four acre East Street Shops, the former home of the Whiteley, Fassler and Kelly's Champion Reaper Works. The twelve thousand pianos Krell-French would produce the first year would only be the beginning. Merged with six other piano manufacturers, the company had a goal of sixty thousand pianos a year.

One year into production, disaster struck Krell-French and nine other companies housed in the rambling brick factory buildings. Early on a cold February morning in 1902, the worst fire in Springfield history turned the East Street Shops into a smoldering ruin. The fire department was helpless in the face of the inferno and Albert Krell watched his dreams literally go up in smoke. Standing nearby, William Whiteley witnessed the last monument to his reaper empire disappear in the flames. Krell-French would never be up and running again, but the O. S. Kelly Company, a threshing machine manufacturer which had started making piano plates in 1890, is one of a small number of businesses around the country still making plates for the Steinway Grand Piano.

Edwin D. Parker created a success story stretched over thirty years. His father had brought the family to Springfield from England in the 1870s, looking for an opportunity to participate in the Golden Age manufacturing boom. Success came slowly, with a pattern business linked to the town's many machine shops and foundries.

Parker saw a potential market in replacing the time consuming raking of lawns with a mechanized sweeper. His first sale of a lawn sweeper was in 1921, but, as he developed nineteen models in the 1920s and 30s, most of the business went to cemeteries and parks. American homeowners still saw lawn sweepers as an unnecessary luxury. After a World War Two detour assisting with the war effort, the Parker Company found new interest in the sweepers in the postwar consumer economy. Edwin Parker's son, Richard, became general manager of the new Parker Sweeper Company. With renewed emphasis on lawn sweepers, blowers and vacuums for the sea of grass in middle class suburban yards, Parker's sales expanded rapidly from coast to coast and then across the world. After more than three decades, Edwin Parker had finally found a home for his innovative product.

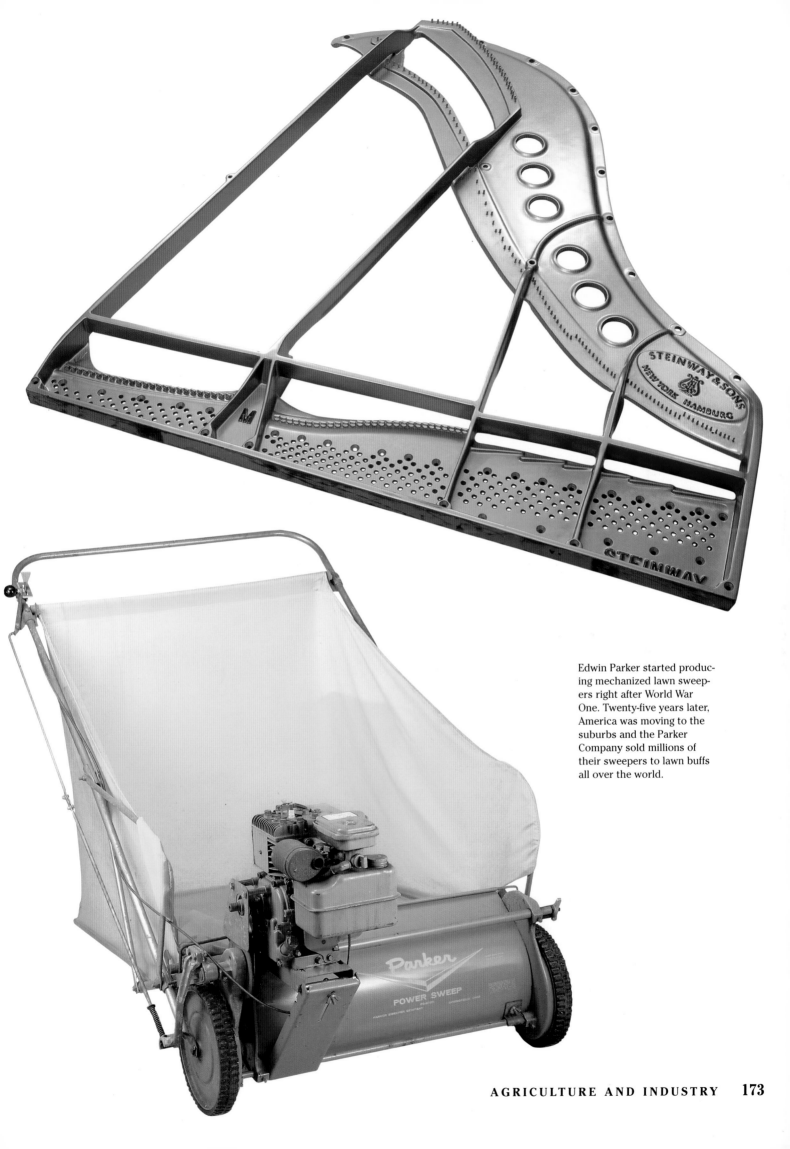

Edwin Parker started producing mechanized lawn sweepers right after World War One. Twenty-five years later, America was moving to the suburbs and the Parker Company sold millions of their sweepers to lawn buffs all over the world.

Labor Saving Devices on the Farm

Phineas Mast made another fortune by providing tools to help with time-consuming farm tasks. His "Buckeye Agricultural Works" was most famous for its durable cider presses (above) which made the fall apple harvest much easier and its incubators which kept newly-hatched chicks alive and well (opposite page). Both products came in a variety of sizes.

Many of the products of Springfield's agricultural revolution were aimed at the family farms that then dominated American life. Much of the consumer market in that era revolved around making the incessant hard work on a farm easier. If there was a task that could be mechanized, some enterprising inventor was tinkering to find an answer.

Farm wives were often ignored in the early days of mechanization. The emphasis was getting as much out of the fields as possible, but farm existence was a rhythm and a balance of large and small tasks day in and day out. A wife and her daughters were expected to prepare all the meals to feed a hard-working family and to help with the crops and livestock. Much of the food came out of a large and demanding kitchen garden that needed regular attention. It took hours and even days to slice potatoes, grind sausage during the fall hog killing or crush apples for cider. One of the most demanding tasks was keeping hatching chicks warm and alive under the stove in the kitchen.

It didn't take long for the Springfield entrepreneurs to see a big market in the making. Inventive farmers had dabbled with helpers of their own and homemade slicers and grinders were the result. Ingenious inventors had put together small machines that swirled and whirled as they magically sliced the skin off an apple. But it was Phineas P. Mast who did the most to develop an industry devoted to farm aids, large and small. His "Buckeye Agricultural Works" faced the often neglected but important tasks head on. "Buckeye's" two biggest contributions were cider presses and incubators in a wide variety of sizes. They made Mast another fortune and he paid his community back by developing magazines, *Farm and Fireside* and *Ladies Home Companion*, that catered to the needs of rural families.

Two things became obvious as labor saving devices flooded the farm markets of Victorian America.

No amount of new gadgets seemed to lessen the amount of work. The arrival of portable steam and gas engines in farmyards changed everything.

As Springfield and the rest of America moved from the farm to the city and suburbs, a local inventor made another groundbreaking contribution to the age of the consumer. The "victory garden" of World War Two spawned a growing interest in backyard gardens. A Springfield machinist named Clyde Quick replaced his spade and hoe with a "garden tractor," pieced together with a small Briggs and Stratton gas engine. Quick's neighbors soon wanted "tractors" of their own. When Clyde's son James returned from the war, the pair created the Quick & Son Manufacturing Company and Springfield had another major innovation, the "rototiller," to market to the world.

After a humble start, the incorporated Quick Manufacturing Company introduced the "Champ," a prototype for the front-tine tiller

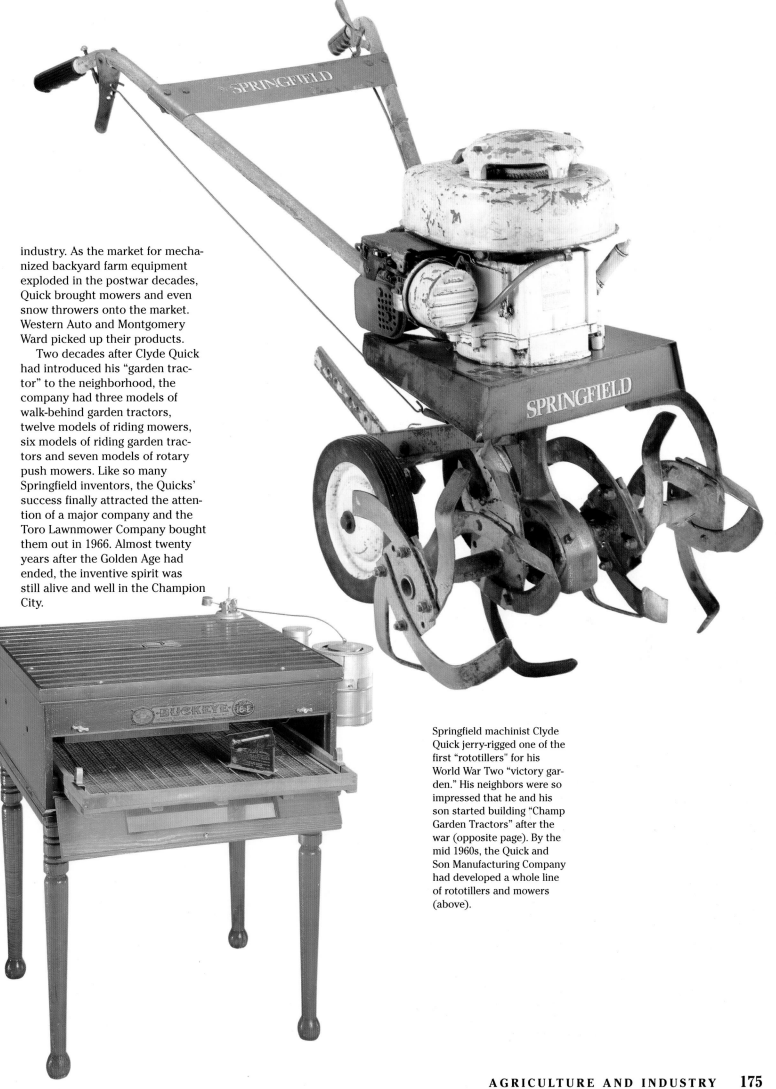

industry. As the market for mechanized backyard farm equipment exploded in the postwar decades, Quick brought mowers and even snow throwers onto the market. Western Auto and Montgomery Ward picked up their products.

Two decades after Clyde Quick had introduced his "garden tractor" to the neighborhood, the company had three models of walk-behind garden tractors, twelve models of riding mowers, six models of riding garden tractors and seven models of rotary push mowers. Like so many Springfield inventors, the Quicks' success finally attracted the attention of a major company and the Toro Lawnmower Company bought them out in 1966. Almost twenty years after the Golden Age had ended, the inventive spirit was still alive and well in the Champion City.

Springfield machinist Clyde Quick jerry-rigged one of the first "rototillers" for his World War Two "victory garden." His neighbors were so impressed that he and his son started building "Champ Garden Tractors" after the war (opposite page). By the mid 1960s, the Quick and Son Manufacturing Company had developed a whole line of rototillers and mowers (above).

Steam versus Gas

The battle between the large and cumbersome steam engines and the smaller gas engines was joined in the early 1900s. The Leffel Company became the local purveyors of steam engines (top of opposite page). Companies like Edwards Motor (right) competed with efficient and economical gas engines and won on all fronts.

The colorful ad below promotes both the six-horsepower portable steam engine and its companion "separator." The opposite page illustrates that steam can even shell corn.

When portable steam and gas engines invaded American farms and backyards, the victory of the industrial revolution was complete. The machine had conquered every garden in the country.

Steam was never very portable. Even the inventive James Leffel Company, originally devoted to waterpower but now converted to steam, couldn't get away from the cumbersome, black monsters that once huffed and puffed in farmyards. It took an experienced hand to run a steam engine efficiently, feeding the fire and fiddling with the valves and gauges to keep the level of steam just right. And they were never practical as tractors. Big, awkward and slow, farmers abandoned them quickly as soon as alternatives were available. A

steam engine puffing away in a farmyard was another matter. Belts running off the bright red fly-wheels could drive all kinds of devices. It could be dangerous if the belt slipped, but the extra power made farmers' lives easier.

The race to develop a practical internal combustion engine went all the way back to the Civil War. The ability to harness explosive power had been fascinating inventors for centuries. First a Frenchman and then a German proved in the 1860s, that a liquid fuel engine could work. The German, N. A. Otto, brought his "Otto Silent" four-cycle engine to America in 1876, the year of the Centennial Exposition in Philadelphia.

Otto patented his engine and launched a business with the Schleicher Brothers of Philadelphia. From that point on, American inventors became obsessed with improving on Otto's design.

The problem was getting the fuel to vaporize or carburet. It remains an elusive quest even today, but it was not until the 1890s, when Otto's original patent ran out, that thousands of hopeful inventors went after the design that would have the most commercial success. The "Charter" Engine, from Sterling, Illinois, was claimed to be the first successful gasoline engine. Springfield entrepeneurs, always ambitious to cash in on new technologies, soon entered the fray. The prolific Foos family was the most successful local manufacturer of portable gas engines. John Foos introduced his first vertical engine in 1893, and the Foos brand competed successfully in the market for decades, always improving their models to keep up with the new developments. Other businesses, like the Superior Gas Engine Company of P. J. Shouvlin, also took advantage of the exciting new market.

Gas engines were exciting because a relatively portable internal combustion motor gave farmers new flexibility. They were noisy and smelly, but they were also smaller, cheaper and much more efficient than steam engines. When they were attached to moving vehicles, the "horseless" tractor became a reality and the agricultural revolution in farm fields continued to accelerate.

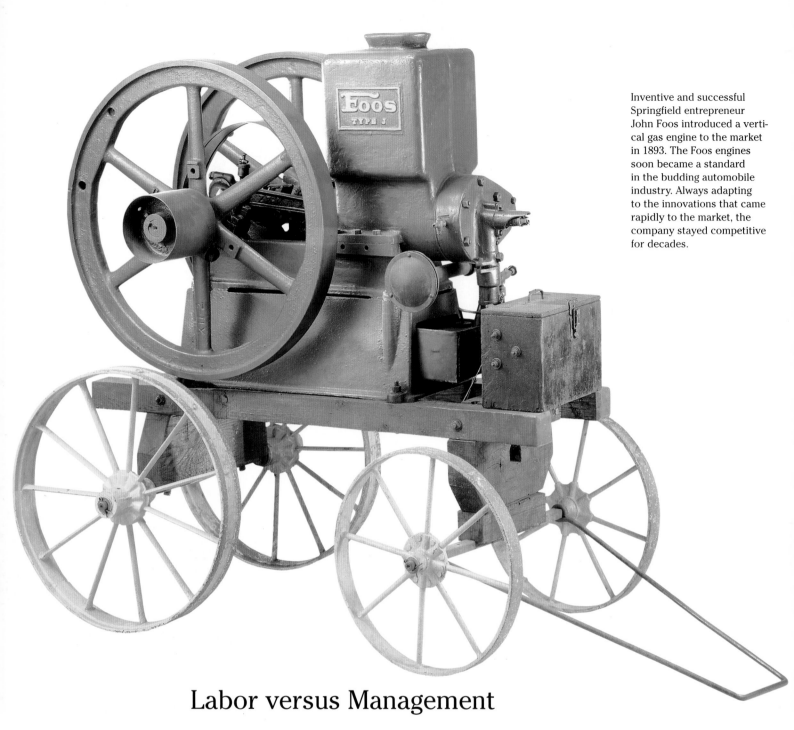

Inventive and successful Springfield entrepreneur John Foos introduced a vertical gas engine to the market in 1893. The Foos engines soon became a standard in the budding automobile industry. Always adapting to the innovations that came rapidly to the market, the company stayed competitive for decades.

Labor versus Management

Labor unrest was inevitable in a suddenly industrial place like Springfield. The real story of the community's labor trouble is that there wasn't more of it. After an initial explosion in the 1880s, there was an uneasy truce and occasional strikes until another blowup a century after the initial collision.

The first generation of Springfield business tycoons, led by William Whiteley, could not understand the need for unions. As far as they were concerned, a job and a decent wage were enough. They had been raised in an economic world with no safety net. Everyone, no matter what their background, had the same opportunity to become rich.

The Iron Molders formed the first union in 1864 to help sick workers. Along with unemployment benefits, this first twenty-two member association organized a committee to discuss disputes with their employers. By 1868, the Typographers had followed the lead of the Molders and organized another labor brotherhood. After this initial burst of labor fever, the workers were relatively quiet until the Knights of Labor came to town in 1883.

Organized among the Philadelphia garment workers in 1869, the Knights were the first great national labor organization and had grown to more than a half million members by 1886. They wanted to protect all working class opportunities with political action and social reform. The Mad River Assembly of the Knights was one of sixteen local unions formed in the 1880s. A serious recession early in the decade increased the tension between employers and workers.

William Whiteley was a natural target for this

newly-organized unrest. He had just completed his huge East Street Shops and now employed two thousand workers. A self-made man, Whiteley was not unsympathetic to the needs of his employees. The Champion Company had created savings banks and home loan associations and he personally had helped families in need. But he could not abide labor agitation and believed the unions were violating his property rights. A thousand of his employees felt the need to join the Mad River Chapter of the Knights. Whiteley responded with a sign across the red brick front of his factory proclaiming "free and independent workingmen only."

The thousand rebels, now "locked out" of their livelihood, asked the Knights of Labor to boycott Champion products. The standoff continued for weeks and then a strange event intervened. On "Blue Friday," June 17, 1887, Whiteley's empire suddenly crumbled. Others, like Oliver S. Kelly, had abandoned him because his fast and loose attitude about business frightened them. Now, a so-called "friend" and associate in Cincinnati lost everything in futures speculation and took Whiteley with him. The "Reaper King" was responsible for his associate's debts and could not make payment.

Springfield was in the worst financial crisis in its history. Others continued to manufacture the famous reapers, but Whiteley had to sell his East Street Shops and only received a fraction of his original $1.2 million construction costs. As the huge factory stood idle, two thousand workers were out of work. Both sides had paid dearly for their first battle over the workers' right to unionize. The emergency stirred Springfield's

A line of workers poses in front of the Champion East Street Shops in the 1880s. Thousands of men labored at the plant that sprawled over forty acres. Many of these men joined the "Knights of Labor," creating Springfield's first great labor crisis in 1887.

The new era of photography created a generation of laborers who posed proudly in their workplaces. This stern-looking group works for the O. S. Kelly Company, makers of farm machines and later piano plates. Note the small pillbox caps, common among laborers of the era, and the confident looking man at the right of the second row with large handlebar moustache and hands on suspenders.

city fathers into action. They formed a Board of Trade that evolved into the Chamber of Commerce. In 1890, the unions organized a Springfield Trades and Labor Assembly to work together on mutual issues and problems. Each Labor Day celebration saw another national labor leader trotted out for the city's working class. In successive years, Terrence Powderly, Eugene V. Debs and Samuel Gompers spoke to big, enthusiastic crowds.

The uneasy "era of good feelings" between labor and management continued through the rest of the Golden Age. The hundreds of surviving photographs of proud workers, staring con-

fidently at us over the generations, attest to the security and prosperity of those decades. The 20th century has brought different dynamics, shaking the foundations of an economic compact our ancestors took for granted.

The Great Depression threatened everything. In 1932, desperate workers at the Springfield Metallic Casket Company sat down on the job and took over their factory. But they could not alter the terrible financial emergency that affected worker and owner alike. World War Two brought economic relief along with the terror of world conflict, but another creeping change would again alter the rules of labor relations.

American labor has always been fond of signs and banners. The AFL-CIO sign, from the local "Labor Temple," has a stern warning. The banner below belonged to the Brotherhood of Painters, Decorators and Paper Hangers.

The thousands of Springfield workers were members of the United Auto Workers Union, one local among the 35,000 UAW members who worked for I H. The Chicago-based company, a huge out-of-date industrial manufacturer, brought in Archie McArdle from Xerox in the late 1970s to modernize operations. One of his targets was the UAW. Many felt that the company had become a "patsy" of the union. The "cushy" contracts for workers were thought to be one reason why I H was losing its competitive edge.

In 1979, the year that International Harvester had its best profits ever, McArdle began negotiations with the union on a long term contract. In the early give and take of the negotiations, it became obvious to the union that the company was going to play hardball. Some of the points of discussion, like seventeen days of mandatory overtime each year, might seem trivial to outsiders, but the union was continuing to fight for the prerogatives that previous generations had fought tooth and nail to achieve. Negotiations soon broke down and the union called a strike. One hundred and seventy days later, the longest strike in UAW history, the company capitulated on most of the union demands. Both sides could only wonder why it had taken so long to reach a place where they were at the beginning. During the six months of the strike, the country had entered a recession and International Harvester was awash in red ink. Another CEO was brought in and the hard-earned gains of the strike were lost as one-third of the work force received pink slips.

The Springfield workers had loyally supported the strike to the end only to find that the events, spiraling International Harvester toward bankruptcy, were totally out of their control. In fact, the important events of the whole saga had occurred somewhere else. And, to add insult to injury, now the company was threatening to close the Springfield plant as a cost saving measure. Only timely and intelligent intervention by city leaders saved the jobs and kept the county's biggest employer from closing its doors. From cottage industry to shops to locally run factories and finally to multi-national corporations, job security and a fair wage remained the worker's goal, but the playing field seemed to get more complex as the world got smaller.

The management of Springfield companies began to move elsewhere. Workers no longer could know their employers and the security and negotiating power of national labor organizations became more important than ever. There could be little redress if absentee owners simply closed a plant down, but there was room for negotiation, and if necessary, agitation, when a company's very existence was at stake.

The second great crisis in Springfield's labor history came almost a century after the fall of William Whiteley. The last surviving giant from the old days, International Harvester, had been making trucks in town for almost six decades.

A labor union marching group, sporting a banner and group of young drummers, sits on the steps of a downtown Springfield public building. Undoubtedly direct from a parade, this group must have been quite a sight strutting down the street with top hats and twirling canes.

The sturdy-looking railroad workers appear to be picking up cinders left on the roadbed by passing steam engines. Note the very young boy. Without child labor laws, young boys often worked side by side with the men.

Most of the group to the left have put on their best "bib and tucker" for the photographer. It was an important matter of pride for workers of the Gilded Age to be photographed with their companions at their place of work.

The workers in the front row (below) have all brought their "Sunday go to meeting" hats for the photograph. Note the burly, bearded man, hammer in hand, on the right of the top row.

This large group contains a few African Americans, working side by side with their counterparts. Note the dandy at the top left, remarkably out of place among these working class faces.

Burton Westcott's Motor Car

Originally from Richmond, Indiana, Burton Westcott brought big city sophistication to Springfield. As a young man, he posed for a portrait with a loyal companion.

Burton J. Westcott brought a sense of class and taste to Springfield. One look at his photograph and you know you're in the presence of a gentleman. Some men looked comfortable in the stiff shirt collars of the era.

Mr. Westcott built motor cars; not just "flivvers" and "gas buggies," but motor cars for adults. His father loved big horses and built beautiful carriages. Westcott, however, was a man of the twentieth century.

A Westcott may be driven harder and farther because of the long life that has been built into it. "Long life" of the right kind! Not brute strength bought at the price of riding comfort, and looks. Not endurance secured by sheer weight of metal, at the cost of gas, oil and tire economy. But stamina engineered into a fine mechanism as the watchmaker – and a few automobile

engineers – know how to do it…judge it carefully and see what you think of it as a twenty-six hundred dollar investment.

All the family money originally came from a seed drill company, in Richmond, Indiana. Richmond was Burton Wescott's home until his father's business sent him to head a branch office in Springfield in 1903. He and his wife Orpha enjoyed the vitality of the Champion City. They brought big city sophistication with them. On a 1905 trip to Chicago, they met the up and coming architect Frank Lloyd Wright. Soon, Wright designed and built them the first "Prairie House" in Ohio. It was low, modern and a little bit oriental looking – quite a contrast to the ornate Victorian estates of their neighbors on upscale East High Street.

After the death of his father, Westcott turned his attention totally to motor cars. His aim was quality at an affordable price – "The Car with a Longer Life," he called it. He

entered a Westcott in the first Indianapolis 500 Race in 1911. His driver, Harry Knight, was one of the best, but Knight crashed the car into the pits, swerving to miss another driver who had been thrown from his car onto the now famous "Brickyard."

Burton Westcott moved his motor car business and his entire career to Springfield in 1916. The city bought into his elegant life style. He was the only man in Ohio with a one million dollar life insurance policy. His Westcott Motor Car Company offered the best chance the community ever had to compete in the auto market. He was put on a city commission that reshaped city government and then was elected mayor. His leadership helped make Springfield finances solvent. He went into the streets to bring calm when black neighborhoods were caught in a flare-up of racial tension.

In 1920, Westcott sold 1850 of his "Lighter Sixes," the best annual sales he ever had. His classy ads, in the *Saturday Evening Post*, boasted about a special car, sporting the distinctive orange hubcaps and radiator plate.

> The Westcott makes an excellent showing as to the first cost, mileage and economy in operation – but the real reason for selecting a Westcott is that above everything else, it is the car with a longer life, and the car with less trouble, more genuine comfort, and greater distinction in action and looks during all the years of its long life.

The Westcott was a luxury car at an affordable price. The twenty-six hundred dollar price tag bought you a "hand tailored top, with dust cover, rear curtain of Gypsy type, with large plate glass rear window, cigarette lighter, walnut instrument board and eight-day keyless clock." Westcott was old-fashioned about his forward-looking vehicle. He resisted attempts by Detroit to buy him out because he wanted his workers to get the best treatment and his cars to be top quality.

By 1923, Westcott's fairy tale world started to crumble. His wife Orpha died suddenly and his independent company, swimming upstream against the monopoly of the Detroit giants, was in danger of being washed away. He tried a new balloon–tired model called the "Closure."

The Westcott Motor Company began in Richmond, Indiana, in 1909, and moved to Springfield in 1916. Until the company capitulated to the Detroit cartel in 1925, the Westcott, with its distinctive orange logo (reminiscent of Volkswagen), offered a luxury automobile at an affordable price.

THE SATURDAY EVENING POST   71

A Westcott may be driven *harder* and *farther* because of the long life that has been built into it. "Long life" of the right kind! Not brute strength bought at the price of riding comfort, and looks. Not endurance secured by sheer weight of metal, at the cost of gas, oil and tire economy. But stamina engineered into a fine mechanism as the *watchmaker*—and a *few* automobile engineers— know how to do it.

The man who admires a workmanlike piece of machinery will appreciate this description of a Westcott car—"*Wonderful Works in a Beautiful Case.*" When next you see a Westcott car (which you'll recognize by its orange hub-caps and radiator plate), judge it carefully and see what *you* think of it as a twenty-six hundred dollar* investment.

THE WESTCOTT MOTOR CAR COMPANY
SPRINGFIELD, OHIO

BODY TYPES
7-Passenger Touring
5-Passenger Touring
3-Passenger Roadster
(Single Seat)
7-Passenger Sedan
5-Passenger Sedan

WESTCOTT
The Car with a Longer Life

Westcott sold 1850 of its sporty 1920 "Lighter Sixes," the best year the company ever had. This model featured a hand-tailored top, a rear curtain of the "Gypsy" type, a cigarette lighter, a walnut instrument board and an eight-day keyless clock. Westcott resisted Detroit attempts to buy him out and was soon forced out of business.

The open car is rapidly passing…perfect weather protection is provided. Sliding windows on either side instantly ventilate the interior…

The "Closure" didn't sell well, in fact nothing sold well. Westcott had to borrow on his life insurance and turn his house over to a bank in order to absorb the losses. By 1924, the company, with so much style and so much promise, could not buck the tide that was moving the auto industry to Detroit. Bankrupt and broken, the elegant Mr. Westcott was dead two years later at the age of fifty-seven. He gambled when he took on the auto monopolies and he lost. Westcott's death was headline news in Springfield. The city mourned for an adopted son who had won its trust and carried its hope for the future.

Mr. and Mrs. Westcott met architect Frank Lloyd Wright on a 1905 trip to Chicago. The result was the first "prairie house" in Ohio, quite a modern contrast to the high Victorian homes on Springfield's posh High Street.

Trucks That Rain Death Upward

THE INTERNATIONAL HALF-TRACK is a truck that carries its own pavement. It can speed over bog, sand, mud and mountain ... carrying armed-to-the-teeth personnel to seize and hold a position, or toting fast anti-aircraft firepower that rains death upward.

The International Half-Track is proving on the world's battlefronts that it can take it, as well as dish it out. It should. It's a brother under the armor to the International Truck that was the *largest selling heavy-duty truck* on the market when civilian trucks were still being made.

When the story of this war is written, trucks will contribute one of the most glorious chapters. A vital part of this war is being waged on the highways of America, where trucks haul materials to keep the wheels of America's war production turning, and other trucks haul food sup-plies to feed America's great army of industry.

Trucks must work harder and longer, to the last possible mile, because there aren't any new trucks to take their places. That means that every truck on the road today must be babied and serviced to give better and longer wear than was ever expected of trucks before.

And International civilian truck service—*the largest company-owned truck service organization in the world*—is now a wartime truck *service*. More alert and more efficient than ever to keep your trucks on their jobs. Whether they're International Trucks or any other make, bring them to an International Branch or Dealer. You'll find International service close at hand—pledged to keep your trucks rolling—*pledged to Victory!*

INTERNATIONAL HARVESTER COMPANY
180 North Michigan Avenue   Chicago, Illinois

★ INTERNATIONAL TRUCKS ★ ★

KEEP 'EM ROLLING—FOR VICTORY

SERVICE TO THE NATION

From Piqua to Desert Storm

A Proud Military Tradition

Sadly, much of American history is defined by war. Hardly a decade has gone by without a conflict that has created veterans, each wrestling with the meaning and frequently the horror of their experience. Clark County has its own proud, two century tradition of commitment and sacrifice. When city, county and country have called, local men and women have always stepped up to put their lives on hold and meet the challenge of war. Often, the conflicts have been fought against long odds in faraway places.

There were veterans living and working on the land before there was a city or a county. They were the closest thing to minutemen the Ohio Country ever knew. There had been a big battle in the neighborhood during the American Revolution. In fact, the 1780 Battle of Piqua was the largest fight west of the Appalachian Mountains during the War for Independence. Veterans of that engagement returned a generation later looking for the beautiful and fertile place they had seen while fighting the Shawnees. These settlers were familiar with the potential danger of living amidst the Native Americans. The French had called frontier fighting, "le petit guerre," quick, terrifying strikes on log cabins by small bands of warriors. The American "Long Knives" had to be ready to defend themselves without warning. No one who risked his life to claim unsettled land was immune from the threat.

The Indian troubles simmered and sometimes erupted for more than half a century. When the new United States sent its small regular army to invade and conquer the Indian lands,

local settlers went along as scouts and militia. The invaders were often defeated and even sometimes destroyed, but the settlers kept coming back until their invasion finally overran the Indian nations. After the wars of conquest, Ohio settled into the "Middle Period" of the American saga.

Tucked between the Wars of Independence and the War Between the States, the early 19th century, when Springfield grew from a village into a small city, saw small town America grow a militia culture. Meeting regularly to practice their martial skills, townspeople remembered their battle-tested minutemen grandfathers as models of military effectiveness. In truth, the militia musters were excuses for males to show off the splendor of their homemade uniforms, engage in some politicking and party to excess. There were always "colonels" and "generals" present. "Colonel" Harvey Vinal remembered how he reached his auspicious rank.

> I got [my title of colonel] under the old militia law. At an early date, Clark Chipman organized a uniformed company [one hundred men], the first in the county. Later the boys raised a second company and made me captain. Our company was called the "Clark-Guard." Peter Sintz had a company of horsemen, west of town, and an uncle of [Mayor] Oliver S. Kelly, had a company of infantry, south of town. Well, we got them together, there was another company or two – there were six companies altogether – and formed a light battalion, of which I was given the command with, the rank of lieutenant-colonel.

"Uncle" John Reid was only a "high private."

> ...I guess I had just as good a time. You see, every man who was able bodied, between the ages of 18

Springfield-made M-17 "Halftracks," featuring twin 20mm gun mounts, "rain death from the ground" in this World War Two International Harvester Company patriotic poster. The Champion City made thousands of trucks to support American armed forces all over the world. *(International Truck and Engine Corporation Archives)*

This giant eagle and shield, measuring twenty feet across, was carved for the stern of the sailing ship Columbia by J. Nabors of New Orleans. With wings majestically spread, the bald eagle has been the symbol of the American martial spirit since the birth of the republic. *(Jerome Hoxie, Eagle, Index of American Design, Photograph ©2000 Board of Trustees, National Gallery of Art, Washington, DC)*

and 45 years, was required to attend muster. There was generally two muster days each year, a company muster in April, and a regiment muster in September. From about ten o'clock in the morning until four in the afternoon we would drill.

They used to call us the Cornstalk Soldiers; but I guess we did very well. The officers had to buy their own uniforms – some of them got very fine ones, too. Every man brought his own musket, and the privates had no uniforms at all. The government provided some of the "light infantry companies" with arms, and they all wore uniforms, usually a pair of white trousers with red or blue stripes down them. These two days drill were all we had in the year; the officers, however, would drill oftener, so as to be able to properly instruct us.

Judge John C. Miller had a different experience at the musters.

General muster was held in a large field north of Main St., opposite the Pennsylvania House. Every fall every man went to camp for three days. There were certain regular organizations that kept up their drill all year, but other companies were formed of the raw recruits who only thought of military affairs on those occasions…Capt. Peter Sintz commanded the "Mad River Spies," an organization of horsemen, who wore helmets with long horsehair plumes. Col. Putnam of South Charleston was distinguished for his immense epaulets, and the big red and white ostrich plumes on his chapeau.

Col. Vinal remembered that musters could turn into homespun dueling grounds.

Muster day was a great time for settling up old scores. Whenever two men would have a little trouble, they would always say, "Well, we'll settle this at general muster," and they would too.

Like every schoolboy, Judge Miller couldn't resist the thrill of a military ceremony.

A hero of the town for many years was Freeman Vicory, the last surviving soldier of the American

Revolution. He was buried with the honors of war in 1845; I remember that I ran away from school (and for which running away I got a whipping) to see the militia march and fire cannons over the grave.

Whatever their military prowess, the local militia, like the volunteer fire companies, served an important community social role and provided a measure of security. They were occasionally called out to help stop a riot or clean up after a natural calamity. They could also be called up for a federal emergency. When volunteers on both sides were called to arms in 1861, the militia companies formed the first regiments that the states sent into the federal service. Suddenly bandbox soldiers were facing the threat of a real war. William Diehl was proud that Springfield pulled its weight during the rebellion.

Springfield made a good record in the war; she never failed to furnish her quota of men and money when needed; everybody took hold without regard to party, and many people who were opposed to the war in principle helped to sustain the city's reputation in doing her share.

In 1861, no one could know the hardship a civil war would inflict on the nation. Among the thousands of Union counties, Clark County sent at least thirty-four hundred of its own men to the battlefront and then waited for news. The war, unlike any American event before or since, took over 600,000 lives and measured everyone's will and commitment.

The Civil War produced a generation of battle-tested veterans who ran the country and trained a state national guard for future contests. There was always some faraway trouble and young men had a choice of joining the regular federal army and navy or training, like their

Admiral Clarence Williams, Clark County's highest ranking officer, at the time of his retirement in 1927. His four-star admiral's flag as the commander-in-chief of the U. S. Asiatic Fleet is below. Admiral Williams saw the American Navy evolve from sail to steam and wood to steel.

local militia fathers and grandfathers, with the state guard in anticipation of an emergency closer to home.

A war with Spain at the end of the century suddenly made the United States a world power. The perspective of the country changed as 20th century ideologies and technologies aided new global strife, involving millions of civilians along

with the armies. The separation of federal and state armed forces became blurred as wars called for the rapid mobilization of millions of men. As the century went on, the wars became life and death struggles for control of the planet. New weapons made it possible to annihilate millions. Through World War One, World War Two, Korea, Vietnam and Desert Storm, Clark County has continued to provide its share of men, and now ever increasing numbers of women, each in their turn willing to endure danger and sacrifice for city, county and country. It is a noble record, reflected in the Clark County Heritage Center's commitment to the memory of valiant deeds and service to the modern community of veterans.

The record is also epitomized by the career of the highest ranking officer ever to hail from Clark County. Clarence S. Williams was appointed as a midshipman to the U.S. Naval Academy in 1880. It was a time of dramatic change for the

Among the thousands of Civil
War flags and banners, this
thirty-four star survivor is
almost unique. It was presented to the people of Clark
County by the Great Western
Fair to aid the Union soldiers,
held in Cincinnati in December
of 1863. Thanks to the efforts
of the local ladies, the county
contributed more to the wel-
fare of the troops than any
other Ohio county.

United States Navy. Steam-powered "ironclads"
had revolutionized naval warfare during the
Civil War. Sail was giving way first to steam and
then to internal combustion. Heavily-armored
"battleships" were replacing seventy four gun
"ships-of-the-line." The United States, already a
potent land power, took its developing naval
fleet onto the high seas and to every major
world port.

Ensign Williams entered the fleet in 1886 and
rose steadily through the navy's command structure as America entered the world stage. He
commanded a torpedo boat that carried dis-
patches through the Caribbean during the
Spanish-American War. Having commanded
cruisers, he was soon the skipper of the U.S.S.
Rhode Island, one of the "dreadnoughts" made
famous by the country's "Great White Fleet."

During World War One, now Admiral Williams
was Chief of Staff of Battleship Force 2. By the
20s, he was first the commander of the Battleship
Force in the Asiatic Fleet and then Commander-
in-Chief of the entire fleet. Upon his retirement in
1927, after forty years of capable service,
Admiral Williams was awarded the Yangtze
Service Medal, recognizing his role in representing American naval interests in the Far East.

Unlike the Civil War generation before him
and the World War Two generation after him,
Admiral Clarence Williams was not a "blood and
guts" combat officer. His role, as a transitional
leader, helped the U. S. Navy evolve from sail to
steam and wood to steel. He commanded battleships, with revolutionary speed, armor and
firepower that took American interests around
the world.

Fighting for the Union (1861-1865)

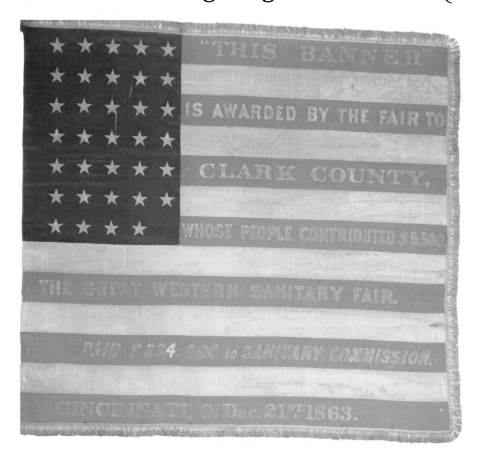

Clark County was a hundred miles north of a
slave state. In its early days, it had known slavery. Whole neighborhoods in Springfield were
called "Old Virginia" and were filled with immigrants from Kentucky and Virginia. And yet,
after a shaky start, the Abolitionist Movement
took hold in the county. When war came, Clark
County, having supported stops on the Under-

ground Railroad for decades, had its share of
southern sympathizers but went solidly for the
Union. Scores of county freedmen, many
escaped slaves, went back to the South to join
the new regiments of United States Colored
Troops.

Young men kept going off to war. First, they
went off by the hundreds, militia companies
assembling at Camps Chase and Jackson in
Columbus, Dennison in Cincinnati and Clark at
the fairgrounds outside of Springfield. In that
first rush of patriotic enthusiasm, they listened
to flowery political orations. In October of 1861,
the brand new 44th Ohio Volunteer Infantry
heard a stirring send off from visiting Senator,
soon to be President, Andrew Johnson. The
local newspaper described the address as
"strikingly affecting throughout, at times
brought tears to manly eyes and again thrilled
all hearts with high resolve to do or die for our
country." Private John A. McKee had his own
homespun version of the event.

> Andy Johnson spoke on the fairgrounds last
> Saturday. The whole regiment was called out to
> escort him from the town to the fairgrounds. We
> formed in line and marched over to town through
> a drenching rain. When we got there, there was
> no Andy Johnson there, so you see we had the
> satisfaction of marching back through the mud
> and rain without seeing him. However, when we
> got back, we found him on the grounds. He spoke
> about two and one-half hours and made about
> the best speech I ever heard. While he was
> speaking, a Democrat came up and said that he,
> Johnson, was a G-d d-m liar. He had not more

Captain Richard Mountjoy, Company C, 129th Ohio Volunteer Infantry (near right), strikes a casual pose, with his hand on an ornate chair. *(U.S. Army Military History Institute, Carlisle Barracks, Pennsylvania)*

Sergeant Joseph Simpson, Company E, 13th Ohio Volunteer Cavalry (far right), was photographed with his saber on April 4, 1864, at the East Main Street Excelsior Art Gallery.

than got it out of his mouth when he was knocked nearly down. He then ran across the guard line where no one was allowed to follow him. He was only saved by the interference of Colonel Wilson who detailed a guard to conduct him to some place of safety.

A month later, the 44th was in the real war in West Virginia. Private McKee and his comrades were beginning to experience the grinding boredom, punctuated by sudden danger and death, that would test a whole generation for almost four years.

> A sad accident happened here last Friday. As Captain Bell was crossing the river with eleven of his men to go on picket in a canoe, it was upset and they were all drowned but three privates. In consequence of which, we are ordered by the colonel to appear at dress parade every day for ten days in the position of reversed arms. That makes ten men drowned in our regiment and not one shot.

The 44th Ohio would see its share of the fighting, "seeing the elephant, head and tail," as the Civil War armies called it. There was a horror to the war that the soldiers could never communicate to the folks on the home front.

The "folks," who received so many letters from the first literate armies in history, had to wait and watch as the fighting ebbed and flowed through the rebellious South. The war never touched Clark County directly, although two swings through southern Ohio by Confederate raiders had the home guard out chasing a phantom enemy. But the families of absent soldiers could not simply stand by and do nothing. Women bucked tradition and joined the armies to minister to the overwhelming numbers of sick and wounded. In the process they invented the nursing profession. As Clara Barton, Red Cross founder, so aptly put it,

> I would fain be allowed to go and administer comfort to our brave men, who peril life and limb...
> I ask neither pay or praise, simply a soldier's fare and the sanction to go and do with my might, whatever my hands find to do.

Future Temperance crusader Eliza Stewart was one of those pioneer women. With a husband in the Confederate service and a son with the Union side, she decided to follow Clara Barton's example and help any way she could at the hospitals, camps and even battlefields. Her devotion to the wounded and sick of both sides so impressed the soldiers that she earned the honored title of "Mother."

Most women stayed home and did what they

could to help with relief efforts. The local ladies aid society joined forces with the national "Sanitary Corps." Designed to step in where the army was wanting, the Sanitary and Christian Commissions did everything they could to fill the physical and spiritual needs of the men at the front. Local journalist Clifton Nichols remembered relief efforts in wartime Springfield.

Of course, during the war the excitement ran high in Springfield, but we were pretty much of the same mind, there being few persons in the community who were not loyalists; the women of the town did much noble work in preparing clothing, and hospital supplies, vegetables, and delicacies for the sick and wounded. It was grand to see the unselfishness they displayed and the sacrifices they made to help the boys at the front... The ladies held fairs and in other ways raised money and supplies; there was an immense sani-

tary fair held in Cincinnati in which the Springfield ladies had a department and materially assisted. After the war was over the ladies turned their attention to the poor of the town, and from their labors in this direction grew the associated charities. During the war the farmers of the town held a "bee," and hauled wood to the widows and wives of soldiers. I organized a wood-saw regiment in town, and with several companies of men and boys, armed with wood-saws, we marched behind a band of martial music from house to house, sawing wood for the families of soldiers. I got the title "Colonel" in that campaign. I remember that one of the Bruce boys...was wounded in one "engagement," being slightly injured by a too violent contact with his saw.

Virginia Hunt, a descendant of the Hunts of Kenton Farm, recounted how the family was caught up in the drama of the war:

The Civil War soldier's accoutrements and personal effects, so familiar to hundreds of thousands of troops on both sides, are laid out around a rifled musket. The band box knapsack on the upper left was made by B. F. Paige of Springfield. Private Daniel Kurtz of the Jefferson Guards, 16th Ohio Volunteer Infantry, carried it to war in 1861.

OPPOSITE PAGE:
The millions back in the Civil War's home fronts waited and worried through the fighting. Many wanted to help and display their patriotism. The shadow box, with a valiant and well dressed lady of spirit and virtue wreathed in the stars and stripes, was a centerpiece in a Springfield parlor. A Hunt family basket used to collect lint for the wounded and a souvenir log, filled with shot and shell from a forgotten battle, are also poignant reminders of a cruel war.

Fifteen-year-old Private Edward Middleton joined the Fourth Ohio Cavalry as a bugler in 1864. In spite of his father's concerns, including a letter to President Lincoln, Pvt. Middleton went to war and was captured in the Atlanta campaign, spending nine months in the infamous Andersonville Prison. Surviving his ordeal, he became a successful local businessman and lived to 1908.

…our little [rail]road [the Mad River and Lake Erie founded by William Hunt in the 1840s] got some business hauling Southern prisoners of war to Sandusky [site of Northern prison camps]… With half the able bodied men away we wonder how the farms were run, especially as people could not always count on the kind of help they had received from each other before this time… Of course, the women had been organizing to help their fighting men. When the troops were near enough they sent down delicious food; jellies, pickles, chickens, broth, etc. This house [the Kenton Farm] was headquarters and Great Grandmother Mary McCord Hunt, president of the Sanitary Corps… They would assemble here. Can't you picture all the buggies and horses tied in the yard and the women at work in the house rolling bandages, picking lint to make absorbent dressings, packing food, medicines, and things to read, writing letters to lonely soldiers, and planning how the shipments were to be sent?

A grim time! And when the men came back they were often broken in health and many died young, leaving the women to carry on.

The United States Sanitary Commission, at first ignored by the War Department and President Lincoln who made the mistake of calling the efforts, "a fifth wheel on the wagon," became "a great artery that bears the people's love to the army." Nursing, better sanitation, missing soldiers' bureaus, better diets; nothing that could improve the soldiers' chances was ignored. At the "Great Western Sanitary Fair," held in Cincinnati near Christmas in 1863, Clark County was awarded a Star Spangled Banner for raising $5,580 for the war effort, more than any other county at the fair. What the President referred to as "the better angels of our nature" stepped up in the dark days of the Civil War to make a terrible situation better.

continued on page 210.

"The Boys of Springfield"– The 44th Ohio Captures an Old Cannon

Springfield's most famous Civil War artifact, an old cannon captured by the 44th Ohio Infantry in the 1862 Battle of Lewisburg, West Virginia, sat for decades in front of Memorial Hall. An iron six-pounder cast in the 1820s, it is now fully restored and has a permanent place of honor in the Civil War Gallery.

The 44th Ohio Volunteer Infantry, one of scores of fighting Civil War regiments from the Buckeye State, found immortality with an old cannon captured at a battle few remember. After the First Battle of Bull Run, President Lincoln called for 500,000 volunteers and the "Boys of Springfield" went to war as the 44th in the fall of 1861. The regiment soon found itself in western Virginia, a military backwater where small armies fought a war of maneuver and skirmishes to protect the flanks of the larger armies to the east and west.

The date was May 23, 1862. The war was a year and a month old. The 44th had been marching all over the hills and valleys of western Virginia, but had yet to fight a real battle. The future Indian fighter Colonel George Crook had led his Union force from Charleston a hundred miles east to the mountain town of Lewisburg. The community was set in a valley surrounded by peaks and one Union soldier called it a "saucer village." While enormous battles raged in the Shenandoah Valley and around Richmond, Lewisburg became a target because it was on the road to the strategic Virginia and Tennessee Railroad.

The Yankees, camped on the outskirts of the "secesh" town, were unaware of a Rebel force, commanded by career soldier General Henry Heth, approaching from the south. Before dawn on May 23, the Confederates moved into the outskirts of Lewisburg with six cannons and 2,200 men. Captain H. E. Titus, the last survivor of the 44th, recalled the first moments of the attack.

> We were eating breakfast – what breakfast we had – when shouts along the sentry posts caused some excitement and warned us that the rebels were coming.

The Union forces, who had no artillery, watched helplessly as shells started falling in the town. One old iron cannon sent a solid shot into a corner of the Methodist church. The 44th and 36th Ohio formed up to sweep through Lewisburg and attack the rebel line waiting on the other side. As the men dressed their lines, a shell burst overhead, killing and wounding three men. But the long winter of drilling had paid off. The ranks were steady as the men waited for the order to advance. For Pvt. Sam Harrison, the wait was an eternity.

> The shells were bursting in every direction, the pieces whizzing about our heads so close we could scarcely keep from dogging sometimes.

Captain Titus also felt the moment before the advance was dramatic.

> The battle [soon] reached a point… which lets us know that we either had to go ahead and beat them or all of us would probably be killed.

Finally, at the command "forward," the bluecoats swept through the streets and yards of Lewisburg, "climbing fences, breaking open gates, and marching through gardens, yards and fields." The 44th had no idea they were attacking rebel troops that were greener then they were. The disciplined Union assault quickly turned the gray defense into a "confused rout." Pvt. Harrison was amazed at the Confederate panic.

> They threw away knapsacks, guns, accoutrements, even shirts. I noticed some cut loose belts and snaps in order to escape quicker.

Pvt. John McKee was surprised that he was so cool under fire.

> At the command 'forward' we all started off on quick time and in the short space of twenty minutes we had possession of four out of six of their field pieces and the other two were in full retreat thus silencing their whole battery. When the rebels found that we had silenced all their pieces, they commenced to waver and soon they were in full retreat in such haste that the road over which they went was literally strewn with blankets, overcoats, pistols, knives, guns, cartridge boxes, etc…Our wagon have gathered up about five hundred stand of arms while wagon after wagon might be filled with clothes that are laying along the road. Although our company [G] was in the thickest of the fight, it came off without anyone being hurt. Part of the time we were crouched down under a fence while the shots passed over us like hail. One shell bursted nearly over our company but did no damage and a ball passed just over our heads. I do not know whether I hit anyone or not but I had several fair shots at the distance of about one hundred yards and do not think I was any more excited than if I were shooting at a squirrel.

The early morning fight turned into a complete rout. Confederate casualties outstripped Union by six to one. The Battle of Lewisburg

was just a skirmish by the bloody standards of the war, but it produced a gift from the 44th Ohio to its network of supporters in Springfield. The now captured old cannon, thought to be a relic from the Revolutionary War, was too out of date to be of any use to the Union army. The 44th claimed it and sent it home as a souvenir of their first battle.

A year and a half later, the 44th, now a battle-hardened unit of veterans, returned to Ohio to be refitted as a cavalry regiment. Besides their obvious pleasure at coming home to loved ones they had a rendezvous with the iron cannon that was their "gift of honor" after they had faced the enemy so gal-

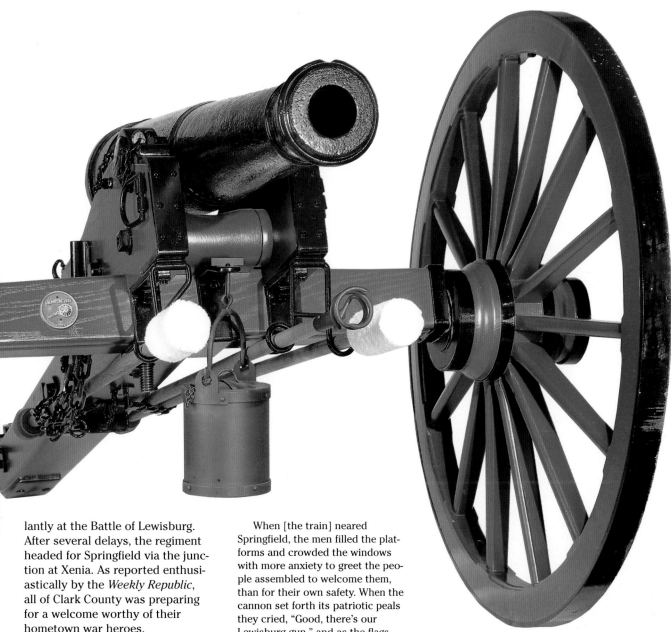

lantly at the Battle of Lewisburg. After several delays, the regiment headed for Springfield via the junction at Xenia. As reported enthusiastically by the *Weekly Republic*, all of Clark County was preparing for a welcome worthy of their hometown war heroes.

Two parallel tables were erected in the City Hall, the Council Chamber was taken possession of as a store room, a table was built on the platform – the \windows were decorated with flags – over the platform, festooned in red, white and blue drapery, hung this motto, "Welcome our Brave," and the walls were placarded with this complimentary motto, "Lewisburg was the neatest little stand up fight of the war – [General] Rosecrans…"

Contributions of meats, fruits, cakes, pies, relishes, indeed of all manner of appropriate edibles and potables poured in upon the committee faster than they could arrange them, and long before the hour at which the regiment was expected to arrive, enough had been received to enable the Aid Society to set before the veterans of the Fourty-Fourth a supper which in variety, excellence of materials, fitness and taste, was never excelled in our city, and has been rarely equaled in other cities on like occasions.

When [the train] neared Springfield, the men filled the platforms and crowded the windows with more anxiety to greet the people assembled to welcome them, than for their own safety. When the cannon set forth its patriotic peals they cried, "Good, there's our Lewisburg gun," and as the flags in the western part of the city met their gaze, they swung their hats and cheered as only veteran soldiers can cheer.

The depot was surrounded with a dense crowd of people when the train came in, and a general rush was made at the cars the moment they were stopped. Husbands, brothers, fathers and sons were greeted as only the dearly loved, long absent on perilous and patriotic service can be granted.

The 44th marched to the Market Square and was ardently welcomed by the Abolitionist Congressman Samuel Shellabarger.

Wherever your flag has gone, there, too, have gone the eyes of mother, wife, father, sister, brother and country – eyes only less wakeful than the eyes of God who watches you…By our share in your country's gratitude, by our property in your gallant deeds, by our memories of your dead and admiration of your living, by our appreciation of the momentous disasters and successes of the past, and by our faith in the future, and in the name of this State, and of all the States, and of the Union of these States, and of all the people of this Union, and of all the high interests of the people in that Union, Soldiers of the Republic, I welcome you.

The high emotion of the occasion, repeated so many times in towns throughout the wartime North, faded into Springfield's memory. But the "Boys of Springfield" left behind a prize of war, an old monument that is now restored and preserved in the Heritage Center. The Lewisburg Cannon survives to tell the story of sacrifice and commitment faced by an entire generation of men in blue and gray.

General Joseph Warren Keifer

One of the faces staring out from the 1859 framed portraits of volunteers with the "Rover" Independent Fire Company (pages 32-33) belongs to a smart, young lawyer and recent Antioch College student. His radical Abolitionist politics fit right into the "Rovers" Republican agenda for Springfield and Clark County. During ordinary times, J. Warren Keifer would have been cut out for a successful career with the city's business elite. But the times were anything but ordinary. Mr. Keifer was destined for a much larger arena. This is how he told the story.

Five days after President Lincoln's first call for volunteers, I was in Camp Jackson, Columbus, Ohio, a private soldier. April 27, 1861, I was commissioned and mustered a Major of the 3rd Ohio Volunteer Infantry and with the regiment went forthwith to Camp Dennison, near Cincinnati. Here real preparations for war began. Without the hiatus of a day I was in the volunteer service for four years and two months... I served and fought in Virginia, Kentucky, Tennessee, Alabama, Georgia, West Virginia and Maryland and campaigned in other states. I was thrice slightly wounded, twice in different years, near Winchester, Virginia, and severely wounded in the left forearm at the Battle of the Wilderness, May 5, 1864. I was off duty on account of wounds for a short time only, though I carried my arm in a sling, unhealed, until the close of the war. Although wholly unprepared by previous inclination, [I] quickly metamorphosed into a soldier in actual war.

Joseph Warren Keifer was modest about his achievements but he was a born fighter. The Civil War gave him a national stage to demonstrate his special skills. Most of the generation "touched by fire" simply survived the horrors of the battlefield and returned home to pick up their lives as best they could. Others, like Keifer, thrived on the danger and rigid structure of military life.

The twenty-five-year-old major attracted attention as soon as he went to the western Virginia battlefront with the Third Ohio Infantry. General John Reynolds, later killed at Gettysburg, noticed his ability to read the mountainous terrain.

"...There was not a cow path in all that region with which he was not thoroughly acquainted."

After a series of campaigns in Kentucky and Tennessee, young Keifer was picked by the Ohio Military Command to lead a new regiment. The 110th Ohio Infantry spent the next eight months endlessly drilling as garrison troops in western Virginia. The regiment's moment arrived in June of 1863. General Robert E. Lee's Army of Northern Virginia, on its fateful march to Gettysburg, collided with a few thousand Federal troops at Winchester, Virginia. The Confederates should have brushed the Yankees aside, but Colonel

General Keifer's headquarters flag, from his 1863 promotion to brigade commander, bears the "lozenge" of the Union Army of the Potomac's Third Corps.

OPPOSITE PAGE: Direct from the battlefront in 1865, Brevet Major General Joseph Warren Keifer was photographed in a Washington studio. His long hair and beard and dusty, worn uniform give him the look of the battle-hardened veteran he was. Just four years earlier, Keifer had entered the service as a private with no military experience. *(U.S. Army Military History Institute, Carlisle Barracks, Pennsylvania)*

Private Daniel J. C. Polley, a member of Company C, 110th Ohio Volunteer Infantry, General Keifer's own honored regiment, stands with a friend. Note the cuspidor at the bottom of the photograph. *(U. S. Army Military History Institute, Carlisle Barracks, Pennsylvania)*

carrying his unhealed arm in a sling for the rest of the war.

Battle after battle and honor after honor piled up in the Shenandoah Valley and the trenches of Petersburg. Brigadier General Keifer's brigade was the first to charge through the shattered Confederate defenses on April 2, 1865. His command then so vigorously pursued the fleeing enemy to Appomattox Court House that Keifer was brevetted a Major General of Volunteers on the very day that General Lee surrendered his army. In one of the war's greatest success stories, a Clark County farm boy heroically went up the army ladder from private to major general with no prior training or experience. At age twenty-nine, Major General J. Warren Keifer returned to his Springfield law practice, a highly-honored hero of one of the greatest wars in American history.

General Keifer could never again be just a local lawyer. He brought his experience on the national stage to a city bustling with the energy and success of its Golden Age. In his long life, he was a mover and shaker, both as an attorney and a banker, among the local business aristocracy. He was also a congressman for many terms, the Speaker of the U. S.

The regimental standard of General Keifer's 110th Ohio Infantry, showing the wear and tear of years of hard fought battles, has been carefully preserved.

General Keifer ended the war a division commander in the Sixth Army Corps (surviving headquarters flag at right).

Keifer's courageous attacks on an entire Rebel corps, "ten thousand strong," held Lee's army up for three days and allowed the small Union garrison to escape.

The army commanders noted the bravery of Keifer and his Ohio regiment. After a rest at Harpers Ferry, the colonel and the 110th were brought to the Army of the Potomac. Shaken by horrific losses at the Battle of Gettysburg, the army brought in reinforcements and Colonel Keifer was suddenly in command of a three thousand man brigade of Ohio, Maryland and Pennsylvania troops in the Third Army Corps. For the next two years, the Springfield citizen soldier would blossom in a high stakes setting dominated by professional soldiers and politicians.

One of the colonel's first assignments was enforcing the Union draft in New York City after bloody riots early in the summer of 1863. This delicate task, performed with prudence and diplomatic skill, indicated how much faith the Union

commanders now placed in a talented young officer. Keifer and his brigade soon returned to the Army of the Potomac and spent the rest of the war attached to the Sixth Army Corps at the center of the fierce fighting that aimed to capture Richmond and General Lee's army. Caught up in the life and death struggle to save the Union, soon to be General Keifer placed himself "in the hands of Providence." Like other officers and men in the armies, he stoically put himself in harm's way amidst the shot and shell on many battlefields. On horseback at the Battle of the Wilderness in May of 1864, he suffered a devastating wound as both bones of his left forearm were shattered by a bullet. His own regiment suffered one hundred and twenty-five casualties in the tangled confusion of the battle. The 110th would go on to lose a total of seven hundred and ninety five men before war's end. Sent home to recover, Keifer was back against his doctor's orders three months later,

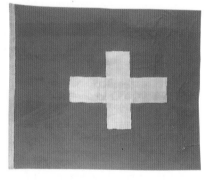

House of Representatives and an advisor to presidents during the era of the "Grand Army of the Republic." As one of the founders of the Clark County Historical Society, he entrusted his hometown with the precious objects that he had used in the war. Through his sixty year postwar career, the general never lost the abolitionist fire of his youth and the rock hard principals of brave service to his cause and his community represented by that proud photograph among his colleagues in the "Rovers" Volunteer Fire Company.

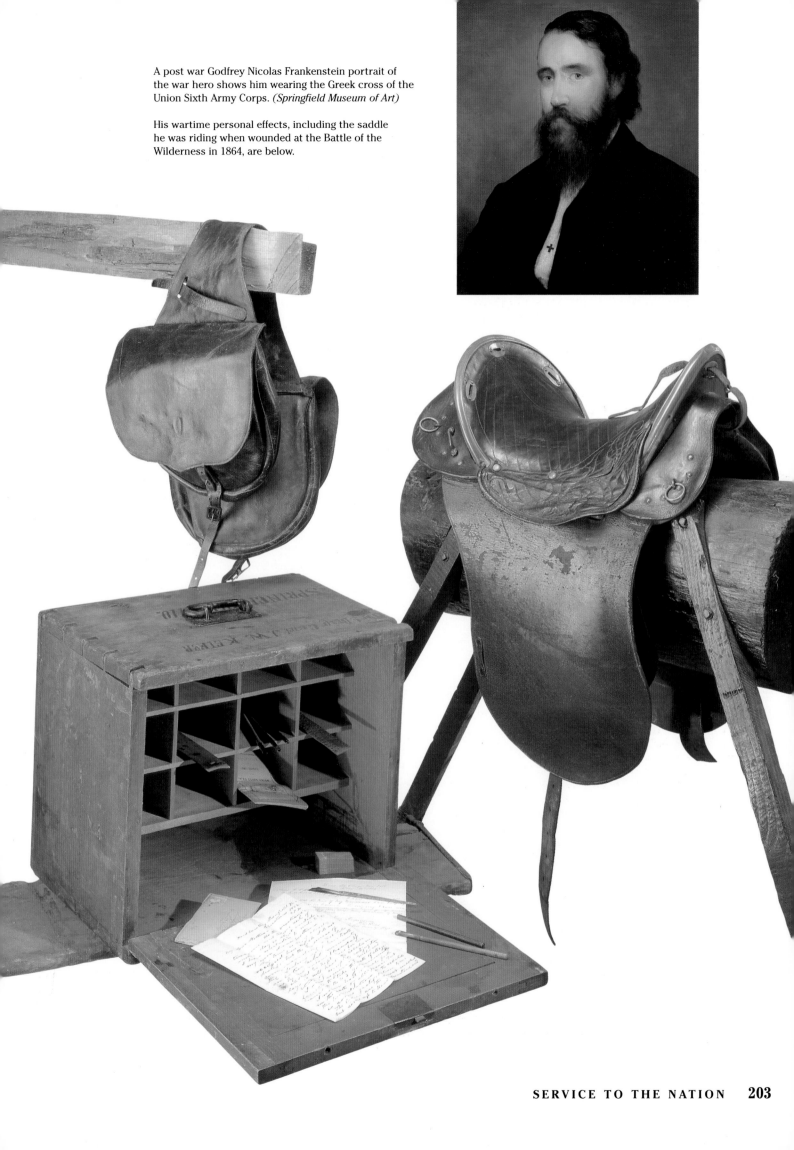

A post war Godfrey Nicolas Frankenstein portrait of the war hero shows him wearing the Greek cross of the Union Sixth Army Corps. *(Springfield Museum of Art)*

His wartime personal effects, including the saddle he was riding when wounded at the Battle of the Wilderness in 1864, are below.

The Hunt Brothers

The Hunt Brothers were Clark County aristocracy. Their Princeton, New Jersey, family had been interested in the Ohio Country since the days of speculator John Cleves Symmes. The Hunts finally migrated west in the 1820s. Franklin moved in as one of the area's first physicians. His seven children came next and he purchased the Simon Kenton Farm between Springfield and Urbana. They built a substantial brick house in the style of the homes they had left in New Jersey. After a stint as postmaster and then mayor of Urbana, William Hunt moved to the Kenton Farm. It was William, called "Major" by the local

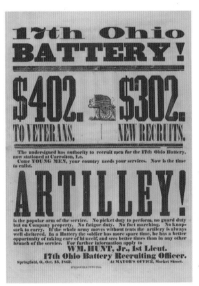

Ralph Hunt's younger brother William (left) joined the 17th Ohio Battery in 1863 and soon became the battery's recruiting officer. The surviving recruiting posters illustrate how difficult it became to lure recruits to the obvious dangers of the battlefield. Note the recruiting poster to the left. A Springfield printer forgot to spell check his work for Lt. Hunt.

community, who worked almost two decades to bring one of the first railroad lines to Springfield in 1848. By the time of the Civil War, the Hunts, noted, like the Warders, for their activist abolitionist views, had two generations invested in Clark County.

No family was more devoted to the Union. During the war, local Southern sympathizers burned cabins built by free blacks on the Kenton Farm to intimidate the Hunts. But Mary McCord Hunt remained a leader of local efforts to help the Union soldiers cope physically and spiritually with the demands of army life. The Clark County Ladies Aid Society won awards from the national organizations. Mrs. Hunt had a vested interest in the well being of Union soldiers. She had sent two of her sons to war.

The first to go joined in the war fever of 1861. Ralph Hunt belonged to the "Mad River Tigers," Company C of the First Kentucky Infantry. From Camp Pendleton, Ohio, the regiment went to the 1861 campaigns in western Virginia. During that early war mountain fighting, Lieutenant Hunt was captured and sent to Libby Prison in Richmond, Virginia. By January of 1862, he was exchanged for a North Carolina officer and sent to Fortress Monroe, near Norfolk, Virginia. After rejoining the First Kentucky, Lieutenant Hunt became a captain and finally a major as his regiment fought in all the major battles of the west from Shiloh to the Siege of Chattanooga. Mustered out when its three year enlistment ended in June of 1864, the thousand man unit was spared the worst of the fighting in the

Atlanta Campaign. And yet its muster rolls recorded that the First Kentucky had lost one hundred and forty-two of its members to battle and disease.

Ralph's younger brother William waited until 1863 to enlist. He chose the artillery rather than the infantry. The 17th Ohio Independent Artillery Battery was already a year old when Lt. Hunt joined its ranks right after the capture of Vicksburg, Mississippi. In the winter of 1862-63, the Battery had suffered substantial losses to disease and deprivation during the cam-

paign to capture Arkansas Post. After Vicksburg, Hunt participated in all of the unit's many engagements to the war's end. In just one battle alone, the 17th lost twenty-five men, twenty-one horses and an artillery piece. When the Battery was mustered out in August of 1865, it had fought in ten major battles, fired 14,000 rounds, lost more than forty men and marched ten thousand miles.

The Hunt Brothers were fighting veterans, lucky to survive the fierce combat. But their experience was similar to tens of thousands of

their comrades. Their connection to the family house, standing through so many generations of Clark County history, made their sacrifice special. Returning from the battlefronts, Ralph and William Hunt put the everyday items of their military life in the attic at the Kenton Farm. The survival of their unique officers' tent, along with their camp chairs and cooking gear, has given Clark County a singular remembrance of the days when millions left homes and loved ones to face the hard realities of a tragic war.

The Hunt brothers used this tent and these chairs in the field during the Civil War. The tens of thousands of tents used by the armies have all disappeared, victims of long use both during and after the war. This lonely survivor sat folded up in the attic of the family house for over a century before it was rediscovered and donated by the Hunt family.

The Music
of the Armies

Standing precariously on a balcony, probably decorated with Springfield-made cast iron, the Hawken's Regimental Band is ready to join the Union army in the field. The specialized over-the-shoulder horns, played so the music would be heard by the troops as the band marched ahead of the regiment, were universal in military bands during the Adolphe Sax era.

Along with the Hawken cornet, these rope-tension drums and the fife saw service with Civil War armies. The fife and drum corps or "field" music was critical to armies before phones and walkie-talkies. It communicated commands in battle and beat out the orders for all to hear in camp.

Music has always had a special hold on the military world. For centuries, the drum, fife and bugle regulated the rhythms of camp life and communicated commands over the noise of battle. All armies have their own songs, created both to praise and lampoon the soldier's life.

The Civil War, fought before the introduction of radio communication, married several musical elements that pointed both to the past and future. Soldiers still marched shoulder to shoulder and depended on the drum and bugle to pass along commands when voices were helpless against the noise of shot and shell. The fife and drum corps still controlled the soldier's routine in camp and inspired troops on the march. It was the culmination of an era of old style, rope-tension drums and fife melodies that often were borrowed from old fiddle tunes and military marches by the likes of Mozart and Haydn.

There were other musical fashions that amused and inspired the Civil War generation. In the 1850s, Stephen Foster helped invent the American popular song and, during the war years, a songwriting industry developed in the North. Soldiers at the front and families around the piano at home sang rousing patriotic calls to action and tearfully sentimental ballads of loss and suffering. Some of the most powerful images from the war, like the "vacant chair," were popularized by ballads, and America is still singing hundreds of the stirring songs almost a century and a half later.

Bands had been traveling with European armies for centuries, but an ingenious Belgian instrument maker named Adolphe Sax revolutionized military band music. Sax introduced his "saxhorns" to the French army in the 1840s. The bells of his new horns faced back toward the troops as the band marched ahead of the column. He also did away with most of the reed instruments, so the troops were hearing music with a decidedly German "oom-pah" flavor. For a few decades, the Sax approach to military music was the rage in European and American armies. In the 1880s, a new star named John Phillip Sousa appeared on the scene and military music again went through a dramatic transition as the "saxhorn" disappeared.

America fought the Civil War at the height of the Sax era. The curious looking horns carried by bandsmen from both North and South survive to remind us of the

all but forgotten band music that inspired the troops and began the transition to modern military music. Some of the Clark County regiments that fought for the Union were particularly noted for their bands. The ensembles featured pairs of horns, from cornet to bass, playing with bass and snare drums. They could perform the popular waltzes, gallops, polkas and schottisches for dances, or patriotic airs and marches for concerts and military ceremonies. In the seemingly incongruous theater of actual combat, the bands would often perform to steady the troops while shells and bullets whizzed around them.

Henry Hawken is the Springfield star of the Civil War band circuit. A friend and colleague of General J. Warren Keifer and a member of the "Rovers" Fire Company, it was natural that bandleader and cornetist Hawken would go to war with his Radical Republican associates. After service with the Sixteenth Ohio Infantry, he put together a sixteen piece band for the famous 110th Ohio Infantry and went to Washington in late 1863.

> At camp distribution, the band found themselves, with two or three hundred others, standing in a drizzling rain, in front of the tent of the commanding officer, who was to assign them to quarters. One of the men, who was nearest the door of the tent, spoke up promptly, 'Where you going to put us fellers?' 'A-going to put you where we please when we get ready,' was the reply, and he did put them into a lot of old bell tents with plenty of mud, where one or two of the boys began to play for amusement. This brought an officer to the spot, who introduced himself with, "Why in h—l didn't you tell us you had a band along? And you would have had better quarters." He then gave them quarters in a house, where they were during the cold New Year's of 1864.

From there they joined the Army of the Potomac in winter quarters, and, as the band of General Keifer's Second Brigade, Third Division, Sixth Army Corps, they were in the thick of the campaigns with the Union soldiers until the end of the fighting in 1865.

Henry Hawken's 110th Ohio Band became an army favorite. The Clark County Historical Society has the cornet that was played by Hawken at the Battle of the Wilderness in May of 1864. While the 110th was suffering enor-

mous casualties in the confused fighting and Colonel Keifer went down with a serious wound, the band struck up a rousing rendition of "Yankee Doodle" that steadied the troops. A few days later, Milton Myers of the 110th commented in his diary that the band cheered the camp after the bloody Battle

of Spotsylvania with a version of "Hail Columbia". The "Hawken's Band" stayed in business after the war and became a fixture at military ceremonies until the end of the century. In 1876, the band enlisted in the National Guard of Ohio and became known as the "Seventh Regiment Band."

Among surviving Civil War instruments, this cornet has a special and heroic history. Henry Hawken, the leader of the band of General Keifer's 110th Ohio Infantry, played "Yankee Doodle" on this horn to steady the troops during the fierce fighting at the Battle of the Wilderness in May of 1864.

After two years in the field, the band of the 44th Ohio Infantry, famous for capturing a cannon at Lewisburg, gathers stoically around its drums for an unusually candid photograph. *(Ohio Historical Society)*

"A Splendid Little War"

The United States ended the nineteenth century with a war that thrust the country onto the world stage. A Cuban war for independence from Spain threatened American business interests, and, when the American Battleship *Maine* mysteriously blew up in Havana Harbor in 1898, President William McKinley declared war on Spain. In a few short months, American forces captured Cuba, Puerto Rico, Manila and Guam and destroyed most of the Spanish fleet. The war cost the U.S. about five thousand lives, but most died from yellow fever outbreaks in the tropical war zones. At the end of 1898, the country had become an international power broker with a colonial empire of 120,000 square miles and 8,500,000 new subjects. It was a monumen-

tal change from conquering a continent to playing an increasing role in world politics that would dominate the 20th century and send Clark County servicemen and women all over the globe.

The Spanish American War had little effect on daily lives in the Heartland. The newspapers brought exciting news of world events to Clark County breakfast tables. But two quite different Clark Countians became national celebrities as the drama of the war unfolded in Cuba and the Philippines. General J. Warren Keifer was one of the Civil War heroes called up by President McKinley to lead the American troops into Cuba. At sixty years of age, Keifer had been Speaker of the U.S. House of Representatives

Called back to active duty during the Spanish American War, Major General J. Warren Keifer perches on a railing next to President and fellow Civil War hero William McKinley along with other, prosperous looking generals. The sixty-year-old Keifer was used to moving in high circles. He had been a Congressman, Speaker of the U.S. House of Representatives and lawyer to the rich and powerful.

and was an insider with the national Republican establishment. During the brief war in Cuba, while most of the attention was directed at the fighting around Santiago, he led the division that captured Havana.

The other celebrity was born in New Carlisle and was far from a national hero when the Spanish American War started. "Fighting Fred" Funston's father was a Civil War veteran who moved his family to Kansas when Fred was only two. After a checkered career as a student, Funston first exercised his adventurous spirit working for the Department of Agriculture. He spent time in Death Valley and then canoed fifteen hundred miles up the Yukon River on the Alaskan frontier. In 1895, he joined the Cuban revolution and within eighteen months was a lieutenant colonel in the Cuban artillery. Returning to America in 1898, he was given command of the 20th Kansas Regiment, but was soon sent to the Philippines rather than back to Cuba. It was in the newly-annexed Philippine Islands that Funston won a place in American history books.

The Americans had won the Philippines from Spain only to be faced with a nasty insurrection led by Emilio Aguinaldo, a Filipino freedom fighter bent on liberating the islands from all colonial domination. After two years of violent guerrilla warfare, the Americans were no closer to capturing Aguinaldo. On the eve of an American

withdrawal, Fred Funston discovered the location of Aguinaldo's headquarters and hatched a plan to capture the rebel commander. He sent a forged message to Aguinaldo offering reinforcements and five "important" American prisoners. In a real life adventure right out of a Hollywood movie, Funston, with four other American officers and seventy-five loyal natives traveled down the coast in an American gunboat and then marched ninety miles to the insurgent camp. Aguinaldo fell for the ruse, was captured and within a few weeks called for an end to the rebellion. Thirty-six-year-old "Fighting Fred" Funston became the talk of America. He had singlehandedly pulled off a feat that the entire U. S. War Department couldn't accomplish in two and a half years of fighting.

No one can know what role General Funston might have played in the First World War. He again distinguished himself in relief efforts after the 1906 San Francisco Earthquake and commanded American troops during the 1916 border troubles between the United States and Mexico. Funston was a favored son to lead American Expeditionary Forces into the trenches of the "Great War's" western front. But fate intervened when the homespun military leader died of a heart attack in 1917 at age fifty-two.

After mysteriously blowing up in Santiago Harbor, the Battleship *Maine* became an important symbol for the United States in the 1898 War. "Souvenirs" of the wreck ended up all over the country. Clark County has a decorated fender salvaged from the ship (below). "Fighting Fred" Funston (left) burst on the national scene as a American hero fighting the Philippine Insurrection. The New Carlisle native who grew up in Kansas captured Filipino Leader Emilio Aquinaldo after he had eluded the Americans for almost two years. *(Kansas State Historical Society)*

OVERLEAF:
Almost lost to history except for this photograph, a turn of the century African American military band, natty in their five-button coats and canvas gaiters, sports the look of the "Sousa Era." Abandoning the Sax horns of the Civil War period, John Philip Sousa again added reed instruments to bands and created his own special sound that is still very popular today.

The 20th Century Wars — World War One to Desert Storm

At the beginning of the 20th century, American troops found themselves in strange, exotic places. The United States had conquered a continent and then moved its interests overseas. Soldiers were stationed in the Caribbean, the Philippines, even China. American fleets were anchoring at ports of call throughout the world. It was a prelude to the most violent century in history. World wars would call the Stars and Stripes to every part of the globe.

The United States was a reluctant player on the international stage. Many felt there was enough to keep Americans busy at home. The rest of the world was a minefield best avoided. When a long peace unraveled in Europe and millions mobilized for what came to be called "The Great War," Uncle Sam stood on the sidelines for more than two years. In the face of unimagined violence, German "U-Boats" on the high seas and the bloody stalemate of trench warfare, the country was unable to protect its "neutral rights." Declaring that "the world must be safe for democracy," President Wilson finally declared war on Germany in the spring of 1917.

A year and a half later, America had mobilized a four-million-man-army. More than a million of those "doughboys," both volunteers and draftees, made it to the western front in France. What they found was a new type of warfare noted for its mud, rats, barbed wire, never ending artillery barrages, poison gas and "over the top" assaults on fortified positions that slaughtered tens of thousands of men every day.

Springfielder Frank Kronk was in the trenches near the infamous Verdun sector a month before the Armistice that ended the war. He was serving with Battery A of the 324th Field Artillery, attached to the 32nd Army Division. The Battery was assigned French 75 millimeter cannons, the most common artillery pieces on the Allied side.

> Tuesday, October 8 – Awakened at 4 A.M. Both light and heavy firing started at 5 A.M. The enemy is sending a few back. 5 men hurt in the 322nd [Light Artillery]. The breach block of a 75mm blew up. I prepare the fuses and powder charges. Our infantry went over the top at 7 A.M. and captured several prisoners. We are firing a shell a minute. Gun is red hot. Have a gang with buckets throwing water and laying wet sacks over them. We expect to advance this P.M. after we stop firing at 12:30 P.M...Saw 200 planes going for a raid at 7:30 P.M. All got back but 2.

> Wednesday, October 9 – Fired off and on all A.M., guns still hot from barrage...Left about 5 P.M. without supper advanced about 5 Kilo's arrived at new position we drove the enemy from yesterday at 12 midnight. Had supper and laid down in the frosty brush and slept until daylight. They say the shells were coming over us very lively last night but I only heard a couple that burst close to me. I was too tired to pay any attention to the shells. On way here I saw them carring[sic] dead and wounded away from the field we fired on yesterday.

Fred Kronk provided a snapshot of the often boring but always dangerous routine of trench warfare. In four years of that nightmarish environment, troops were ground into the mud and filth, too exhausted to care what happened to them.

The American Expeditionary Force provided a fresh and powerful boost to the Allied side. The enthusiastic "doughboys" arrived in France singing unforgettable songs like "Mademoiselle

Pvt. Ferdinand Smith found himself in the Meuse-Argonne sector of the western front when his unit, Company A of the 368th Colored Infantry, went into the trenches in the summer of 1918. He brought home his uniform and a "Souvenir de France" handkerchief when he returned in 1919.

Corporal Roth Carries a Message

Corporal Leon Roth was part of the first generation raised in the era of the motor car. He loved the new "horseless carriages" and became a truck driver as soon as he was big enough to manhandle the big, lumbering rigs that were replacing horses on city streets. When he joined the army, determined to play his part in defeating the Germans, he was a natural candidate to drive the American "Liberty" trucks. But Uncle Sam had other plans for Corporal Roth.

It was the early morning of November 11, 1918. Dispatch rider Roth shook off the chill and waited. His job with the 319th Signal Battalion was rushing by motorcycle from one headquarters to another and then waiting, sometimes for long hours, for his orders to move on to another location. It was a dangerous job. Just a month earlier, Roth had been in the middle of the hotly-contested Meuse-Argonne sector and had won a decoration for gallantry riding through the shelling to deliver messages. Now, standing idly near the railroad car that was Marshal Foch's French Army headquarters, he had no idea what he was waiting for.

At 5:15 A.M., an orderly emerged from the railroad car and gave an order to Corporal Roth to deliver to the First U. S. Army twenty-five miles away. As he stuffed the order into his red canister, the orderly

told him to "ride like hell. This is one message that you must get through." Roth faced a merciless ride through the "No-Man's Land" of the Western Front. "I dodged shell holes only to be thrown off my motorcyle by the impact of a nearby hit." A little later, a German sniper almost picked him off and he finished his ride, with shells landing all around in the dim morning light, thinking that he might already be dead.

At breakneck speed, it had only taken a half hour to cover the twenty-five miles. Covered with mud, Corporal Roth delivered his message and stood around waiting

for the inevitable reply. He was not looking forward to another ride through the eerie and dangerous front lines. Suddenly the corporal was surrounded by joyous shouting. Inquiring into the commotion, he was told that the war was finally over. Without vaguely suspecting the importance of his mission, a Springfield, Ohio, doughboy had delivered a message pronouncing the armistice that ended the Great War. Corporal Roth's harrowing early morning delivery, just doing his duty, won him a Distinguished Service Cross from the U. S. Army and a Croix de Guerre from the French.

Corporal Leon Roth, a dispatch rider with the 319th Signal Battalion, unknowingly made history in the early hours of November 11, 1918. He won medals from both the Americans and French for carrying a message in his red canister through twenty-five miles of shot and shell. That message, delivered to the Americans, ended the First World War.

---

of Armentieres" and "Over There." The Germans still had two million soldiers in the trenches, but an Allied offensive in the Fall of 1918 that claimed thousands of American lives, finally ended the fighting. Back home, many self-appointed spy hunters went on a hate crusade against German Americans. Springfield, with Wittenberg College and many ties to German culture, struggled with a new wave of bigotry. Businessman Henry Kissell joined other community leaders, bringing former president Theodore Roosevelt to the Wittenberg campus to settle the community down. But, while zealots muddied the local waters, Clark County sent thousands of its young men into the army and navy in a burst of homegrown patriotism.

The local servicemen who sailed to France found a world transformed by years of total war. Sergeant Arnold Sonander served as a Signal Corps aerial photographer. He was assigned to the 225th and 496th Aerial Squadrons, part of the units associated with the new brand of fighting "air aces" Lt. Eddie Rickenbacker, Col. "Billie" Mitchell and future New York mayor Fiorello La Guardia. Sgt. Sonander carried his heavy camera equipment into the air riding in the fragile biplanes just introduced to war. The allies had faced the Great War with just fifty-five planes. By 1918, the value of aircraft was apparent to both sides. The Allies had over three thousand hastily developed planes engaged in dogfights, aerial reconnaissance and

Battery D of diarist Frank
Kronk's 324th Field Artillery
stood at formation in the win-
try weather of Ohio's Camp
Sherman before they were
sent to France in 1918. Note
the icicles on the barracks
and the French 75mm can-
non, the favorite field piece of
the American Expeditionary
Force.

Twenty-one thousand officers
and men engage in a popular
First World War art form at
Camp Sherman, Ohio. The
lively profile of the president
is reminiscent of the later
card tricks at football games.

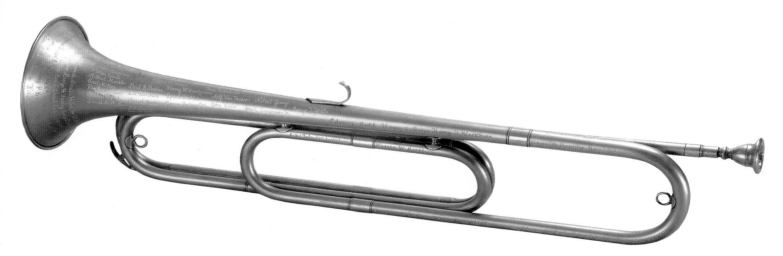

The bugle of the "Last Man's Club," an organization formed in the 1930s by a hundred World War One veterans, was blown for the "Last Man," ninety-nine-year-old Ralph Bruce, who passed away in 1996.

some bombing of military targets. Some visionaries predicted that the skies would become increasingly important in future wars.

Clark County also sent a contingent of African American men to the Western Front. Serving in segregated units, the black soldiers were challenged by prejudice and inferior, hand-me-down equipment both at home and abroad. Overcoming these obstacles, they fought alongside the white units with gallantry and commitment. Private Ferdinand Smith of the 368th Colored Infantry Regiment faced the dangers of the 1918 Meuse-Argonne Offensive and returned home with his "Souvenir de France" handkerchief proudly stuffed in his duffle bag.

Most of the County men who served never went overseas, but "doughboys," like Pvt. Lewis Tuttle of the 58th Infantry Regiment, experienced the agony of all-out war. They came home with memories of the horrors tucked away and resumed their lives. Their relationships with

Lieutenant Colonel Robert Hanes served in the United States Army for thirty-five years. He was photographed on Guadalcanal where he won the Silver Star for bravery in early 1943.

veteran comrades remained important as the years went by and one hundred local veterans bought a bugle and formed a "Last Man's Club" in the 1930s. The "Last Man" was sworn to blow the bugle at the death of the 99th club member. Ralph Bruce blew the bugle for Carleton Davidson in 1994, passing on himself in 1996 at the age of 99.

Just two decades after the "war to end wars," the madness returned, more frightening than before. Along with the rise of Adolf Hitler's "Third Reich" in Germany, the warlords of a militant Japan sought an empire in the Far East. The United States remained determined to avoid the foreign conflicts as country after country fell to menacing new tyrannies. On December 7, 1941, the Japanese attack on Pearl Harbor shattered America's illusions. A leading isolationist remarked that, "We learned that the oceans are no longer moats around our ramparts." As he declared war, President Franklin Roosevelt predicted, "Never before has there been a greater challenge to life, liberty and civilization."

The whole country, faced with an emergency even more threatening than its own Civil War, mobilized as never before. After a year of setbacks all over the world, the allies began to turn the tide. Step by step and island by island, German and Japanese forces were forced on the defensive. America became a vast industrial war machine and fifteen million served in the armed forces. It was a fight to the finish and Clark County played a major role in making the country an "Arsenal of Democracy." Local industrial giant International Harvester even sent service battalions overseas to fix its damaged military vehicles on the battle front.

Clark Countians found themselves fighting on every battleground. Ensign Daniel Shouvlin was aboard the brand new U. S. Destroyer *Walker* in 1943. He quickly realized that no place was safe during a world war.

...We were assigned to anti-submarine patrol off South America. On that duty we caught a German

sub on the surface, after it had been damaged by U. S. Navy aircraft, and sank it with our main battery. We took quite a few prisoners and had them on board for about five days before turning them over to the Marines in Trinidad. They seemed to be glad to be out of the war.

I was put in charge of the officer prisoners, several of whom spoke English. One young ensign was quite friendly, and during a conversation said he was from Dusseldorf. A few years earlier Superior Gas Engine [a Shouvlin family company] had an agent, Hans Von Loesel, who lived in Dusseldorf also. This young ensign knew the family quite well. Small world!..

A short time after we were hit by a torpedo just off Trinidad. It put a major league hole in the bow even though it didn't detonate, fortunately. After getting a soft patch in Trinidad, we went back to the Portsmouth, VA. Navy Yard for repairs. We were there for several weeks before being assigned to escort the [U. S. Cruiser] *Augusta* to Casablanca – the Augusta was taking [Secretary of State] Cordell Hull to a conference with President Roosevelt and Joseph Stalin… I remember the rats of Casablanca – they were as big as cats.

Shouvlin served with the *Walker* as it "island hopped" with the American fleet in the Pacific. When the war ended, he was a Lieutenant Commander assigned to the Commander of the Destroyer Fleet in the Pacific.

Lieutenant Colonel Robert Hanes was a career soldier for thirty-five years in the U. S. Army. He was on Guadalcanal Island in early 1943, only six months after the first U. S. Marine invasion in the Pacific. Control of the island was still very much in doubt. Hanes was on foot under "withering enemy fire," when he guided armored vehicles through thick jungle terrain. His "aggressive leadership and capable direction of fire against enemy positions" won him the Silver Star for bravery.

African Americans continued to serve gallantly with U. S. forces. Private later Major James Caldwell began his twenty-two year career with the military in the 761st Tank Battalion. Assigned to Camp Hood, Texas, the Battalion faced the familiar generations old prejudice. "At the post, German prisoners of war were actually afforded more privileges than these Black soldiers who were preparing to fight and, if necessary, die for their country." And fight and die they did as the 761st joined the European fighting in the fall of 1944. They fought in their Sherman Tanks for 183 days straight,

Sergeant Willis Tiemann, photographed on one of the self-propelled 105mm howitzers in his battery, served with the 696th Armored Field Artillery in Europe.

Like tens of thousands of G.I's before him, young soon-to-be Seabee James Walsh (far left) is photographed as he enters the U.S. Navy in 1944.

Seaman First Class and "Wave" Helen North Tiemann was one of over two hundred thousand women who joined the military in World War Two. After serving as a personnel secretary at the Great Lakes Naval Center, she married Sergeant Willis Tiemann after the war (Page 219).

taking three towns from the Germans on their very first day of combat. The Battalion played an important role in the terrible events of the Battle of the Bulge, eventually winning a "Presidential Unit Citation" for its sacrifice.

Most of the millions of veterans who fought in the fierce combat were anything but regulars. They were simply part of a generation unlucky enough to come of age at an intense moment of worldwide crisis. Yet they met the danger and the loneliness in faraway places with courage and determination. Sergeant Harold Locher survived the dangerous job of rifleman and radio operator with an army tank destroyer unit fighting the Japanese in the Philippines. Motor Machinists Mate Third Class James Walsh kept a book of snapshots that documented his life as a "Seabee" on Guam. The Navy construction battalions followed the fighting men into the Japanese-held islands and often started constructing airfields as the fighting still raged around them.

One Clark County story demonstrates the changing nature of 20th century war. More than ever before, the increasingly violent fighting was spilling over into the civilian populations. Millions died as whole cities were destroyed in bombing raids with weapons of mass destruction. In the midst of this new terror, women could not stay at home and do nothing. On some battlefronts they joined the fighting. Millions of

American women joined the work force, while over two hundred thousand served in non-combat roles with the military. Seaman First Class Helen North volunteered to join the "Waves" in 1944. She served as a personnel office secretary at the Navy's Great Lakes Training Center while her husband-to-be, Sergeant Willis Tiemann, was assigned to the 696th Armored Field Artillery in the European theater. Sergeant Tiemann was a crew member of a self-propelled 105 millimeter howitzer battery. Both the sergeant and the seaman put their lives on hold as they and their generation faced a global life and death drama.

When the World War Two generation returned to their homes, their lives were rewarded by the prosperity of the post war years. But international tension and danger have continued to vex our lives in the last half of the twentieth century. "Hot" wars have been replaced by "cold." So-called "brush-fire" wars and "police-actions" have required commitment from Clark County's sons and daughters. Each conflict and duty station, from Korea to West Germany to Vietnam and Kuwait, has defined a special group of veterans and demanded a special brand of service. The County in the Heartland has sent its own to every trouble spot during a tumultuous twentieth century. It will play a proud role as long as Americans face a dangerous world.

OPPOSITE PAGE: Motor Machinist Mate Third Class James Walsh was a "Seabee," building airfields and repairing equipment alongside the fighting men on Pacific islands. Walsh kept a book of snapshots, documenting his adventures with his buddies and the tedium of long years away from home.

Souvenirs of War

Clark County has a rich collection of war souvenirs dating back as far as the Civil War. A rare Confederate political ribbon (far right) and Philippine leader Emilio Aguinaldo's inkstand (right) are among the most significant. The inkstand might have been captured by Clark County native "Fighting Fred" Funston and sent to an important county military figure like General J. Warren Keifer. Other souvenirs, include enemy flags that come from every part of the globe (opposite page).

Collecting mementos from life's adventures is an important part of the human experience. When the adventure is life threatening, like participation in a war, collecting can sometimes appeal to man's most primitive instincts. Along with the usual items remembering ports-of-call around the world and special relationships with comrades in arms, there can be a need to memorialize the special demanding valor of the battlefield.

A French handkerchief, an autographed coconut, a photo album of buddies smiling for the folks at home, any of these can end up in a military duffle bag. A veteran might also take away captured books, newspapers, leaflets and political ribbons. But the most powerful evidence of his ordeal is the arms, equipment and personal items important to his enemy. Historical societies are filled with captured rifles, ammunition and accoutrements. In addition, there are letters, diaries, snapshots, money and government forms, most of these effects taken from dead enemies. In midlife, veterans have been known to try to establish a connection with their enemy's loved ones and sometimes give back the "souvenirs" taken after the heat of battle. The souvenirs of combat provide a powerful connection to the passions of war.

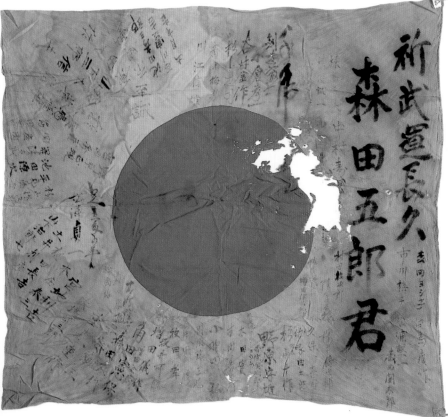

Epilogue

A Springfield G. I. Comes Home to the American Dream

It is a pleasure to meet Howard Weber. Whoever, long ago, gave him the nickname "Howdy" hit the nail right on the head. At seventy-five years young, he still has the twinkle of a schoolboy with mischief on his mind. Within moments of a greeting the stories from a busy life start flowing. He soon has you engaged, traveling back to fifty-year-old adventures that could have happened yesterday.

Howdy is a full-fledged member of what many are now calling the "Greatest Generation." Born in 1925, he was raised in a crippling economic depression and came of age during a world war. Like the Civil War three generations earlier, World War Two consumed the lives of millions of the best and brightest. Howdy couldn't wait for his chance and joined the U. S. Army Air Force as soon as he graduated from Springfield's South High School in February of 1944.

> They sent me to Keesler Air Force Base in Biloxi, Mississippi, for my basic training. The segregated South was a real eye-opener. You know how the military is so good at finding out what your skills are and then assigning you to something else? As long as I could remember, mostly because of my dad, I was interested in photography, so the Air Force made me a gunner. I trained at a school in Las Vegas. It was just a little dinky whistle stop. Boy, if I would have bought some land out there in the middle of nowhere!

Eighteen-year-old Sgt. Weber was soon sent to the 100th Bomb Group, 351st Bomb Squadron, 8th Air Force, stationed in England.

> They called my unit the "Bloody Hundredth," because of an incident that caught the attention of Goering, the Luftwaffe commander. Whenever a B-17 went down below 3,000 feet and lowered its landing gear, that was a sign it was surrendering so the German fighters would escort it in. Once, one of our bombers went down and lowered its gears. When the FW 190s [German fighters] gathered around our gunners shot them out of the sky. Goering commanded the Luftwaffe to show our unit no quarter after that.
>
> I flew sixteen missions over Germany and started out as a tail gunner. The officers who were bombardiers were getting killed so fast, they sent us enlisted to a school in England for bombardier training. We learned how to use a top

secret piece of equipment that was supposed to jam the German anti-aircraft radar, but I'm not sure it ever worked. One thing I know, they put the fear of God into us about never letting that equipment get captured. On one mission, we thought we were going down and I dumped my equipment out of the plane. We got home all right and I guess I cost Uncle Sam a few dollars.

> I was never actually a bombardier. We were called "toggle-atiers." Bombers would go over the targets in groups of three. The lead plane would have a bombardier officer with a Norden Bombsight and we would drop our bombs at the same moment he dropped his.

Howdy's last bombing mission was on April 3, 1945, only a month before V-E Day.

> We were bombing a German sub pen near the North Sea. We couldn't drop our bombs on the target and we were running low on fuel so our pilot was trying to get us to safety in Holland or Belgium. As we crossed over one of the Frisian Islands, we took a big barrage of flak. I was in the midsection of the bomber and the whole front end blew up ahead of me. I pushed open a door and went out, door and all, and opened my chute.

Howdy Weber's father gave him his love of photography. Here the senior Mr. Weber is on the other side of the camera, enjoying a promotional visit to Springfield by flyer Amelia Earhart in the 1930s.

OPPOSITE PAGE: Howdy (third from left in third row) and future comedian Jonathan Winters (first on left in third row) were choirboys in 1939 at Christ Episcopal Palm Sunday services on High Street in Springfield. "Johnny and I weren't good friends until after the war. He lived in a different neighborhood and went to a different school. But we did have fun together after we came back from the service."

Teen-aged airman Weber with the 8th Air Force in 1945 and fifty-five years later (below) after a long career as a news photographer in Springfield.

All photographs, on pages 227-35, unless otherwise credited, are by Howard O. Weber.

Only two of us got out. The other eight didn't make it. I heard that one got out but his chute got mixed up with the tail section and went down with it.

Having hit the water safely, Howdy could not get out of his rig and was blown out to sea in a modern version of a whaler's "Nantucket Sleigh Ride."

I was blown five miles out to sea before I could get separated from the chute and by that time I was close to dead because of the cold and exhaustion. I didn't know it but two Dutch fishermen had seen me come down and chased me out to sea trying to run me down. They got to me just in the nick of time and one of them pulled me out by my hair. When they got me back to the beach, I was still out. The Germans came by and thought I was dead, but they came back the next day and picked me up.

Howdy spent the next month in a moving prisoner of war camp. The few German guards were constantly marching the group to avoid the allied soldiers closing in from all directions.

We would watch the dogfights overhead. When an allied plane got shot down, it often wouldn't be long before we had another airman join our group. During that whole month, I never changed my clothes and never brushed my teeth. I had "scabies" and was sore from walking all the time. One day I just sat down and said I wasn't going any further. Then I heard the German guard click a bullet into the chamber of his gun. I did ten more miles that day and never complained again. We were eventually liberated by the British.

Forty years later the Dutch Government brought Howdy Weber and other veterans back to honor them for their war service.

We were there for four days with Georgian [Russian] veterans who had liberated the Frisian Island area. We were all treated like royalty and given special medals. While I was there, somebody came up and grabbed me by the hair. It was the brother of the fisherman who had saved me. He had been in the boat that had chased after me. I was unconscious at the time and had never met either one of them. My rescuer had died the year before my visit.

Still a teen-ager, Howdy had "been touched by fire" in 1945 and was one of the lucky ones who came home. He used the "G. I. Bill" to go to Miami University and then Wittenberg College.

I wanted to be an artist. A photographer from the *News and Sun* came over one day, took one look at my work and thought I might make a better photographer. I ended up working at the newspaper for thirty-eight years. I was a general news photographer so I had an opportunity to keep up with everything that was going on, good and bad. I guess the biggest story I covered was the "bionic woman" over at Wright State University in the 1980s. Nan Davis, a paralyzed lady, was able to walk to receive her diploma with electronic equipment that was developed on campus. That moment got international attention.

Except for his war service, Howdy Weber has lived in the same Springfield neighborhood for seventy-five years. He has been an active and enthusiastic participant in more than a third of the Champion City's eventful history. He is living proof that this community in the Heartland is "rich in people against whom misfortune and failure seem powerless."

Newsweek Magazine discovered Springfield in 1983. They wanted to celebrate their fiftieth anniversary by exploring a community that held the keys to the American dream. They soon found Howdy Weber and learned that the real story of every community is people simply living their lives. Howdy helped guide them to the keys they were looking for and they traced the life and death dramas of five families through several generations. It was a proud moment for the *News and Sun* photographer and his cherished hometown. As the *Newsweek* reporters investigated the Champion City, they found America's "Our Town," important because it was such a fine example of the rest of us.

Howdy Weber has followed his own version of the American Dream in his own special time and place. When he passes the torch to the next generation, the past will be there to instruct the future and we will all be the better for it.

"I think my colleague Bill McCuddy at the *News and Sun* took this photo of Springfield in the early 1950s before so many of the downtown buildings disappeared." The City Building is still flanked by other buildings at the lower left. The massive Crowell-Collier Building at the upper left was closed in the mid-fifties. One corner of the Historic Arcade Building is visible at the bottom.

"The editors always used to send us out to get pictures of snow when there was a snow storm. As if everybody didn't have enough snow to look at during a blizzard. This was the winter storm of 1950, the biggest I can remember. That car was buried right in front of the City Building."

227

OPPOSITE PAGE: "This is a photo of the aftermath of the 1950 blizzard looking up Limestone Street past the county building on the left. People are just starting to dig out."

"TWA started transcontinental service to the Springfield Airport south of town in the late 1940s but it didn't last very long."

"Dr. Howard Dredge ran a big tennis school in the 1950s. He made tennis a big deal around Springfield. That guy on the left in the chair is Nick Bolletieri who went on to create the famous Tennis and Sports Academy in Sarasota, Florida."

"They always wanted me to go out and get a photo of the county fair when it ended each year. One year I got this bright idea to get the fair director, Byron "Putt" Sandles to climb up the tower at the fairgrounds. He was game and this was the result."

"This photo was taken the first year the county fair moved to its present location on the site of the old airport southeast of town. You can still see some of the airport hangars in the background."

"We had two railroad stations close to each other. The Pennsylvania and the "Big Four" stations. You could get on the train and spend the night in a "Pullman" going up to Chicago. Five million *Collier's* Magazines were trucked over to the Pennsylvania Station and shipped out by train every week."

"I had to fight my way through a big crowd, ten thousand people, to get these closeups of Ike when his train stopped in 1952."

"JFK came through in 1960 on his presidential campaign. I had a chance to photograph him at Wittenberg and here, in London, Ohio. I'm proud of this shot."

"I remember Nixon visiting twice, once in 1952 and once in 1960. One time, he wasn't planning to speak, but we got him and Pat Nixon to interrupt their lunch on the train and pose for us."

"President Ford spoke right in front of the Art Museum in 1976. Here he is flanked by two Ohio politicians, Senator Bob Taft and Congressman Clarence J. Brown."

OPPOSITE PAGE: Howdy Weber gathered all the contestants from an annual ritual of the late 1940s and 1950s, the Soap Box Derby competition (right). "I lined them up at the Springfield City Garage and told them to tip their helmets. This was the very satisfying result."

"I had many opportunities to photograph visiting celebrities like actor Charles Laughton, especially when they appeared at Wittenberg."

"This was an amazing moment for all of us. To think that Neil Armstrong had recently been standing on the moon!"

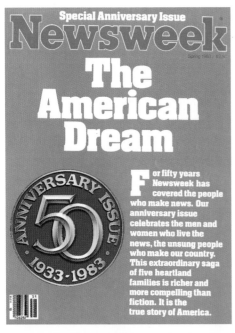

The Staff of *Newsweek* Magazine spent six months in Springfield researching the community for its Fiftieth Anniversary Issue in 1983. The "Champion City" was featured as the "Our Town" of America. Five local families, "the unsung people who make America," are introduced on these pages. The Bayleys represent the successful families of the Golden Age. The immigrant Cappelli's are thriving in Springfield's flower business. The Bacons have broken barriers between African Americans and whites. The working class Nuss family lives near Snyder Park in the west end and the Gramms have a farm south of town.

Bibliographic Essay

The 1983, Fiftieth Anniversary, issue of *Newsweek* Magazine introduced modern America to Springfield, Ohio. It was as thorough an exploration as any national periodical might give a local subject. *Newsweek* saw the value of going to the Heartland to find the country's "Our Town." It seems fitting to recall that almost twenty-year-old milestone and keep those important stories of local families in the public eye.

The *Newsweek* issue tapped into a gold mine of primary information about Springfield and Clark County in the Clark County Historical Society Archive. That Archive was the source of most of the information collected for this volume. A large collection of original newspapers, including the *Daily News*, the *Sun*, the *Republic*, the *Tri-Weekly Republic* and *Farm and Fireside*, reaches well back into the nineteenth century and has provided hundreds of facts and anecdotes for two decades of Society newsletters. Besides many sets of business and personal letters and publications that date back to the Golden Age, the Society has every important city and county atlas, directory, gazetteer and report as far back as the 1840s travels of Henry Howe and Warren Jenkins and the 1852 and 1856 *Sketches of Springfield*.

Since 1947, the Historical Society has been reprinting important early histories and reminiscences. The wonderful six volumes of *Yesteryear in Clark County* has been a rich source that is woven all through this book. Starting with John Ludlow's *Papers on the Early Settlement of Springfield, Ohio*, first delivered in 1871, the community has an extraordinary window on how the frontier village developed. In addition, William Kinnison and Mary Skardon have published numerous pamphlets culminating in Dr. Kinnison's 1985 *Springfield and Clark County, an Illustrated History*, which is also an important beginning for anyone interested in city and county history. The *Illustrated History* has a comprehensive bibliography that lists all of these sources. Along with the information on presidential visits, the Westcott family, Gus Sun and local African American history, Professor Thomas Taylor of Wittenberg University provided a copy of *Updating the Dream, Springfield looks at 2000 and beyond*. This most recent look at the challenges and opportunities faced by the Champion City was sponsored by the University and featured David Rusk and William Julius Wilson, two nationally-recognized experts on modern cities. A 1985 publication, *A Corporate Tragedy, the Agony of International Harvester Company*, by Barbara Marsh, provided background on the troubles in the company that impacted Springfield so severely in the early 1980s.

The National Road is a major thread in the Clark County story. A renewed interest in the old road is producing new scholarship, but an article entitled *The National Road, Main Street of America*, written by Norris Schneider in 1975 for the Ohio Historical Society, has become a standard and is in its third printing. In recent years, the Ohio Historical Society has been publishing its handsome *Timeline* periodical. The publication has regular features and illustrations that often touch on Clark County as they explore Ohio history.

General background on the pre-Civil War era period of roads, canals and railroads was garnered from two standard histories, Samuel Eliot Morison's *Oxford History of the American People* and Page Smith's *The Nation Comes of Age*, volume four of his *People's History of the Ante-Bellum Years*. About the Civil War itself, a 1966 volume, *Life in the North During the Civil War, a Source History*, by George Winston and Charles Judah, provided useful information on changes in agriculture and life on the homefront. The neverending interest in the Civil War provides more and more detail about every facet of the conflict. Two recent studies, *To See the Elephant, the Civil War Letters of John A. McKee (44th Ohio)*, by James R. James and an article in a 1998 issue of *America's Civil War* entitled *War in the Streets of Lewisburg*, by James T. Silburt, profiled the Battle of Lewisburg in 1862.

Along with the colorful eyewitness accounts of early Springfield found in the Historical Society's *Yesteryears* volumes, a 1996 study, *The Ohio Frontier, Crucible of the Old Northwest*, by R. Douglas Hurt, is an essential history of the early years. Professor Hurt's interest in agricultural history was useful in portraying the challenges facing frontier farmers. John Sugden's 1997 biography of *Tecumseh* was also helpful, tracing the hopeless dilemma facing the Shawnees and their great leader. Martin West of Fort Ligonier, Pennsylvania, was kind enough to share his original research on George Rogers Clark's 1780 Miami River campaign against the Shawnees.

Finally, the story of Clark County's important role in the nineteenth century agricultural revolution was enhanced by Robert Leslie Jones's *History of Agriculture in Ohio to 1880*. The role of fairs and agricultural exhibitions was an important part of that study. The Internet provided colorful background on the 1893 World's Columbian Exposition in Chicago. In fact, the Worldwide Web was there to answer questions ranging from the role of cowcatchers on streetcars to General Fred Funston's hometown of Iola, Kansas.

The aim of this volume was not only to trace the rich history of one community in the Heartland, but also to open eyes to the continued importance of state and local history in our shared heritage as a nation. Every page in this journey opens doors to the continuum of human experience contained in ordinary lives. We hope that others will find time in the busy present to step through those doors into a fascinating and instructive past.

Index

Illustration references are indicated in italic.

240